Curious About Cannabis™

2nd Edition

Curious About Cannabis™

A Scientific Introduction to a Controversial Plant

2nd Edition

Jason Wilson, MS

Natural Learning Enterprises, LLC

Published by Natural Learning Enterprises, LLC

Natural Learning Enterprises is a mission-driven science and philosophy education and media company dedicated to enhancing critical thinking skills and public scientific literacy about the natural world. Curious About Cannabis is just one of many learning initiatives managed by Natural Learning Enterprises. To learn more, visit www.NaturalEdu.com

Curious About Cannabis™: A Scientific Introduction to a Controversial Plant

Second Edition

ISBN 978-0-9985728-5-7

www.CACPodcast.com

www.CuriousAboutCannabisBook.com

Curious About Cannabis: A Scientific Introduction to a Controversial Plant

© *Jason Wilson, First Edition 2018, Second Edition 2020.*

Cover image of Cannabis inflorescence copyright Adobe Stock, image number 123629851

Disclaimers:

Every good faith effort has been made to secure required permissions for all text, images, and other art reprinted in this edition. To the best of the author and publisher's knowledge, all images and excerpts used in this book have either been reproduced with permission, relinquished to public domain, used within perceived appropriate "fair use" standards, or distributed under a creative commons license allowing reproduction for commercial use with or without attribution.

None of the statements in this text should be interpreted as medical advice or health claims, therapeutic or otherwise. **This text does not provide medical advice.** *None of the information in this book is intended as a substitute for the medical advice of physicians. The reader should regularly consult a physician in matters relating to his/her health and particularly with respect to any symptoms that may require diagnosis or medical attention. Pharmacological effects listed within this text should not be considered medical claims or health indications whether explicitly or implicitly stated or implied.*

This text is for informational and educational purposes only. Be aware that THC-rich Cannabis and its cannabinoids are illegal substances in the United States and many other countries. Neither the author nor the publisher condones or encourages illegal activity. The author does not endorse, recommend, or encourage the use of any products, techniques, procedures, opinions, or other information mentioned or implied in this book. Reliance on any information in this book is at your own risk. The author is not responsible for any actions taken with the information provided. The author has made every effort to ensure the accuracy of the information within this book was correct at time of publication and assumes no responsibility for errors or omissions.

References to any specific companies, organizations, or their affiliates are not to be interpreted as indications of endorsement or support for this book, its content, the publisher, or the author.

Acknowledgements

Special thanks to my wife for tolerating the exorbitant amount of time that it took me to research and write this book. And thank you for inspiring me to press forward when I considered giving up.

This book is certainly not just a result of the work that I put into it, but the foundation that so many others have laid before me. Immense thanks to the Cannabis and cannabinoid researchers that have been publishing their work and publicly sharing their data to help further our understanding of this plant. Many researchers chose to share their publications as open source publications that allow for sharing figures and data in this book with attribution, which has allowed this book to present a lot of critical content including images and figures that would otherwise have not been shared. Thank you, thank you, thank you!

Special thanks to all the amazing contributors to the Curious About Cannabis Podcast which helped me restructure my thinking on many Cannabis science topics and informed many revisions that took place in this edition. Your contributions of your time and energy to publicly share your expertise with myself and our podcast listeners is immensely appreciated and respected.

Special thanks to the many science educators working in the Cannabis space that actively share Cannabis and cannabinoid science research findings and interpretations with the public. You have stimulated all manner of ideas in my head and many expansions and revisions in this edition would not have happened without your contributions to spreading awareness and education.

Special thanks to my various mentors throughout the years. You have gotten me to where I am now, and I hope my work brings honor to our time spent together.

Special thanks to those of you that contributed images for the book!

And finally, immense thanks to all of the Curious About Cannabis supporters, including our patrons on Patreon.com/CuriousAboutCannabis. Your support has allowed me to do things I never imagined I would be able to do.

Thank you, all. You are very much appreciated.

Jason

Contents

Index of Tables and Figures

List of "Try This!" Activities

Photo courtesy of Cheryl Johnson

ABOUT THE SECOND EDITION

Greetings!

Thanks so much for purchasing the second edition of the Curious About Cannabis™ book. It was a pleasure having the opportunity to update some of the content from the first edition as well as add new content that was not in the first edition. This edition is approximately 100 pages longer than the first edition!

So, what's different about this edition? It would be impossible for me to list everything, but here are some highlights.

Since the first edition was released, I have had the pleasure of working on the production of the Curious About Cannabis podcast (www.CACPodcast.com) where I have been able to interview a wide variety of people including Cannabis researchers, doctors, nurses, patients, dispensary owners, cultivators, and more in order to broaden my understanding of Cannabis and deliver that knowledge and range of perspectives to others. Those discussions have had profound influences regarding content that I have chosen to add into this second edition of the Curious About Cannabis™ book.

You might notice that some of the chapters and sections within chapters are in a different order compared to the first edition. After getting feedback from readers, I decided to condense, separate, and rearrange things a little bit to help the book have a slightly better flow – at least I hope that's the effect it has.

The taxonomy chapter has been updated to reflect a host of new research that has come out since the final draft of the last edition of the book was complete. This includes updated information regarding the origins of Cannabis, as well as updates on the debate over the taxonomy of Cannabis, including the most recent official taxonomical model for Cannabis that was proposed by leaders in the field in 2020.

You are going to notice that this edition contains information about even more chemical compounds found in Cannabis, including entire sections on things like quinones, esters, stilbenoids, aldehydes and phytosterols (plant steroid alcohols) found in Cannabis. There is more information about Cannabis flavonoids available, as well as clarifications about some of the common Cannabis cannabinoids and terpenoids.

This edition also highlights many more compounds found in other non-cannabis plants which interact directly with the endocannabinoid system. As more and more research is being conducted, examining how other plant compounds interact with the cannabinoid receptors in our bodies, we are learning that a lot of plants are interacting with our endocannabinoid systems regularly, which highlights the importance of diet in managing health.

The chapter on Cannabis extraction science and technology has been expanded to cover a number of different extraction and refinement technologies that have become popular that were not so commonly used when I was writing the first edition, like rotary centrifugal partition chromatography (RCPC) to isolate cannabinoid fractions from Cannabis extracts and the use of color remediation cartridges (CRC) to remove color from extracts.

Another big change for this edition is a significantly expanded chapter on hemp and a new chapter dedicated to CBD. In the CBD chapter, I describe the scientific history of CBD, leading to the production of CBD pharmaceuticals and the modern CBD industry. In the expanded hemp chapter, I describe the differences between CBD products, how to evaluate CBD products and CBD companies (which really applies to Cannabis companies broadly), and other considerations that consumers should keep in mind when considering using a hemp product.

You will find more information in this edition about cannabinoid pharmacology, including expanded information about how cannabinoids move throughout the body, as well as information about bioavailability, absorption and elimination, in an attempt to understand how different consumption methods affect the body differently. There is also expanded information about how Cannabis affects different types of people in different ways.

Those are just *some* of the updates that you will find in this edition, compared to the first edition. You can also look forward to seeing more information about how to evaluate Cannabis product manufacturers, how to manage quality control in Cannabis product manufacturing environments, expanded information about Cannabis product drug interactions and contraindications, expanded information about Cannabis safety and harm reduction, and more. And of course, there are lots more research citations and recommended resources to help you as you take your educational journey beyond the content offered in this book. A number of great books have been published since I collected resources for the first edition of *Curious About Cannabis*™, and I tried to highlight some of my favorites in this edition.

I truly hope that this book can be a resource for any inquisitive minds interested in laying a strong foundation for future learning about Cannabis. Thanks again for your interest in this book and I hope it serves you well.

Stay curious and take it easy.

Jason Wilson

Chapter 1:
ARE YOU CURIOUS ABOUT CANNABIS?

Marijuana. Hemp. Ganja. Bud. Reefer. Mary Jane. Hash Plant. Weed.

It's a plant that goes by many names...

Call it what you will - it's Cannabis. And it's got a lot of people curious...

There may be no other plant that is as controversial as the Cannabis plant. It not only has many names but also many uses such as food, fuel, fiber, medicine, intoxication, and more. The plant has been utilized by human civilizations for varying purposes for thousands of years, but until recently, there was little that was scientifically known about the plant or how it affected the human body. What little that was known was not generally available to the public.

Cannabis prohibition around the world throughout the 19th, 20th and 21st centuries has greatly limited the research that has been possible to conduct on Cannabis thus far and, as a result, consumers, producers, and curious minds have had to rely on hear-say, pseudoscience, prohibitionist propaganda, and Cannabis culture lore to learn about this plant. It is my hope that this book may help the reader transcend unreliable sources of information and begin developing a more mature perspective about the Cannabis plant, its potential risks and harms, as well as its potential benefits and opportunities.

To illustrate how young the science of Cannabis is, consider the fact that although modern pharmacological research into cannabinoids began around the 1940s, it was only in the late 1990s that the concept of the "endocannabinoid system", the human body's own cannabinoid-centered physiological system was described. It took nearly 50 years or more to piece together one of the most significant physiological systems in the human body, which upcoming nurses and doctors often still do not learn about in their studies. At the time of this writing, most health care workers are still unfamiliar with the term "endocannabinoid system" and medical science curricula either only briefly touch on the subject or ignore it altogether. In addition, most cannabinoid research that took place throughout the 1900s was largely focused on THC, only one of over 100 cannabinoids and hundreds of terpenoids found in the plant – not to mention the multitudes of other chemical compounds also found in Cannabis. We still have a long way to go toward understanding how Cannabis and cannabis compounds interact with the body.

You've probably picked up this book because you are curious about Cannabis, for one reason or another. Perhaps you are taking a Cannabis science course that uses this book as a reference text. Perhaps you are interested in trying Cannabis for the first time and want to understand more about this controversial plant before you consume it. Maybe you or someone you know uses Cannabis to treat a medical condition and you want to better understand how Cannabis affects the body and human health.

Or moreover, maybe you are a dispensary worker, Cannabis cultivator, processor, or product manufacturer and you want to brush up on your Cannabis science knowledge to improve your business, product, or process. Whether you are a Cannabis novice or a well-seasoned Cannabis connoisseur, *Curious About Cannabis*™ has something for you.

Curious About Cannabis™ is intended to be a launching point for Cannabis education. While this book covers a broad range of Cannabis science topics, it is by no means totally comprehensive. There are numerous references to other reliable resource texts throughout this book to help fill in information that was chosen to be excluded.

At the end of this chapter you will find essential questions to consider while reading this text. It is my hope that these questions may help provide direction and guide you in your quest for quality information about Cannabis. By the time you finish reviewing this text, try to answer these essential questions yourself. Remember to **utilize the citations** throughout the text to learn even more about the topics mentioned in this book!

Essential Learning Questions

Use the following questions to help guide your journey toward learning more about Cannabis science using this text:

1. What is the difference between CBD and THC?
2. What are the therapeutic promises and limitations of Cannabis?
3. How have Cannabis medical claims arisen?
4. How is Cannabis consumed and how does it affect the body?
5. How long does it take for Cannabis to leave the body?
6. How do THC and CBD interact with other drugs/medications?
7. At what concentration does THC or CBD become toxic?
8. What adverse health effects might arise from Cannabis consumption?
9. What is the endocannabinoid system?
10. What is the endocannabinoidome?
11. What contaminants might be found in Cannabis products?
12. How is Cannabis tested for potency, pesticides, microbiology, residual solvents, and terpenes?
13. What sorts of challenges exist to interpreting the results of Cannabis research?
14. What are some of the environmental impacts of Cannabis cultivation?
15. How are endocannabinoids produced in the body and what roles do they serve?
16. What effects does Cannabis consumption have on driving?
17. What are synthetic cannabinoids?
18. What are semi-synthetic cannabinoids?
19. How does Cannabis use affect pre-existing mental health conditions?
20. Why is vaporization an often-preferred whole plant drug delivery system for Cannabis?
21. How do terpenes enhance skin penetration of drugs like cannabinoids?
22. What are the metabolic products of phytocannabinoids and endocannabinoids?
23. How does Cannabis use affect blood sugar and insulin levels in the body?
24. How are Cannabis extracts produced?
25. What variables affect the consistencies and textures of Cannabis extracts?

Use the Notes section of this book to document answers to these and any other question you come up with. If you cannot find the information you need in this book, just use the references and resources listed in the appendices to find information from a variety reputable books, articles, and websites.

Good luck on your journey exploring the science of Cannabis!

PART I

INTRODUCING THE CANNABIS PLANT

Essential Questions:

What do the common colloquial terms for Cannabis products mean?

How many species of Cannabis are there thought to be?

What are the various parts of the Cannabis plant?

What are trichomes and how many types of them are there?

How is Cannabis commonly propagated, harvested, and processed?

Chapter 2:
CANNABIS TERMINOLOGY

Deciphering the Vocabulary of the Cannabis Culture

Learning Questions

- What does the term "strain" mean?
- What are the colloquial terms used to describe various styles and consistencies of Cannabis extracts?
- What are some technical terms that may be used as alternatives to colloquial Cannabis terminology?

There are a plethora of words, phrases, and terms used colloquially to describe Cannabis and Cannabis products which can be very confusing to anyone that is new to Cannabis. In this chapter you will find a short breakdown of some of the most common colloquial Cannabis terms used in the Cannabis industry.

CANNABIS STRAINS

Unique varieties, or cultivars ("cultivated variety"), of Cannabis are commonly referred to as "strains." Although the term "strain" is commonly used to refer to Cannabis cultivars, it is technically inaccurate. In botany and botanical taxonomy, there is no category called "strain," like there is in microbiology. For instance, there are various strains of the flu, or of E. coli. But this level of classification does not exist for plants. Instead unique varieties of a plant species are often referred to as variants, cultivars, or forms.

The recognized number of Cannabis strains in existence is highly disputed. The Cannabis-friendly website Leafly lists 2388 strain names in their "Cannabis Strain Explorer" (www.leafly.com/explore) at the time of this writing. Although strain names are heavily used in commercial Cannabis activities and Cannabis culture, according to recent genetic research, strain names are unreliable and often do not adequately reflect genetic lineage (Sawler et al, 2015). This could be for a variety of reasons. Strain names are sometimes accidentally mislabeled during cultivation, harvest, and processing. Sometimes strain names are purposefully mislabeled to enhance the value or marketability of a product.

Another reason strain names are unreliable is that it is common for strain names to follow both the sexual and asexual progeny (children) of the genetic progenitor (parent). When plants reproduce sexually by seed, genetic variation is introduced, and the progeny, or child plants, will not be true-to-type representations of their parent(s), yet they may be propagated under the same strain name as the parent. Alternatively, if a plant is reproduced asexually, as through cloning, the resulting child plant should be genetically similar to the parent, warranting an extension of the parent's strain name.

Some common strain names include:

"Blue Dream"	"Jack Herer"	"OG Kush"	"Sour Diesel"
"Chocolope"	"Strawberry Cough"	"Super Silver Haze"	"Z7"
"Trainwreck"	"Harlequin"	"Swiss Tsunami"	"Koala"
"Vortex"	"Hash Plant"	"G13"	"CBD Therapy"

A variety of biotechnology companies have begun work on sequencing the genomes of Cannabis varieties to catalog them and better understand the relationships between them.

PRODUCTS OF THE CANNABIS PLANT

FLOWERS, BUDS, NUGGETS AND NUGS

The term "bud" or "nug", short for "nugget", refers to a Cannabis inflorescence, or group of flowers. Usually this is in reference to dried, cured, and trimmed Cannabis flowers (see following image). The term "flower" is sometimes used as both a singular and plural term referring to collections of Cannabis inflorescences.

TRIM

"Trim" generally refers to the leaf material and small "buds" left behind after trimming a Cannabis inflorescence in preparation for retail sale. Trim contains cannabinoids and is often used to produce cannabinoid extracts or infused products.

Sugar Leaf

The term "sugar leaf" refers to leaf material that is densely covered in trichomes. "Sugar leaf" is often collected during the trimming process and used to produce cannabinoid extracts or pre-rolled Cannabis cigarettes.

Extracts, Concentrates, Dabs, and Dabbing

These are terms referring to Cannabis extracts and the act of smoking or vaporizing Cannabis concentrated extracts. The act of "dabbing" typically involves the use of a smoking device referred to as a "dab rig" which houses a receptacle that can withstand very high temperatures, often referred to as a "nail". The receptacle is heated with a torch until it is sufficiently hot. Then a small amount of Cannabis extract, or "dab", is touched to the hot surface, instantly burning or vaporizing the product while the user inhales the resulting smoke or vapor.

These concentrated extract products come in a variety of forms and consistencies. The various consistencies of "dabs" has led to the development of unique terms to differentiate them such as "shatter", "taffy", "honey oil", "budder", and "wax" which are profiled in the following sections.

Some of the variables that influence the consistency of a Cannabis extract include things like terpene content, as terpenes are often liquid at room temperature and can act as solvents for cannabinoids, as well as things like the concentration of cannabinoids that want to be solid at room temperature, like THCA or CBD. Additionally, the way that an extract is refined or handled can influence its texture or consistency. For instance, budder can be turned into badder by whipping it enough that it becomes aerated and fluffy. Additionally, extracts can be formulated, as with sauce or diamonds, where the ratio of crystallized cannabinoids to terpenes and liquid cannabinoids is altered to create a desired consistency.

The following is a chart that demonstrates the spectrum of Cannabis extract types, their consistencies, and their presumed chemical constituents. However, as with most things, there are exceptions to these rules, and formulated extracts like sauce and diamonds have been excluded from the chart to keep things simple. Sauce and diamonds would be examples of extracts that could have both high terpene content and high THCA or CBD content since the products are defined as crystallized cannabinoids soaked in a terpene rich liquid. Additionally, distillates can exhibit a wide range of consistencies, depending on chemical profile, but often it is the consistency of hot glue, which is why it has been placed in the middle of the chart.

Dry/Wet	THCA or CBD Content	Terpene Content	Extract Type
Very Dry/Solid	High	Low	
↕	↕	↕	Crystalline Isolate
			"Shatter"
			"Pull n Snap"
			Distillate (w/ terpenes)
			"Honey Oil" / "Hash Oil"
			Essential Oils
Very Wet/Liquid	Low	High	

DIAMONDS/DIAMOND OIL

"Diamonds" is a relatively new term, generally referencing a product consisting of crystallized cannabinoids, soaked in essential oils, or terpenes. The THCA or CBD crystal somewhat resembles a diamond – hence the term "diamonds".

DISTILLATE/DISTTY/DISTY

A distillate is an extract that has undergone a distillation process, typically a "short path" distillation process, which is described in the Cannabis Extraction Technologies chapter. Distillate extracts are commonly referred to by the slang terms "disty" or "distty" among some circles of Cannabis extract producers.

HONEY OIL

"Honey oil" is a term typically referring to hash oil that is light in color and runny at room temperature. The light color is generally thought to indicate purity, though this is not always the case. Honey oils tend to be rich in terpenes and cannabinoids like THC or CBDA which are more liquid at room temperature.

ISOLATE/ZIRCONIA

An "isolate" is a product that generally appears as a white, off-white, or slightly yellow powder or crystal which is thought to be >95% pure – generally either isolated THCA or isolated CBDA. Isolated cannabinoids are sometimes referred to as "zirconia", referencing their diamond-like appearance.

KIEF AND HASH

The term "kief" refers to mechanically sifted trichomes that have been separated from Cannabis flower and leaf tissue. This can be accomplished by simply tumbling Cannabis over a mesh screen placed above a collection receptacle. Sometimes the terms "kief" and "hash" are used interchangeably.

ROSIN/ROSIN TECH

"Rosin" is a term referring to Cannabis extracts produced through a solvent-less heat pressing method. Cannabis material is placed within wax paper and then heated and squeezed to remove the oils from the plant material.

SHATTER

Extracts called "shatter" have a semi-solid structure at room temperature. Shatter will usually easily break or shatter when handled. "Shatter" extracts typically have higher concentrations of either THCA or CBD, which tend to be more solid at room temperature, as opposed to THC or CBDA, which are more liquid at room temperature.

TAFFY, SNAP, PULL 'N SNAP

"Taffy", "Snap", or "Pull n Snap" is a concentrate product with a consistency between that of shatter and oil. It is sticky, but still semi-solid, and will stretch apart like gum or taffy. It will pull and eventually break or snap.

WAX/CRUMBLE

"Wax" or "crumble" has a light fluffy appearance at room temperature and is often orange to pale yellow in appearance. It is a "dry" extract which is brittle and crumbles when handled. Wax extracts tend to contain higher concentrations of either THCA or CBD, which tend to be primarily solid at room temperature.

LIVE RESIN VS CURED RESIN

Live resin refers to Cannabis extracts produced from freshly harvested ("live") Cannabis material, which is typically frozen, commonly referred to as "fresh frozen", rather than dried, and then run through an extraction system. The result is an extract typically very high in monoterpenes compared to more traditional extracts produced from Cannabis materials that have already dried and volatized off some of their monoterpenes. Because of the high concentration of monoterpenes, live resins have a more pungent smell and is reported to have strong flavors during smoking or vaporizing.

The term "cured resin" simply refers to extracts produced from Cannabis biomass that was allowed to dry and cure in storage prior to extraction. While it is often claimed that it is possible to distinguish live resin extracts versus cured resin extracts by their color and fluidity, this is not always the case. While live resin extracts often feature brighter colors and a more fluid consistency, it is entirely possible to get a very similar outcome with cured biomass, depending on the extraction method.

Nug Runs vs Trim Runs

If Cannabis buds, as opposed to leaf material, are used for producing Cannabis extracts, the extraction is considered a "nug run", referring to the use of "nugs", or inflorescences. An extraction that utilizes the trimmed off leaf material is referred to as a "trim run." It may be possible to obtain greater extraction yields using trim or "sugar leaf" due to the excess surface area available compared to dense inflorescences.

Vac Purging and Vac Ovens

"Vac purging" refers to vacuum purging of solvents during extract production. Once solvent has passed through the extraction vessel filled with Cannabis material, the resulting oil is placed in a vacuum chamber so that the volatile solvent may be pulled out and recycled in a closed loop extraction system. A "Vac oven" is a vacuum oven used to heat items while applying a vacuum to remove all water, solvent, or other volatiles that enter the air.

Topicals

Topicals are products that are intended to be applied to the skin. Cannabis resins can be formulated into different topical products like balms, skin creams, lotions, and transdermal patches.

Edibles

Cannabis infused foods are often referred to simply as "edibles". Common Cannabis edibles range from chocolates and gummies to sodas and hot sauces, and everything in between.

Cannabis Consumption Devices

Blunt

A "blunt" is a Cannabis cigarillo, also called a "'rillo", usually made by opening a tobacco cigarillo, discarding the tobacco contents, filling with Cannabis, and resealing the cigarillo. Blunts often contain anywhere from 0.75 to 1.5 grams of Cannabis, traditionally.

Bong, Bubbler

A "bong" or "bubbler" is a smoking pipe that features a chamber that holds water which the smoke passes through before entering the user's body. It is often assumed that bongs, or water pipes, effectively filter Cannabis smoke, however research has brought that idea into question. Some studies indicate that bongs may actually expose users to more tar than using an unfiltered pipe or Cannabis cigarette.

Bowl

The term "bowl" refers to a pipe bowl. Cannabis smokers often use the phrase, "load a bowl" or "spark a bowl" to refer to engaging in the act of smoking Cannabis. A typical bowl usually holds somewhere between 0.25 to 0.5 grams of Cannabis.

Dab Rig

A "dab rig" or "dab pipe" is a device specifically used for the smoking of concentrated Cannabis extracts, colloquially referred to as "dabs", as in, "a dab will do you." Dab rigs often feature significantly smaller receptacles compared to other Cannabis smoking devices and are made of materials that can withstand the considerably higher temperatures often used to smoke "dabs". Some dab rigs feature electronic receptacles, called "e-nails" that heat up to programmed temperatures to allow for controlled vaporization or smoking.

Unlike a typical pipe, dab rig receptacles are heated *before* introducing the Cannabis product, allowing the product to vaporize or burn once it touches the hot surface.

Joints and Pre-Rolls

A "joint" is a slang term referring to a Cannabis cigarette. Joints can be filtered or unfiltered, just like traditional tobacco cigarettes. Joints often contain somewhere between 0.5 to 1 gram of Cannabis, traditionally. As consumer products, joints are usually called "pre-rolls".

Vaporizer, Vapes, and Vape Pens

A vaporizer, or "vape", is a temperature-controlled device that is designed to heat Cannabis materials up to a point at which the chemicals in the plant will lightly volatize into a vapor stream, avoiding combustion of the plant material or extract and limiting exposure to tars and toxic compounds that would be found in the smoke. Some vaporizers are portable and referred to as "vape pens" or "electronic cigarettes".

MISC. TERMS YOU MAY COME BY

DANK, FIRE

The terms "dank" and "fire" are often used to refer to highly desirable or very **potent** Cannabis products. For instance, a consumer might comment, "That Afghan OG was super dank!" or "That Afghan OG was fire!", meaning that the Cannabis was potent and pleasurable.

DECARB'ING/ACTIVATING CANNABINOIDS

The term "decarb'ing" is a shorthand term referring to the process of **decarboxylation**. Decarboxylation is the process of removing a carboxyl group from a molecule, often through exposure to heat or simply old age. All cannabinoids produced in Cannabis start off as cannabinoid acids, like THCA, before becoming decarboxylated and converting to their neutral forms, like THC. This process is often referred to as "activating cannabinoids".

PHENO/PHENO HUNTING

This is a shorthand term referring to the word "**phenotype**". The phenotype is the physical or morphological profile of an organism. This contrasts with genotype, which is the genetic profile of an organism, and the chemotype, which is the chemical profile of an organism. Breeder that cultivate many different plants of a strain by seed in search of varieties that exhibit desired characteristics are said to be "pheno hunting." Although it would be more correct to say they are both "pheno and chemo hunting".

TERP(S)/TERP JUICE

This is a shorthand term referencing **terpenes** and terpene products. Often this is a term used to bring attention to monoterpenoids present in Cannabis products, as these terpenes are more pungent and have stronger flavors than other heavier terpenoids.

The term "terp juice" refers to liquid lightweight terpenoids, usually in reference to particularly runny extracts like "diamonds" where the cannabinoids are not fully dissolved and well blended with the terpene fraction of the extract. "Terp juice" is also sometimes used more broadly to refer to essential oils or flavoring additives.

ALTERNATIVES TO COMMON COLLOQUIAL CANNABIS TERMS

Cannabis Colloquial Terminology Translation Guide		
Colloquial Term	Alternative Term	Description
Banana(s)	Anther	Pollen releasing structure of the male Cannabis plant, which somewhat resemble small bananas
Blunt (large)	Cannabis Cigar	
Blunt (thin)	Cannabis Cigarillo	
Bong, Dab Rig	Water Pipe	Pipe, often glass, featuring a chamber to hold water for purposes of smoke filtration
Buds, Nugs, Flower	Inflorescence(s)	Groups of Cannabis flowers
Crystals, Sugar	Trichomes	
Dank, Fire	Potent	Adjective describing desirable or potent Cannabis or cannabinoid products
Decarb, Activating	Decarboxylate	Applying heat to Cannabis products to convert cannabinoid acids (THCA, CBDA, etc) to neutral cannabinoids (THC, CBD, etc)
Distty, Disty	Distillate	The resulting refined cannabinoid-rich extract after distillation
Hairs	Fused Stigma and Style	Part of the pistil that extends away from the plant to help guide pollen into the ovaries
Joint	Cannabis Cigarette	
Oil, Dab, Wax, Rosin, etc	Resin	Resinous secretions from the Cannabis plant that may be extracted and/or concentrated
Pheno	Phenotype	The physical attributes of an organism such as size, shape, color, etc.
Raw Oil; Crude	Oleoresin	A primary extract of plant essential oils and resins
Strain	Cultivar, Variety, Varietal, Form	A cultivated variety of the Cannabis plant, typically with a unique morphology or chemical profile
Terp Juice	Essential Oils, Terpenoid Solution	A solution comprised primarily of mono and sesquiterpenoids
Terp(s)	Terpenoid	
Trim	Trimmings	Whole or trimmed Cannabis leaves, separated from Cannabis flowers during harvest and post-harvest processing.
Vac Purge	Desolvate	Removing solvent or volatiles from a Cannabis extract using heat and a vacuum
Zirconia	Isolate	Crystalline cannabinoids resembling diamonds

FIGURE 1: CANNABIS COLLOQUIAL TERMINOLOGY TRANSLATION GUIDE

Enduring Understandings

- The term "strain" is not a term used in botany. A more appropriate term to describe unique Cannabis varieties would be **cultivar**, meaning cultivated variety.

- There are a myriad of Cannabis extract products of different consistencies and formulations, each with unique colloquial names.

- There are many formal alternatives to most of the colloquial terms used to describe Cannabis and Cannabis products.

- Understanding the colloquial meanings behind commonly used Cannabis terms can help eliminate confusion for consumers, healthcare professionals and others that may be new to Cannabis.

Chapter 3:
CANNABIS TAXONOMY

"...We would all prefer simple nostrums to explain complex systems, but this is futile and even potentially dangerous in the context of a psychoactive drug such as Cannabis."

Ethan Russo, MD (Piomelli and Russo, 2016)

Learning Questions
- How has Cannabis been classified throughout history?
- Where did Cannabis originate?
- How many species of Cannabis are there?
- What do the terms "sativa" and "indica" mean?

Cannabis sativa. Cannabis indica. Cannabis ruderalis. For those readers already well versed in Cannabis lore, these names are often referred to as the three-definitive species of Cannabis. But the fact is, the taxonomy of Cannabis is not well understood or agreed upon among scientists, and for the sake of consumers, a better model is needed. This chapter will explore the ways in which Cannabis has been named and categorized throughout history, and what modern science is telling us about the differences between Cannabis varieties.

There has been a long-standing debate over the taxonomy of Cannabis ever since botanists and naturalists began working with the plant and confounded ever more by the chemists and geneticists working with it today. **Taxonomy** is a term which refers to the way that something is categorized and classified. In botany, plants are organized according to the following hierarchy: Kingdom, Class, Order Family, Genus, Species, Subspecies, Variety, Form

Botanical taxonomy utilizes a **binomial nomenclature**, or a "two-name system of naming," when categorizing and naming plants, which focuses on the plant's genus and species. For instance:

Cannabis sativa

➢ The first word refers to the **genus** of the organism and is always capitalized.

➢ The second word refers to the **species** of the organism and is lower case.

➢ **Subspecies, varieties, and forms** are also written lower case.

   o   "ssp." = subspecies   "var." = variant   "f." = form

Cannabis sativa ssp. sativa

The Cannabis genus belongs to the botanical family Cannabaceae, which also contains the genus Humulus, which are known as hops, commonly known as the plants used as bittering agents for beer. And, depending on what botanical reference text you reference, the genera Celtis and Trema may also be included in the Cannabaceae family. These genera consist of small trees commonly used for landscaping. The USDA still lists Celtis as belonging to the botanical family Ulmaceae, although this categorization is often disputed among botanists.

THE ORIGINS OF THE CANNABIS PLANT

The "original" wild ancestor of Cannabis has never been discovered, and likely no longer exists. So where did the Cannabis plant come from? This has been a difficult question to answer, but modern pollen research may provide the clues we need to retrace the spread of Cannabis throughout the world to pinpoint its origins. In 2018, McPartland et al published the results of genetic research of fossilized pollen from Cannabis and Humulus (hops). They separated pollen based on the ecological environment under which they would have existed. Ancient Cannabis is associated with steppe environments, whereas ancient Humulus plants are associated with forested environments.

Plant	Ancient Environment	Accompanying Plants
Humulus lupus (hop)	Forest	*Alnus, Salix, Quercus, Robinia, Juglans*
Cannabis sativa	Steppe (Grasslands)	Poaceae, *Artemisia,* Chenopodiaceae

FIGURE 2: ANCIENT ENVIRONMENTS AND PLANTS ASSOCIATED WITH HUMULUS AND CANNABIS

Cannabis and Humulus are thought to have diverged approximately 28 million years ago (McPartland, 2019). The oldest Cannabis pollen that the researchers could identify was estimated to be approximately 19.6 million years ago from northwestern China (McPartland et al, 2019). Their results led them to posit that Cannabis may have been initially domesticated in Europe, near present-day Bulgaria and Romania, before it spread to Asia and Africa (McPartland et al, 2018). Follow up research that was conducted after this initial pollen study showed that the origins of Cannabis likely extend back to the northeastern area of the Tibetan Plateau. It is thought that from the Tibetan Plateau, Cannabis traveled to Eastern Europe, where domestication of the Cannabis plant started to take hold, before moving to Eastern Asia and elsewhere. (McPartland et al, 2019)

FIGURE 3: SPREAD OF CANNABIS ACROSS EUROPE AND ASIA

Cannabis wouldn't reach the Americas until more recently, in the last several hundred years. It is speculated that Cannabis may have reached South America as early as the 1500s, and North America within the 1800s.

A VERY BRIEF HISTORY OF CANNABIS TAXONOMY

Cannabis was first formally classified by Carolus Linnaeus in 1753 in his *Species Planatarum* (Linnaeus, 1753). Linnaeus is responsible for formally applying the system of naming and categorizing organisms, like plants, that is still in use today. Linnaeus described only one species of Cannabis - *Cannabis sativa*. If you look at a listing for *Cannabis sativa*, it will usually read "*Cannabis sativa* L." The "L" refers to Linnaeus. The specimens that Linneaus used to characterize Cannabis were common forms of Cannabis cultivated throughout Europe, which today we would refer to as "hemp".

Jean-Baptiste Lamarck, a naturalist from the 18th and early 19th centuries who named well over 1600 distinct species in his lifetime, came along thirty years later and categorized a unique Cannabis plant with a sharp smell and intoxicating qualities as *Cannabis indica*. Lamarck approached differentiating Cannabis types by looking at their different **morphologies,** or shapes and sizes, and their geographic ranges, while also considering their aromas and potency, or intoxicating qualities (Hillig, 2004). Lamarck categorized *Cannabis indica* as having more narrow leaflets than *Cannabis sativa*, which is opposite of how the terms are commonly used today (Lamarck, 1785). For Lamarck, *Cannabis indica* was a plant with narrow leaflets from India (hence "indica") which were intoxicating.

Potential Monotypic Species Models of *Cannabis sativa*

Kingdom	Plantae
Class	Magnoliopsida
Order	Rosales
Family	Cannabaceae
Genus	Cannabis
Species	sativa
Potential Subspecies	sativa, indica
Cultivar epithet	'GG #4', 'Koala', 'Moonshine Haze', etc

Potential Polytypic Species Models of *Cannabis*

Kingdom	Plantae
Class	Magnoliopsida
Order	Rosales
Family	Cannabaceae
Genus	Cannabis
Potential Species	sativa, indica, ruderalis, etc
Potential Subspecies	sativa, indica, afghanica, ruderalis, spontanea, kafiristanica, etc
Cultivar epithet	'GG #4', 'Koala', 'Moonshine Haze', etc

In 1929 Vavilov and Bukinich performed research on wild Cannabis populations in central Asia and Afghanistan. They determined that there were two separate Cannabis species: *Cannabis sativa* and *Cannabis indica*. The wild variations of *Cannabis indica* were called *Cannabis indica* var. *kafiristanica*. The wild form of *Cannabis sativa* was called *Cannabis sativa* var. *spontanea*. The researchers felt that what was often called *Cannabis ruderalis* was in fact this *spontanea* variant. "Spontanea" was a term generally reserved to describe plants that had escaped cultivation. This sentiment would be echoed in 2004 when Karl Hillig published a paper that reported so few morphological differences were found between the so-called *Cannabis ruderalis* and the wild biotype of *Cannabis sativa* that Hillig was convinced of a two-species model for Cannabis: *Cannabis sativa* and *Cannabis indica*, with feral (wild) and cultivated varieties between each of them (Hillig, 2004).

In the book *Cannabis Evolution and Ethnobotany*, authors Robert Clarke and Mark Merlin explain that researcher Richard Schultes followed the work of Vavilov and Bukinich and worked to expand it, applying Lamarck's term *Cannabis indica* to a series of *Cannabis* varieties from both Afghanistan and India. However, Lamarck's use of the term *Cannabis indica* was distinctively used to refer to varieties only from India, not Afghanistan. According to Clarke and Merlin, there was no evidence that Lamarck had even studied Afghan varieties of Cannabis. Schultes went on to describe *indica* varieties as Cannabis plants that were short and bushy, while *sativa* plants were characterized as being tall with wide spacing between branches – a model very similar to the colloquial "sativa" and "indica" model used in today's Cannabis culture.

In 1973, Small and Beckstead broke Cannabis plants down into three different chemical phenotypes, or chemotypes (Small and Beckstead, 1973b). These chemotypes were differentiated based on their ratios of delta-9 THC to CBD. They tried to average these ratios among plants to categorize them, but this made it impossible to distinguish the chemotype of an individual plant (Small and Beckstead, 1973a).

In 1976 Small and Cronquist published a paper examining Cannabis taxonomy and claimed that *Cannabis indica* should be reduced to the status of subspecies, resulting in *Cannabis sativa* subsp. *sativa* and *Cannabis sativa* subsp. *indica*. Then each of these was split into cultivated and wild varieties based on cannabinoid content of leaf tissues (Small and Cronquist, 1976). In 1986, Robert Clarke visited the New York Botanical Garden herbarium to examine Small and Cronquist's Cannabis samples and found that varieties from Afghanistan were seemingly absent – revealing a problem with their proposed taxonomical system (Clarke and Merlin, 2013). This problem would later be corrected in a revised taxonomy put forward by John McPartland and Ernest Small in 2020.

Other researchers disagreed with Small's approach. Emboden made the claim that the inebriant effect of a plant (ie. THC content) cannot be a legitimate characteristic for determining taxonomic classification, thus the chemical levels of THC in the plant are completely irrelevant for Cannabis classification (Emboden, 1981).

Researchers looking again at morphological features of the Cannabis plant focused on the size of the leaflets between varieties. The researcher Loran Anderson would later refine Schultes' model in 1980 by stating that *sativa* plants had narrow leaflets, while *indica* plants had wife leaflets. The work of Schultes and Anderson are what largely contributed to the colloquial nomenclature that is popular today – although Schultes and Anderson never intended these terms to be associated with plants of any particular chemical profile, which they stated explicitly. The idea that *sativa* and *indica* plants produce unique effects would come along later as the details of each of these different proposed taxonomical models would get confused in the minds of both lay people and researchers alike.

Along with cannabinoid-centric chemotype research, there is also taxonomical research now looking at how *terpenoid* variation might help reveal more information about how the Cannabis plant varieties should be categorized (Hillig, 2004). The process of examining the chemical profile of something for the purposes of taxonomical classification is called **chemotaxonomy**. The terpenoid variations among plants of known geographic origin, partnered with cannabinoid content and genetic information could help solidify the taxonomy of Cannabis.

Did You Know?

The term "sativa" means "cultivated".

For example, the common cultivated oat is *Avena sativa*. Some researchers argue that all Cannabis is "sativa" because it has been cultivated for thousands of years, casting doubt that any true wild Cannabis plants exist anymore.

Etienee de Meijer points out the deficits of categorizing Cannabis plants based on cannabinoid chemotypes in Chapter 2 of *Handbook of* Cannabis, *The Chemical Phenotypes (Chemotypes) of Cannabis* (2015):

"The great difficulty with such criteria is that **[Cannabis plants] have, directly or indirectly, been subjected to human selection for ages**. *Furthermore, cannabinoid ratios are governed by simple genetic mechanisms and in segregating populations, or even in single plant progenies,* morphologically similar plants can be found with strongly contrasting chemotypes. *This makes the cannabinoid chemotype unsuitable as a taxonomic criterion."* (Emphasis added)

More recently attention has focused away from morphology and chemotypes, instead looking at the *genetics* of these varying plant types to look for **"restricted gene flow."** This means that researchers are trying to find any genetic markers that seem to belong solely to one type of Cannabis plant and not to others. Then, this might be a means of at least differentiating the *varieties* of Cannabis plants and determining whether there may be distinct species or subspecies of Cannabis.

When using DNA evidence to support taxonomical changes, researchers also take the geographic origin of the plants into consideration, as this can help provide more information about how these genetic differences might have arisen. Knowing geographic origin can sometimes help resolve taxonomic disputes by giving researchers an idea of how various gene pools might have interacted with one another. The term **gene pool** refers to the "stock" of genes that are available in an organism's population. As different populations interact, the gene pools mix and change. If part of a gene pool becomes geographically isolated, gene flow is restricted, and the two pools may become substantially unique over time.

In 2014 John McPartland released details of research he and Dr. Geoffrey Guy undertook using "DNA barcoding" to determine if Cannabis *indica* and *sativa* were two distinct species. Their results revealed that they are actually one species, challenging his previous theories of a polytypic species model for Cannabis. The researchers claimed that the nomenclature of Cannabis varieties needed to be corrected so that what is currently traditionally being called "*sativa*" should instead be "*indica*", what is now called "*indica*" should be called "*afghanica*", and what is now called "*ruderalis*" should be called "*sativa*." (O'Shaughnessy's online, 2015)

McPartland described this new model as consisting of *Cannabis sativa* ssp. *indica*, *Cannabis sativa* ssp. *afghanica*, and *Cannabis sativa* ssp. *sativa*. The subspecies *indica* was characterized as being tall with spaced branching, containing much greater THC than CBD, and originating from India. Subspecies *afghanica* was characterized as being short, densely branched, containing more or roughly the same THC to CBD, and originating from Central Asia. Subspecies *sativa* was characterized as a mostly wild or ruderal species with a CBD content greater than THC content on average with variable morphology. (O'Shaughnessy's online, 2015)

McPartland would later revise this proposed taxonomical model with the help of Ernest Small, where they posit that Cannabis truly only consists of one species, *Cannabis sativa*, with two subspecies, sativa and indica, and various varieties within those subspecies. In this revised model, all THC-rich Cannabis varieties fall under *Cannabis sativa ssp. indica*.

A series of work conducted by Karl Hillig examining the genetic history of Cannabis seems to support a model similar to McPartland's proposal. Hillig's research revealed two primary gene pools in the *Cannabis sativa* lineage. One gene pool seems to have started somewhere near Asia or Eastern Europe and consists of hemp type Cannabis landrace strains. The second primary gene pool includes both narrow and wide leaflet drug-type Cannabis varieties as well as a unique variety of hemp type Cannabis. This second gene pool extends from eastern Asia to southern Asia Africa, Latin America, Afghanistan, Pakistan, India, and Nepal; (Hillig, 2003). This data suggests that perhaps there are two genetically distinct Cannabis species or subspecies, but the narrow and wide leaflet varieties of THC-rich Cannabis are still the same species, as reflected by McPartland and Guy's DNA research. Instead, under Hillig's model, it would be hemp forms of Cannabis that fall under multiple species or subspecies.

A Tale of Hillig's Two Gene Pools

Hillig's genetic variation research reveals two distinct gene pools of Cannabis. One gene pool (black arrows) seems to have spread from the Afghanistan region to Asia, Africa, Europe, and South America. This gene pool includes all drug type varieties of Cannabis as well as some hemp varieties of Cannabis. Meanwhile a separate gene pool (orange arrows) primarily consisting of unique hemp varieties spread to Eastern Europe and Western Asia.

THE CULTONOMIC NOMENCLATURE OF CANNABIS

While researchers continue to try to categorize Cannabis, a "cultonomic" (AHP, 2013) nomenclature, or culture-focused system of naming, of its own has already been established in the Cannabis culture which is due for revision. If you visit a Cannabis dispensary today, you are likely to be confronted with products labeled according to the traditional dichotomy of *sativa* vs. *indica* with unique physiological or psychoactive effects associated with each type. Many Cannabis dispensary technicians, also known as "budtenders", tend to advise consumers to use this system for identifying Cannabis products that will deliver the desired effects the consumer is looking for.

The term *Cannabis indica* is today typically associated with Cannabis plants featuring wider leaflets and a bushier appearance that supposedly produce "body heavy" or sedative effects whereas *Cannabis sativa* is associated with Cannabis plants with thin leaflets and effects described as being more uplifting and energetic. Strains are often reported as falling along a spectrum of 100% indica to 100% sativa. A strain may be labeled as a "60% sativa/40% indica" variety, for instance, and would probably be said to be overall an uplifting variety with some pain-relieving qualities.

As revealed in this chapter, strain names are not reliable indicators of genetic lineage. A plant's shape and size do not indicate its biochemistry. There is no such thing as a "60% sativa 40% indica hybrid" per se. Two Cannabis plants may look alike in every way and exhibit distinct cannabinoid and terpenoid profiles. Two Cannabis plants of the same strain cultivated in the same area can even end up exhibiting distinct chemical profiles. In addition, this traditional sativa/indica view assumes that the effects of Cannabis will always fall within a spectrum between only two states of being: sedation and stimulation. This characterization is an oversimplification of human experience and presents a false dichotomy.

While there *are* unique chemical differences between wide leaflet drug type varieties and narrow leaflet drug type varieties of Cannabis (Hillig, 2004), there is little data supporting the idea that the biochemistry or even lineage of a plant can be assumed based on the morphology (size and shape) of the plant. The Cannabis plant is far more complex than the traditional view of "sativa vs. indica" supports and a new view is needed which embraces the available genetic and chemotaxonomic data and advises consumers to focus on the chemotype of a product, not the strain or indica/sativa indication.

In a 2016 interview published in the journal Cannabis and Cannabinoid Research, Cannabis and cannabinoid researcher Dr. Ethan Russo commented:

> *"There are biochemically distinct strains of Cannabis, but the sativa/indica distinction as commonly applied in the lay literature is total nonsense and an exercise in futility. One cannot in any way currently guess the biochemical content of a given Cannabis plant based on its height, branching, or leaf morphology. The degree of interbreeding/hybridization is such that only a biochemical assay tells a potential consumer or scientist what is really in the plant. It is essential that future commerce allows complete and accurate cannabinoid and terpenoid profiles to be available…*
>
> *… We would all prefer simple nostrums to explain complex systems, but this is futile and even potentially dangerous in the context of a psychoactive drug such as Cannabis. Once again, it is necessary to quantify the biochemical components of a given Cannabis strain and correlate these with the observed effects in real patients. Beyond the increasing number of CBD predominant strains in recent years, almost all Cannabis on the market has been from high-THC strains. The differences in observed effects in Cannabis are then due to their terpenoid content, which is rarely assayed, let alone reported to potential consumers."*

Piomelli Daniele and Russo Ethan B.. Cannabis and Cannabinoid Research.
January 2016, 1(1): 44-46. doi:10.1089/can.2015.29003.ebr.

A MODERN TAXONOMY FOR LANDRACE THC-RICH PLANTS

A "landrace" variety of Cannabis is one that has grown to be naturalized to its environment. Despite a popular misconception, "landrace strains" are *not* wild Cannabis varieties, but instead are naturalized varieties, adapted to their environment. It has been found that modern hybridized domesticate varieties of Cannabis can begin re-naturalizing and exhibiting wild-type characteristics in as few as 50 generations (McPartland, 2020). This is one reason why it is so difficult for researchers to determine whether any "wild" Cannabis plants exist. It is very challenging to distinguish between older landrace Cannabis varieties that are truly "wild-type" versus those that have recently escaped cultivation and re-naturalized.

In 2020, McPartland and Small published a paper that sought to formally categorize Cannabis into a new taxonomical model based on morphological, geographical, chemical, and genetic data. Their focus was on THC-rich landrace cultivars of Cannabis and their hope was that a formal taxonomical system for these landrace plants will help researchers identify them in the field and contribute to preserving their genetic diversity before they are hybridized with other landraces or modern hybrid Cannabis varieties.

The table below summarizes their proposed taxonomical system for THC-rich landrace Cannabis varieties.

Cannabis sativa ssp. indica (All THC-rich Landrace Varieties)		
var. indica	Domesticated THC-rich varieties that are tall and widely branched, pleasant aroma, large seeds, THC/CBD ratio > 7	South Asia; Colloquially commonly called "sativa"
var. himalayensis	Wild-type THC-rich varieties (THC/CBD ratio ~7) that are tall and widely branching, pleasant aroma, small seeds that easily drop	South Asia
var. afghanica	Domesticated THC-rich varieties that are short and bushy, skunky aroma, large seeds, THC/CBD ratio < 7	Central Asia; Colloquially commonly called "indica"
var. asperrima	Wild-type THC-rich varieties (THC/CBD ratio <2) that are short and bushy, skunky aroma, small seeds that easily drop	Central Asia

FIGURE 4: MODERN TAXONOMY FOR LANDRACE VARIETIES

It is interesting to note that the South Asian and Central Asian ecoregions for these landrace varieties converge somewhere around the borders of modern Pakistan and Afghanistan, resulting in a fascinating zone of diversity where all four of these varieties, as well as hybrids between them, may be found.

It is important to note that this model does not apply to modern hybridized varieties of Cannabis like you would see in a medical or adult use Cannabis dispensary, which have been hybridized to the point that the major differences found in landrace varieties are largely no longer present. Under this model, what Cannabis connoisseurs refer to as "Sativa" or "Indica" are actually hybrids between *Cannabis sativa ssp. indica var. indica* and *var. afghanica*.

Colloquial Term	Suspected Hybridization	Description
"Sativa"	Cannabis sativa ssp. indica var. indica x var. afghanica	Hybrids of both domesticated THC-rich varieties, leaning toward var. indica traits over var. afghanica
"Indica"	Cannabis sativa ssp. indica var. afghanica x var. indica	Hybrids of both domesticated THC-rich varieties, leaning toward var. afghanica traits over var. indica
"Ruderalis"	Cannabis sativa ssp. sativa var. sativa x Cannabis sativa ssp. indica var. asperrima	Hybrids of domesticated hemp and a wild-type THC-rich variety from Central Asia

FIGURE 5: DESCRIPTIONS OF SATIVA, INDICA, AND RUDERALIS HYBRIDIZATION

HOW MANY SPECIES OF CANNABIS ARE THERE, REALLY?

The problem is not all scientists agree what a species of plant actually is. I know, that may sound weird. How could scientists not agree on something that seems so simple?

For biologists, "species" typically means anything that can mate and produce fertile offspring. However, geneticists and molecular biologists are challenging this definition after revealing diversity present among seemingly similar organisms once examined on a chemical or genetic level.

If we accept the typical biological definition of "species", then there is probably only one species of Cannabis, ultimately. Although Hillig revealed two gene pools in his research, it could be argued that this diversity is on a subspecies level, not the species level.

Varying Definitions of "Species"	
Biological Species	Organisms that can interbreed, form viable offspring, and are reproductively isolated from other groups
Ecological Species	Organisms that can interbreed and are adapted to a particular set of resources in an environment
Genetic/Phylogenetic Species	Organisms comprising a unique gene pool, which can interbreed, and are genetically isolated from other gene pools.

FIGURE 6: VARYING DEFINITIONS OF "SPECIES"

Although McPartland and Small presented a modern monotypic taxonomical model of Cannabis, there are modern polytypic, or multi-species, models that have been proposed as well. A recent polytypic model of Cannabis taxonomy was proposed in *Cannabis Evolution and Ethnobotany*. The authors propose that there are at least two species of Cannabis, which came from a common ancestor which is either represented by some plants labeled *Cannabis ruderalis,* or may no longer to be in existence. These two current species or subspecies, depending on how you define the term "species", would be *Cannabis sativa*, which represents a specific genetic pool of European hemp cultivars, and *Cannabis indica*, which represents all THC dominant "drug cultivars" as well as Asian broad leaf hemp cultivars.

Within the *indica* group, there are wide and narrow leaf varieties of THC-rich cultivars, with *Cannabis indica ssp. indica* representing narrow leaf THC-rich cultivars, and *Cannabis indica ssp. afghanica* representing broad leaf THC-rich cultivars. And among those varieties, there are feral varieties that have escaped cultivation and naturalized to their environments. This model is actually very close to the model proposed more recently by McPartland and Small, with the exception that McPartland and Small proposed a monotypic model, and reduced all THC dominant cultivars to the ranks of varieties of the indica subspecies.

So, how many species of Cannabis are there? It seems as though more and more researchers are leaning toward embracing a monotypic model of Cannabis, as proposed by McPartland and Small, but there will likely always be camps of dissenters that provide compelling arguments for the idea that Cannabis consists of multiple species. This debate may be one that never ends.

Currently, the **Integrated Taxonomic Information System**, which provides authoritative information on plants, animals, fungi, and microbes of the world in partnership between ITIS-North America, Species 2000, and the Global Biodiversity Information Facility, recognizes only one species of Cannabis, *Cannabis sativa*. *Cannabis sativa* is then broken down into two subspecies, *Cannabis sativa* ssp. *sativa* and *Cannabis sativa* ssp. *indica*. This is consistent with the taxonomical model proposed by McPartland and Small in 2020 and is likely to be the accepted model for botanists for the foreseeable future.

CANNABIS TAXONOMY AND THE CONSUMER

How does this taxonomy debate affect the consumer?

If the terms "sativa" and "indica" aren't correct, what terms *are* correct?

Let's make one thing clear: all of these debates about formal Cannabis taxonomy have little influence over the types of Cannabis found in the modern Cannabis industry, which is composed of intensely artificially selected and hybridized forms of Cannabis plants. The taxonomy debate is much more relevant for landrace cultivars and their wild-type forms which are reservoirs of genetic diversity that has been contaminated by modern breeding. With a formal taxonomical model in place, botanists, breeders, seed collectors, and enthusiasts can ensure that underrepresented landrace genetics are collected and classified appropriately. But this doesn't really affect the common Cannabis consumer at all.

While researchers may continue to debate over details regarding Cannabis taxonomy, what modern researchers do agree on is that the different varieties of THC-rich Cannabis colloquially referred to as "indica" and "sativa" actually belong to a single species, regardless of what we call that species, and there seem to be some chemotypical patterns between Cannabis varieties. Just as a single species of plant can exhibit a variety of shapes, colors, and sizes, a single species of plant can exhibit a variety of chemical profiles. Researchers also generally agree that hemp varieties display both narrow leaf and wide leaf varieties just like THC dominant "drug varieties". In addition, more research is revealing that strain names are often poorly correlated with genetic lineage or chemical profile, making their utility highly limited at best.

So, what does all of this mean to a consumer or producer?

1. Recognize that the "indica" / "sativa" language used to describe THC-rich varieties of Cannabis is not scientifically supported and the terms are used inconsistently. Try to describe plants appropriately *without* these terms.
2. Recognize that "indica" / "sativa" labels are *not* reliable indicators of genetic lineage or chemical profile.
3. Recognize that strain names are *not* reliable indicators of genetic lineage or chemical profile.
4. Put more emphasis on **chemotype**, especially CBD:THC ratios and terpenoid profiles. The terpenoid profiles can be correlated with aroma profiles, as well, so pay attention to the smells of Cannabis! Sometimes your nose knows best.
5. Keep an **experience journal** to track how different products, dosages, etc affect you.

For an in-depth examination of Cannabis taxonomy, I recommend checking out the book *Cannabis Evolution and Ethnobotany* by Robert Clarke and Mark Merlin as well as the review article "Cannabis Systematics at the Levels of Family, Genus, and Species" by John McPartland and the paper "A Classification of Endangered High-THC Cannabis (Cannabis sativa subsp. Indica) Domesticates and Their Wild Relatives" by John McPartland and Ernest Small.

Enduring Understandings

- Cannabis is currently thought to have originated from the Tibetan Plateau before it travelled to Eastern Europe where it began to be domesticated before making its way into Eastern Asia, South Asia, and Africa.
- Cannabis is currently considered by most researchers to consist of one species – *Cannabis sativa* – with various subspecies, varieties, and forms
- Cannabis "strains" should be thought of as cultivated varieties, or cultivars.
- Strain names and indica/sativa designations are not reliable in terms of genetic lineage or chemical profile.

Chapter 4: CANNABIS BOTANY AND CULTIVATION

Learning Questions
- What are the various parts of the Cannabis plant?
- What are trichomes?
- What growing conditions do Cannabis plants prefer?
- How is Cannabis propagated?

INTRODUCTION

The Cannabis plant can be a fascinating plant to cultivate, propagate, and observe. It displays dense groupings of highly irregular flower structures, bulbous trichomes, sharp serrated leaf edges, and can grow to be the size of a small tree within a single growing season.

To understand the basic biology of the Cannabis plant, it is important to cover a brief survey of general botany and soil science concepts. Cannabis horticulture deserves its own book and there are many adequate ones already in publication, so this chapter will only focus on broader botanical topics. The topics that will be covered in this chapter include general plant morphology, the components of the Cannabis plant, plant growth, plant reproduction and propagation, and soil science.

FLOWERING PLANT MORPHOLOGY

The plant kingdom is primarily broken up into two categories: **vascular and nonvascular plants**. The term "**vascular**" refers to whether the plant has a vascular system for pumping water and nutrients. The two pieces of the vascular system are the **phloem**, which transports nutrients, and **xylem**, which transports water. Nonvascular plants, like mosses or liverworts, are called **bryophytes**. Cannabis is a vascular plant.

Vascular plants are further broken down into more categories: **Seedless vascular plants, nonflowering plants, and flowering plants**. Ferns are an example of seedless vascular plants. They reproduce through spores rather than seeds. Plants that do have vascular systems but do not produce flowers are called **gymnosperms**. Conifers are examples of gymnosperms. Plants that produce flowers are called **angiosperms** (*angeion* = vessel; *sperma* = seed). Cannabis is an angiosperm.

There are a variety of different **morphologies**, or shapes, of flowering plants. The Cannabis plant is **dioecious**, meaning that it consists of two morphologically distinct male and female plants. The Cannabis plant typically does not pollinate and fertilize itself except under certain situations where the plant may become **hermaphroditic**, expressing both male and female reproductive structures, often due to environmental stress.

Instead, the male plant produces **staminate** flowers and pollen in its **stamen**, which consists of the **anther** and the **microsporangium** and **filament** (or "connective"). Staminate flowers are flowers only containing stamen, the male plant reproductive organs. Pollen is produced in the microsporangium and discharged from its anthers to begin their journey to a female Cannabis plant. The female plant produces **pistillate** flowers. Pistillate flowers are flowers only containing **pistils**, female plant reproductive organs. **Fertilization** and seed production occur if pollen successfully makes its way to the **ovary**.

In the plant kingdom, there are a variety of shapes and forms that flowers can take. Flowers can appear as single flowers or bundles of flowers called **inflorescences**. Female Cannabis flowers grow as a multiple branching inflorescence, called a **panicle**. Each branch of a panicle is called a **raceme**.

"THE 'HAIRS' PROTRUDING FROM CANNABIS FLOWERS ARE THE PISTIL'S FUSED STIGMA AND STYLE USED TO GUIDE POLLEN TO THE OVARIES"

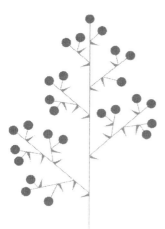

PANICLE INFLORESCENCE TYPE

Each of the flowers of a Cannabis plant contains a pistil, which consists of the stigma, style, and ovary. The **stigma** and **style** are fused to make up most of what is thought of as the "hairs" that extend from Cannabis flowers. The stigma is responsible for catching and guiding pollen or a pollen carrying insect into the **ovary**. The ovary is a swollen mass of tissue housed below the stigma and style in the **calyx**. The calyx is the small pod of leaf like tissue containing a single Cannabis flower. A calyx begins to swell when seed formation begins, as the ovary begins to grow.

Female Cannabis plants are often harvested for their resin production which occurs during the **flowering stage of growth** in Fall. Once fertilization occurs, the plant puts less energy into producing resin, and puts energy into producing seeds. For this reason, Cannabis cultivators typically seek to grow "**sensimilla**", or seedless, plants for maximum resin production. This resin contains high concentrations of cannabinoids and terpenes and is used for a variety of medical and recreational preparations. **Hemp** is a general term applied to low-THC varieties of Cannabis.

The Cannabis leaf is a **palmate** and **compound** leaf, meaning that the leaf shape is similar to that of a hand (palm) and consists of multiple distinct **leaflets**, sometimes referred to as "fingers." A Cannabis leaf can have anywhere between 3 to approximately 13 leaflets. The leaves are **serrated**, meaning that they feature a series of notches, like the teeth of a saw, around the margins of all of the leaflets. Cannabis leaves have a unique **venation**, or arrangement of veins, which can be seen in the image on the next page.

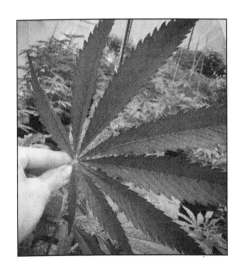

"A CANNABIS LEAF CAN HAVE ANYWHERE BETWEEN 3 TO APPROXIMATELY 13 LEAFLETS."

Cannabineae.

A

B

n

1

8

12

13

9

10

7

6

5

Cannabis sativa L.

W. Müller

CANNABIS SATIVA BOTANICAL DRAWING CIRCA 1900

TRY THIS! CANNABIS PLANT PRESSING

Traditionally, when botanists are researching plants, they create what are called **herbarium vouchers**, which feature a pressed sample of the plant as well as details about the plant and its growing environment. Whether you are studying Cannabis for fun or want to create your own Cannabis herbarium to help with your breeding or research projects – knowing how to press plants is an easy and valuable skill.

Materials

For building the plant press
- Newspaper
- Cardboard
- Planks of wood (2x)
- Saw
- Utility straps (2x)

For collecting samples
- Cutting tools
- Permanent Marker

For creating the voucher
- Herbarium paper or alternative paper
- Adhesive
  - Hot glue recommended

Building the Plant Press

1. Start off by determining how big you want your plant press to be. I recommend making it approximately two feet wide and three feet long, but this is completely subjective. In general, I recommend making the plant press to a size that can accommodate an entire newspaper page, folded.
2. Once you have determined your plant press size, cut your wooden boards to match your specified dimensions.
3. Cut pieces of cardboard that are the same size as the wooden boards. Start off with at least 10 pieces of cardboard.
4. Place one wooden board on the ground.
5. Stack all of the cardboard pieces on top of the wooded board.
6. Place a stack of newspaper on top of the stack of cardboard.
7. Place the second wooden board on top of the newspaper.
8. Tighten a utility strap at either end of the plant press "sandwich"
9. Voila – you now have a plant press!
10. **Cheap Shortcut**: don't have the resources to make a true plant press? Just find a large, thick book that you can fit your cuttings in.

Using the Plant Press

1. Collect a sample, whether it be part of a branch, a Cannabis inflorescence or just a single leaf, and place the sample within a folded piece of newspaper.
2. On the piece of newspaper, write the date, your initials, and any other important information, such as a cultivar name, in permanent marker.

3. Then place the folded newspaper containing the sample in between two of the pieces of cardboard.
4. Reassemble the plant press and tighten the utility straps as tight as possible.
5. Leave the sample undisturbed for several days or weeks until it has dried.

Creating a Botanical Voucher

1. Once the sample has been pressed and is dry, very carefully lift the sample from the newspaper and transfer to herbarium voucher paper or other media.
2. Use hot glue or some other adhesive to stick the sample to the paper.
3. Add any notes or other information that you may desire on the paper.

Congratulations – you just made a botanical voucher with Cannabis!

TRICHOMES

Cannabis plants are one of many types of plants that produce **trichomes**. The word "trichome" is derived from the Greek word *trikhōma*, meaning "hair". Trichomes can aid plants in many ways such as trapping and disabling pests, providing insulation and protection from the elements, preventing water loss from plant tissue, or producing glandular trichomes full of chemicals that may attract pollinators or deter pests.

Aromatic compounds are sometimes produced in trichomes that attract predatory insects which may feed on pests. Sometimes these oils even aid in protecting the plant from bacterial and fungal diseases. The sticky glandular trichomes of Cannabis largely contain cannabinoids and terpenoids, the "active" compounds in Cannabis primarily responsible for its various physiological and psychological effects.

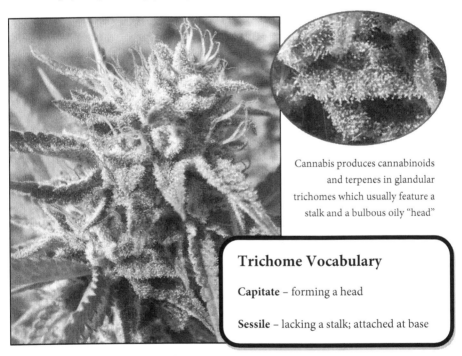

Cannabis produces cannabinoids and terpenes in glandular trichomes which usually feature a stalk and a bulbous oily "head"

Trichome Vocabulary

Capitate – forming a head

Sessile – lacking a stalk; attached at base

The Cannabis plant produces both **glandular** and **non-glandular trichomes**. Glandular trichomes feature a little ball, or head, at the end of a stalk as seen in two of the images above. When a trichome features a glandular ball or head, it is called **capitate.** Cannabinoids and terpenoids are produced primarily in the glandular heads of trichomes. Non-glandular trichomes lack this head and resemble hairs. Trichomes can further be characterized by whether they have stalks or not. *Capitate-sessile* trichomes do not feature a stalk and look like droplets of dew on the plant. *Capitate-stalked* trichomes are shaped like the typical Cannabis trichome featuring both a stalk and head.

One particularly interesting aspect of Cannabis trichomes is that a Cannabis plant's chemistry will affect the shape, or morphology, of its trichomes! For instance, Cannabis plants that produce a lot of the cannabinoid, CBCa, exhibit mostly capitate-sessile, or stalk-less, trichomes. Cannabis plants with little to no cannabinoids produce headless trichomes. CBGa dominant plants produce exceptionally milky trichomes (de Meijer, 2015).

Common Types of Trichomes in Cannabis	
Non-Glandular	**Glandular**
(A) Unicellular Non-Glandular These trichomes are the simplest trichomes, resembling small hairs with no other distinguishable features	(C) Capitate-Sessile These trichomes appear as small spheres on the plant tissue, often said to resemble fish eggs.
(B) Cystolithic These trichomes do not feature a "head" and resemble hairs with small knobs at their base	(D) Capitate-Stalked These trichomes feature a stalk and "head"
	(E/F) Simple and Complex Bulbous Bulbous trichomes are found throughout the plant but do not house cannabinoids. These trichomes produce an irregular glandular head on thin stalks.

FIGURE 7: COMMON TYPES OF TRICHOMES IN CANNABIS

TRY THIS! SKETCH A TRICHOME

Have you ever looked at trichomes carefully up close? In this activity you will take what you have learned about trichomes and find at least two different types of trichomes on a Cannabis inflorescence and sketch them.

Materials

Resinous Cannabis inflorescence (Cannabis bud)

(If Cannabis is unavailable, any resinous plant will do)

Loupe, Magnifying Glass or Microscope (40x or greater magnification recommended)

Pen or pencil (pencil recommended)

Procedures

1. First let's find a glandular trichome. Using a loupe, magnifying glass, or scope, find a glandular trichome in the form of a **capitate-stalked** trichome.
2. Sketch the capitate-stalked trichome below.
3. Are there any **capitate-sessile** trichomes around? If so, sketch and label one below in the "glandular trichomes" section.
4. Find a non-glandular trichome.
5. Sketch the non-glandular trichome below. Is it a **unicellular non-glandular** trichome or a **cystolithic** trichome?

Glandular Trichome	Non-Glandular Trichome

Parts of a Cannabis Plant

Match the following terms to the parts of the male and female Cannabis plants above.

1.___ Anther
2.___ Axillary Bud
3.___ Female Flower
4.___ Leaf
5.___ Leaflet
6.___ Male Flower
7.___ Petiole
8.___ Terminal Bud
9.___ Vegetative Shoot

PLANT GROWTH

Plant growth begins at **germination**, when a seed receives enough water for growth. Cannabis seeds typically germinate within 15 days when regularly exposed to water (AHP, 2013). The **embryo** of the seed uses the water while feeding on nutrition from the **endosperm** in the seed to begin new growth. A root with many root hairs is formed that exits the seed hull in search of more food and water. As the root makes its way into a substrate, like soil, and finds nutrients and more water, the **cotyledons**, or "seed leaves", emerge from within the seed and begin generating energy from sunlight through **photosynthesis**. Eventually **true leaves** appear, the cotyledons die off, and the plant begins to mature.

Photos courtesy of Cheryl Johnson

Plant growth occurs in regions of the plant called **meristems**. There are two different types of meristems, apical and lateral. The **apical meristem** regions are located at the tips of plant roots and shoots and are responsible for the elongation of plant parts while the **lateral meristem** regions are responsible for increasing the girth of plant parts. Plants require four things to grow: energy from the sun, carbon dioxide, water, and nutrients. When these conditions are satisfied, the meristematic regions actively grow.

Cannabis is an annual plant, meaning that it grows out its entire life cycle over the course of one year before developing seeds and dying. This is opposed to biennial or perennial plants which have lifecycles that span multiple years. The Cannabis lifecycle can be extended through a combination of **light deprivation** and **supplemental lighting** to keep the plant in a vegetative or flowering state.

Plants can be grown in a variety of ways through different growing media including **soil**, **hydroponic** solutions, and **aeroponic** solutions. Hydroponics involves growing a plant in a nutritive water solution. The plants rest in pots that are suspended over a reservoir that feeds the nutritive solution to the roots of the plant. In hydroponics, nutrient solutions should be between 5.2 and 5.8 pH (AHP, 2013). Aeroponic systems expose roots to a nutritive solution as a vapor or mist.

CANNABIS ENDOPHYTES

All plants harbor micro-organisms within and around their tissues. These micro-organisms can alter how a plant uptakes nutrients, distributes water, defends itself against pests and more. These micro-organisms that live within the tissues of plants are called **endophytes**. Until recently, little was known about the populations of micro-organisms that live in and around the Cannabis plant. A 2020 review by Taghinasab and Jabaji organized much of the information that is currently known about the endophytes that are associated with Cannabis. A summary of their findings is found below.

Plant Part	Associated Micro-organisms		
Inflorescence (Flowers, Buds)	Pantoea sp. Bacillus licheniformis	Mycobacterium sp.	Peniciillium copticola
Leaves	Bacillus sp. Pseudomonas sp. Aureobasidium sp.	Cochliobolus sp. Penicillium copticola	Alternaria sp. Aspergillus sp.
Petioles (Leaf Stems)	Acinetobacter sp. Agrobacterium sp. Bacillus sp.	Pseudomonas sp. Enterococcus sp. Aspergillus flavus	Alternaria sp. Cryptococcus sp. Penicillium copticola
Stems	Alternaria sp. Diaporthe sp. Schizophyllum sp. Thielavia sp. Curvularia sp.	Aspergillus flavus Aspergillus niger Aspergillus nidulans Penicillium citrinum Colletotrichum sp.	Penicillium Chrysogenum Phoma sp. Rhizopous sp. Cladosporium sp.
Roots	Proteobacteria: Rhizobiales Acinetobacter sp.	Chryseobacteirum sp. Enterobacter sp.	Microbacterium sp. Pseudomonas sp. Glomus sp.
Seeds	Pantoea sp. Bacillus sp.	Enterobacter sp. Brevibacterium sp.	Aureobasidium sp. Cladosporium sp.

FIGURE 8: CANNABIS ENDOPHYTES

Source: Taghinasab M, Jabaji S. 2020. Cannabis microbiome and the role of endophytes in modulating the production of secondary metabolites: an overview. Microorganisms. 8: 355

These micro-organisms can serve many different roles in the Cannabis plant. Some micro-organisms like Bacillus, Pseudomonas, Pantoea, Serratia and Bipolaris can promote growth in the plant. Many of these bacteria and fungi can attack plant pathogens under certain scenarios and may themselves act as pathogens in other scenarios. One of the exciting areas of future research for Cannabis lies in better understanding the roles that these micro-organisms may play in manipulating the production of secondary metabolites, like cannabinoids and terpenoids in Cannabis.

PLANT REPRODUCTION

Angiosperms (flowering plants) reproduce either asexually or sexually. Some plants can reproduce asexually by producing clones of themselves from roots or vegetative material or by generating embryos *without* fertilization. Sexual reproduction occurs through a cycle of germination, vegetative growth, pollen production, dispersal, pollination, fertilization, and seed production. As mentioned previously, the components of the stamen produce **sperm** inside pollen while the ovary produces **eggs** in **embryo sacs**. When pollen is discharged it sometimes successfully meets a female flower's **stigma** and **style**. The pollen must then travel down the style and meet an embryo sac that contains an egg.

When the egg and sperm meet, **fertilization** occurs, and the production of the core contents of the future seed begin: **the endosperm, seed coat, and embryo**. The seed coat helps protect the embryo from harm. The embryo develops **cotyledons** in the seed, which are the first leaves of the plant that emerge from the seed. These leaves and petioles grow as they use up the nutrition of the **endosperm**. The endosperm is a bundle of nutritive material that provides just enough food to help the immature plant reach sunlight and produce roots.

In medical and recreational Cannabis production, seedless, or "**sensimilla**", female flowers are desired, as these are more potent. When a Cannabis plant is pollinated, and the ovaries are fertilized, the plant begins producing seeds and the cannabinoid and terpenoid production is reduced. Male Cannabis plants are typically not allowed near female Cannabis plants being grown for resin production.

The following photographs on the next several pages depict Cannabis plants at varying stages of growth.

CANNABIS SEEDLINGS AND IMMATURE FEMALE PLANTS

IMMATURE FEMALE CANNABIS PLANTS,
APPROXIMATELY 2 MONTHS OLD

MATURING FEMALE CANNABIS PLANTS,
APPROXIMATELY 4 MONTHS OLD

MATURE FEMALE CANNABIS PLANTS ENTERING FLOWERING
CYCLE, APPROXIMATELY 6 MONTHS OLD

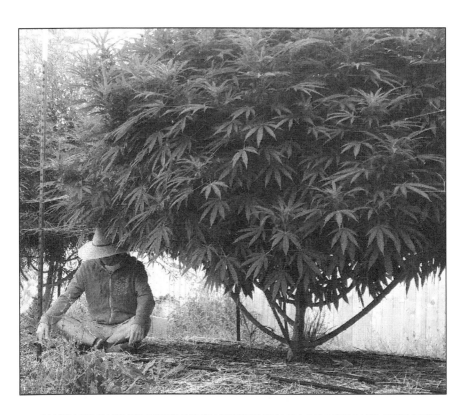

A CANNABIS FARMER RESTS BENEATH THE SHADE OF A FEMALE CANNABIS
PLANT, APPROXIMATELY 5-6 MONTHS OLD

FEMALE CANNABIS PLANTS NEARING PEAK FLOWERING MATURITY,
APPROXIMATELY 7-8 MONTHS OLD

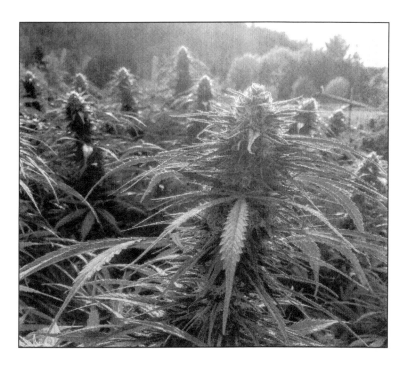

FEMALE CANNABIS PLANT AT FULL FLOWERING MATURITY,
APPROXIMATELY 8 MONTHS OLD

Female Cannabis Fruit Production

Cannabis sativa L.

W. Müller

Which of the following images represents the pistil (stigma, style, ovaries)? _____

What primary components make up the inside of a seed?

1. _____

2. _____

3. _____

What is the term used to describe the plant tissue seen in figures A and E, surrounding the ovary? _____

Parts of a Male Cannabis Flower

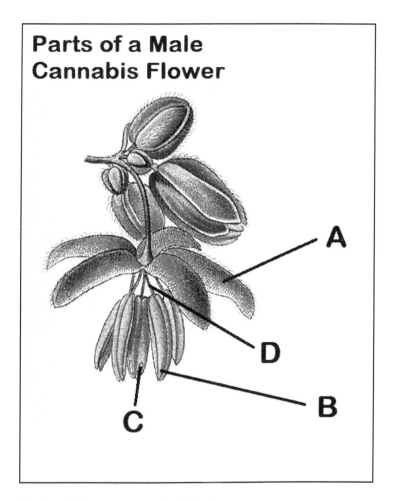

Match the following terms to the labels above:

1._____ Anther

2._____ Calyx or Sepal

3._____ Filament

4._____ Microsporangium or Pollen

PLANT PROPAGATION

Cannabis plants can be propagated a variety of ways. Plant **propagation** refers to how plants are perpetuated. Plants can typically be propagated via seed, cuttings, layering, grafting, and micropropagation. Each method has its advantages and disadvantages depending on what the grower desires.

SEXUAL PROPAGATION: SEEDS

Seed propagation is a sexual form of propagation and usually involves farms that are totally dedicated to seed production. These farms keep crops far apart from other crops that might cross-pollinate with each other. Often bags are placed over the male flowers to collect their pollen and avoid airborne pollen. Pollen from one plant will be collected and manually introduced to female plants to breed and create hybrid plants, or "crosses."

Photos courtesy of Cheryl Johnson

Did You Know?

Cannabis seeds are highly nutritious, containing all the essential amino acids our bodies need but cannot produce on their own!

Try This! Germinating Cannabis Seeds

Want to see the magic of seed propagation yourself? Try germinating some seeds! This simple method is reliable and allows you to see all of the changes happening in the seeds close up. Keep in mind that there are many ways to germinate seeds – this is just one simple way that allows for easy observation. Other methods that many people utilize include placing seeds in moistened peat pellets, placing seeds directly in water until germination, or even just directly sowing seeds into soil.

DISCLAIMER: *Check your local laws before attempting this activity to avoid breaking any laws. Germinating Cannabis seeds may be illegal where you live. If you are in the United States, it is recommended to perform this activity with Cannabis seeds that are legally classified as hemp. Neither the author nor the publisher of Curious About Cannabis™ are responsible for any illegal activities performed, either intentionally or unintentionally.*

Materials

Cannabis Seeds	Paper Towel	Water
Ziplock Bag	Scope or Jeweler's Loupe	

Procedures

1. Moisten the paper towel and squeeze out excess water. The paper towel should be very moist, but not excessively dripping with water.
2. Place the seeds in the paper towel, leaving equal spacing between them.
3. Fold the paper towel over the seeds.
4. Place the folded paper towel into a plastic bag and seal approximately 80 to 90%. The bag should breathe a little, but overall should keep most of the moisture within the bag.
5. Place the plastic bag in a dark, warm area for 48 hours
6. Check the seeds for signs of germination. Use a scope or loupe to see the seeds up close.

Congratulations! You just germinated Cannabis seeds and began the process of life! What will you do now?

ASEXUAL PROPAGATION: CLONING

Cloning involves propagating plants asexually either through **cuttings, layering, grafting,** or **micropropagation**. The **cutting** method of cloning involves cutting off a stem from a parent plant, introducing that stem to growth hormones that will stimulate root growth, and allowing the cutting to rest, heal, and grow in a well-maintained environment called a "rooting chamber" until it develops its own root system and can be transplanted.

Layering involves bending a branch of a plant down to the ground, covering it with soil, and coaxing it to produce roots before severing it from the parent plant. This only works with certain kinds of plants but rarely is used for Cannabis propagation. **Grafting** involves taking a vegetative shoot from one plant and connecting it to the root stock of another plant, fusing the two together into one plant. Grafting can be difficult and many times the two plants will not adopt each other. This is not a common propagation method for Cannabis.

All the previous mentioned methods of cloning have a major disadvantage in that they also propagate plant pathogens and other unfavorable traits. Clones from traditional propagation methods usually do not result in true clones and multiple cloning through generations can cause various mutations and genetic deviations. These drawbacks can be avoided using **micropropagation**. Micropropagation, through a process called **tissue culture,** involves harvesting meristem regions (regions of active growth) from the plant and growing clones from that tissue in sterile environments.

Typically, the apical bud is used for tissue culturing plants. All excess plant matter is removed, and the remaining bits of tissue are washed and transferred to a sterile nutritive growing medium. Once the plant develops in the sterile environment and develops a root system, it can be acclimated to the outdoor or indoor growing environment before finally becoming established in soil or other growing medium.

Tissue culture has some advantages over other methods of cloning. Tissue culture provides greater genetic stability between clones. It can produce high quantities of plants in a small area using very little starting material from a parent plant. A major disadvantage, as with all methods of asexual propagation, is that genetic diversity is reduced in the plant populations. If a disease or pest were to affect one plant, it would most likely affect all the plants. This can lead to total crop failure quickly. Genetic diversity through seed propagation is an effective way to minimize this effect. Another disadvantage of micropropagation involves getting the clones acclimated to the outdoor environment. Because the plants are initially grown in very humid environments in containers, their **stomata**, or gas exchange pores, are not trained to close to hold water in the plant's tissues. Tissue culture plants must go through a delicate "hardening off" phase before fully transitioning to outdoor conditions.

CANNABIS GROWING, HARVESTING, AND STORAGE

While Cannabis can thrive in a variety of conditions, it does seem to have some preferences. **Cannabis reportedly grows best in soils that have a pH between 6.5 - 7.2 (neutral to alkaline) with a clay and loamy soil texture.** The soil should be able to hold water while allowing excess water to drain. If growing hydroponically, the pH of the nutritive solution should be 5.2 to 6. Cannabis plants prefer approximately 18 hours of light (6-8 hours of darkness) during their vegetative growth phase. This is easily satisfied throughout the late spring and summer months outdoors in many areas throughout the world.

Cannabis typically begins to enter flowering when plants are exposed to approximately 12 hours of darkness. Cannabis plants that are "**autoflowering**" will proceed to flower regardless of light cycle (see section "Exceptions to the Rule: Autoflowering Cannabis" for more information).

In indoor growing, lights are automated to mimic the natural light cycle that would occur in Fall as the season transitions toward winter and the days get shorter. Actual harvest times can be optimized according to the desired chemical profile of the plant. Regularly monitoring of cannabinoids and terpenes can help optimize harvest to achieve desired chemical profiles. Optimal harvest times are sometimes determined by the browning and senescence of three quarters of the stigmas on the plant (AHP, 2013).

> *"Light absorption by chlorophyll A peaks at 430 nm in the blue band and 662nm in the red, and chlorophyll B peaks at 453 nm in the blue and 642 nm in the orange-red bands. Chlorophyll synthesis peaks at 435 nm and 445 nm in the blue spectrum and 640 and 675 nm in the red wavelengths."*

Source: Ed Rosenthal's Marijuana Grower's Handbook website
http://mjgrowers.com/book_what_light.htm

Prior to cultivation, any soil or water used for growing Cannabis should be tested for pesticides and heavy metals to ensure the plant will not bioaccumulate these contaminants.

Seed cultivation usually begins between March and April in the northern hemisphere. It takes approximately eight weeks from seed for Cannabis plants to show their complete sexual characteristics so that males can be separated from females should pollination not be desired, as is the case in medicinal Cannabis flower production. The plant then takes approximately 6 to 8 months to reach full maturity before flowering. (AHP, 2013)

The cannabinoid content of the plant reaches its peak when flowers are in full bud and will typically maintain that peak for approximately two or three weeks. Both genetic and environmental conditions affect the concentration of active compounds in the plant resins.

This may result in a greater diversity of chemical profiles present among plants cultivated outdoors than indoors.

When growing indoors, Cannabis growth and yield can sometimes be enhanced by increasing the ambient carbon dioxide in the room. While small increases in carbon dioxide do not stimulate photosynthesis or water use efficiency very much, nearly doubling the ambient carbon dioxide levels *does* have a significant effect, although this effect may differ between cultivars. There is also scientific debate over whether these enhanced growth effects are long lasting or not (Chandra et al., 2011). In addition, new environmental research looking at climate change effects suggest that elevated carbon dioxide levels may lead to certain chemical deficiencies in plants (Davis et al, 2004; Singh et al, 1967). It is unknown how this effect might impact cannabinoid and terpenoid production in Cannabis.

AFTER CANNABIS FLOWERS ARE HARVESTED, THEY MUST DRY AND ARE OFTEN HUNG ON DRYING RACKS AS SEEN HERE

Generally, immature Cannabis plants can thrive in humid conditions (~75% humidity) but require lower humidity levels at maturity (~55-60% humidity), otherwise risking mold growth. According to the American Herbal Pharmacopeia, when drying, a humidity level of approximately 30% is ideal and drying should continue until the plant material is approximately 25% of its starting weight (AHP, 2013). Seasoned Cannabis cultivators often report drying at humidity levels between 40-60% until stems snap cleanly.

Cannabis must be stored properly to protect it from air and light, which lead to the degradation of cannabinoids, like THC. THCA steadily decarboxylates to THC during storage (AHP, 2013), however one study showed that after one year of storage, approximately 90% of the original THC was still intact. Excessive handling of Cannabis material will expose trichomes to air and light, leading to oxidation and chemical degradation (AHP, 2013). Cannabis can be stored at temperatures up to 20 degrees Celsius without causing significant changes to the THC content of the material (AHP, 2013).

AVOID SUFFOCATING YOUR HYDROPONIC PLANTS!

A NOTE ABOUT **DISSOLVED OXYGEN**

In order for plants to grow vigorously, they require oxygen, just like animals. In soil cultivation, plants have access to a lot of oxygen in the air and in spaces in the soil. In hydroponic cultivation systems, the primary source that plants receive oxygen is in water! Water contains varying levels of dissolved oxygen, or DO. The temperature of the water will determine how much DO can be contained in the water. In general, water temperature should be around 70°F to support high levels of dissolved oxygen!

In hydroponic cultivation, it is important to monitor the temperature and dissolved oxygen levels of the growing solution to ensure plant roots do not suffocate in the water!

Glandular Trichome Sketching

Can you recall the differences between the different **glandular trichomes** *produced by Cannabis?*

Phytocannabinoids are produced in **glandular trichomes**. Glandular trichomes can be broken down into two further categories: _____-_____ and _____-_____.

(HINT: head and/or neck?)

Use the space below to sketch these two different types of trichomes.

EXCEPTIONS TO THE RULE: AUTOFLOWERING CANNABIS PLANTS

Not all Cannabis plants follow the basic rule of requiring certain photoperiods to trigger vegetative growth versus flowering. There are a variety of Cannabis plants called "autoflowering" plants, which, as their name suggests, will automatically flower with age, regardless of photoperiod. As Cannabis decriminalization and legalization continues to spread across the world, it is likely that autoflowering Cannabis plants will be the varieties that the average person grows in their home, because they can grow in smaller containers, do not require as much attention, and can produce substantial yields of resinous flowers in a short period of time. Autoflowering Cannabis plants can sometimes be grown from seed to harvest in a matter of 2.5 months or less.

At the time of this writing, breeders are actively crossing autoflowering varieties into other lineages, imparting some of the desirable qualities of autoflowering varieties while still maintaining fairly long growth periods, leading to larger plants and larger yields.

ALL ABOUT SOIL

Cannabis prefers neutral to alkaline clay and loamy soils. To understand how to obtain the perfect soil type for Cannabis, we must first discuss how soils are categorized. Soil is a mixture of broken down rock and organic matter. A combination of humus, mineral fragments, plant residues, and clay form what we normally think of as soil.

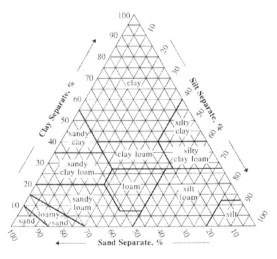

Soils contain three major classes of minerals including: sand, silt, and clay. The ratios of sand to silt to clay determine what soil type is present. A **soil ternary diagram** can be used to calculate your soil type and texture.

The Primary Mineral Components of Soil	
Particle	**Particle Size**
Sand	2-0.02mm
Silt	0.02-0.002mm
Clay	<0.002 mm

FIGURE 9: SOIL TERNARY DIAGRAM

Try This! Soil Texture Activity

Are you interested in trying to learn what the texture of your soil is? Here is a simple activity to help you determine your soil texture using a soil ternary diagram. You will need a quart jar, soil, water, a dispersing agent like table salt or Calgon, and a ruler.

Materials

Quart Jar   Soil   Water   Dispersing Agent   Ruler
(table salt or Calgon)

Procedures

Fill the quart jar with one inch of dry soil.

Fill the jar 2/3 full of water.

Add one teaspoon of salt or Calgon.

Vigorously shake the jar.

Let the contents settle for several days.

Use the ruler to measure the depth of each layer.

Convert the measurements into ratios of sand:silt:clay.

Use a **soil ternary diagram** to determine your soil texture type! If you don't want to use a soil ternary diagram manually, you can also use the Soil Texture Calculator on the USDA NRCS website by visiting
https://www.nrcs.usda.gov/wps/portal/nrcs/main/soils/survey/tools/

SOIL CHEMISTRY

As mentioned earlier, Cannabis prefers an alkaline clay or loamy soil. But what does it mean for a soil to be alkaline? The term alkaline is referring to the pH of the soil, which may be influenced by several factors. The chemistry of soil primarily involves several major parts: the colloidal particles found in clay, the parent rock compounds like sand and silt, the organic matter, and water.

Before we talk about soil pH, we should first talk about soil colloids, which are tiny particles found most often in the clay portion of soil. More specifically, colloids are particles that remain suspended in solution. Colloidal particles carry an electrical charge, and because of this electrical charge, ions (charged elements or molecules) are held very tightly against the surface of the colloids with other ions gathered around them in a less tightly bound ionic "cloud". This helps to keep chemicals in place for a while. Because of this buffering effect, clay soils are packed with nutrients. It is also this buffering effect that causes colloids to have a profound influence on the pH of the soil.

The **pH** refers to the alkalinity or acidity of the soil, which is determined by the concentration of negative and positively charged hydrogen ions, in the form of H+ and OH-. In water, these ions are expressed as hydronium (H_3O^+) and hydroxide (OH^-) ions.

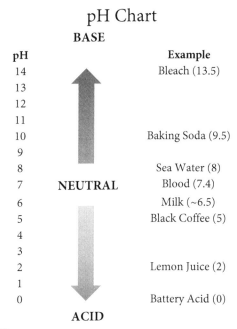

pH Chart
BASE

pH	Example
14	Bleach (13.5)
13	
12	
11	
10	Baking Soda (9.5)
9	
8	Sea Water (8)
7 **NEUTRAL**	Blood (7.4)
6	Milk (~6.5)
5	Black Coffee (5)
4	
3	
2	Lemon Juice (2)
1	
0	Battery Acid (0)

ACID

FIGURE 10: PH CHART

pH is measured on a scale of 0 to 14 with 0 being very acidic and equivalent to battery acid and 14 being very alkaline (basic), the equivalent of bleach. A neutral pH is 7. **Cannabis prefers neutral (7 pH) to alkaline soils**.

Clay soils attract positively charged ions, like H+ ions. This can lead to an accumulation of positively charged hydrogen ions in a soil, causing a change in pH.

pH affects a compound's solubility in water, which affects the chemical forms that various nutrients may take in the soil. Take Phosphorous for example. At a pH of 1, Phosphorous is generally found in the form of H_3PO_4. At a pH of 5 it is usually $H_2PO_4^-$. At a pH of 9 it becomes HPO_4^{2-}. Finally, at a pH of 14 Phosphorous is found primarily as PO_4^{3-}. These changes are due to the changes in availability of positively charged hydrogen ions. Nutrient availability charts can easily be found online detailing the pH levels at which certain nutrients become available or unavailable to a plant.

If a pH is low and soil is very acidic, the solubility of heavy metals in water is enhanced, leading to higher metal accumulations in plants. This is especially relevant for Cannabis plants because they appear to be supreme nutrient accumulators, though much more research is needed on the subject. Cannabis **plants have been shown to accumulate heavy metals from soil into every tissue of the plant** (Linger *et al.*, 2002).

Phosphorous is typically found in the soil as an **anion**, meaning it is negatively charged. Since colloidal particles are usually also negatively charged, the **phosphorous and colloidal particles repel each other and phosphorous is prone to leaching** out of the area.

WATER AND SOIL

Soils do more for plants than just provide a reservoir of nutrients for growth. Soil also affects a plant's ability to receive water. Different textures of soils have varying **water holding capacities**. The water holding capacity is defined as the soil's ability to retain water for periods of time. This is all dependent on the size of the particles in the soil. If you were to pour water into a cup of sand, which consists of relatively large particles, the water would pass through quickly due to the larger spaces between particles.

If you were to pour water into a cup of clay, which are very small particles, the water would pass through slowly and saturate the clay, eventually being held tightly in place as a mud ball. A plant's roots and soil are in a constant battle for water, and it all has to do with **water tension** and **available water**. A plant root is always "pulling" at water. The soil texture affects how strongly the soil holds on to water, resisting the plant's pull. When soil is saturated with water, there is low tension and the water in the soil is easy for the roots to suck up.

Available Soil Moisture Holding Capacity for Different Soil Textures	
Soil Texture	Inches of Water/Foot of Soil
Coarse Sand/gravel	0.2 to 0.7
Sand	0.5 to 1.1
Loamy Sand	0.7 to 1.4
Sandy Loam	1.3 to 1.8
Clay Loam and Silty Clay Loam	1.7 to 2.5
Silty Clay and Clay	1.6 to 2.2

Source: "Soild, Water and Plant Characteristics important to Irrigation" by T. Scherer, D. Franzen, L. Cihacek, NDSU Extension Service, AE1675, 2017; https://www.ag.ndsu.edu/publications/crops/soil-water-and-plant-characteristics-important-to-irrigation/

FIGURE 11: SOIL MOISTURE HOLDING CAPACITIES

As the soil starts to dry, though, the tension increases, and the soil starts to hang ever tighter to the water that is present. The point at which water is present in the soil but unavailable to plant roots is called the **permanent wilting point**. This is one reason why some plants struggle in a heavy clay soil. The clay hangs on to a lot of water, potentially drowning or rotting the roots, while at the same time maintaining high tension and holding tightly to the water so the roots cannot easily draw in water to help the plant grow. Plants can be in deserts even if they are surrounded by water!

LEARN MORE ABOUT YOUR SOILS WITH THE WEB SOIL SURVEY

If you live in the United States, there is a great soil information resource available online provided by the US Natural Resources Conservation Service to help you find out more information about the soil and geology of your area. This information can be a great resource when designing a garden or farm.

The Web Soil Survey NRCS Home Page:
http://websoilsurvey.sc.egov.usda.gov/App/HomePage.htm

For more information about soil dynamics, check out the **Soil Biology Primer**, authored by Elaine Ingham, Andrew Moldenke, Clive Edwards and available **free** through the USDA NRCS:

http://www.nrcs.usda.gov/wps/portal/nrcs/main/soils/health/biology

TRY THIS! WATER AVAILABILITY ACTIVITY

Here is a quick activity you can do at home to easily demonstrate the concepts of water tension, water availability, and permanent wilting point.

Materials

Water   Dry Sponge

Procedures

1. First, obtain a dry sponge. Imagine that the dry sponge represents dry soil.
2. Now soak the sponge in water. This represents rain or irrigation. The sponge now represents a **water saturated soil**.
3. Turn the sponge vertically and let water pour out, but do not squeeze the sponge. The dripping water represents run-off as well as water available to plants.
4. Now squeeze the sponge, releasing more water. This represents the pull exerted by a plant root as the plant pulls in more water away from the soil as it "drinks".
5. Finally, ring the sponge out completely so that no more water drips out when you squeeze it. When you feel the sponge, you should be able to feel that it is wet, but no water will drip out of the sponge. This represents the *permanent wilting point*. This represents water that, though present in the soil, would be totally unavailable to plants because the soil is exerting a greater pull on the water than the plant roots. At this point, the plant may as well be growing in a desert!

Enduring Understandings

- Cannabis is a dioecious plant, meaning that it has distinct male and female forms, although sometimes, usually under stress, Cannabis can appear as monoecious, with both male and female reproductive parts on one plant.
- Cannabis flowers form in groups called inflorescences.
- The Cannabis plant produces various types of trichomes, including glandular and non-glandular varieties.
- Cannabinoids are produced in capitate-stalked and capitate-sessile glandular trichomes.
- Cannabis plants typically don't produce flowers until they experience at least 12 hours of darkness at a time each day, unless they are autoflowering varieties of Cannabis.
- Cannabis plants are commonly propagated either sexually, through seeds, or asexually through cloning, usually through cuttings or tissue culture.
- Cannabis prefers neutral to alkaline clay and loamy soils.

Chapter 5:
COMMON CANNABIS PATHOGENS

Learning Questions
- What insects negatively impact the growth of Cannabis plants?
- What pathogenic fungi affect Cannabis plants?
- What bacteria and viruses can infect Cannabis plants?

INSECT PESTS

Cannabis is affected by many common garden pests, most notably: aphids, russet mites, broad mites, white flies, spider mites, thrips, fungus gnats, and, in flowering Cannabis, caterpillars. Different pests attack various parts of the plant. Fungus gnats reside in the soil and roots. As such, fungus gnats can typically be combated by ensuring that soil dries out in between watering. White fly larvae may start in soil and adults move on to feeding on leaf and stem tissue. Microscopic pests, like broad mites, can use other pests like white flies to travel and spread among plants.

Characteristic leaf curling and yellowing caused by russet mite infestation. Russet mites pictured to the right.

A mature Cannabis plant infested with russet mites.
Although the mites do not kill the plant, the flower and resin yield will suffer.

PATHOGENIC FUNGI

There are many different fungi which may attack the Cannabis plant at varying stages of growth. The most common type of pathogenic fungus that attacks Cannabis is *Botrytis cinerea*, or gray mold (McPartland, 1996). Gray mold is a very common type of pathogenic fungus that attacks diverse types of plants. In fiber type, hemp plants, gray mold tends to attack the stem and cause cankers which girdle the stem and kill off everything above the canker.

In drug type varieties of Cannabis, gray mold tends to attack the dense inflorescences, or buds. Dense buds will retain a lot of moisture which presents a perfect environment for molds to grow and take over the plant material. When a group of Cannabis flowers is infected with Botrytis, the fan leaves will turn yellow and die off, followed by a darkening of the fused stigmas and styles that extend from the calyx of each flower. Eventually the inflorescence will become covered in mold. Cannabis cultivars from arid regions, like Afghanistan, are exceptionally susceptible to mold.

Some fungi attack young Cannabis plants early, causing a condition called "damping off". There are a variety of genera of fungi that cause damping off including *Pythium*, *Rhizoctonia*, *Botrytis*, *Macrophomina*, and *Fusarium*. Another condition that can kill off a plant is "root rot". This occurs when the plant's roots have been saturated with water for too long, leading to a fungal infection of the roots. It is important to allow soil to dry between watering to avoid root rot. When growing Cannabis in containers, it is important to ensure that the container is big enough to allow the plant's root system to extend and grow without becoming bound in the container.

Powdery mildew is another common fungal pathogen common to Cannabis and many other plants. Powdery mildew is often caused by high humidity levels or excess watering. There are several species of powdery mildew fungi including *Leveillula taurica*, *Oidiopsis taurica*, and *Sphaerotheca macularis*.

PATHOGENIC BACTERIA AND VIRUSES

There are four primary species of pathogenic bacteria that afflict Cannabis plants. They include bacterial blight caused by *Pseudomonas syringae* pv. *cannabina*; crown gall caused by *Agrobacterium tumefaciens*; bacterial wilt caused by *Erwinia tracheiphila*; and xanthomonas leaf spot caused by *Xanthomonas campestris* pv. *cannabis*. Of these four pathogenic bacteria, *Pseudomonas syringae* is the most common bacterial pathogen of Cannabis. (McPartland, 1996)

There are several different viruses that may attack Cannabis. Although viruses rarely kill Cannabis plants, they can drastically reduce yield and growth vigor. Once a virus has infected a plant, they are essentially impossible to get rid of. Sometimes viruses may even infect pollen or seeds, effectively passing the virus on to the plant's progeny. Some of the most common viruses that are thought to affect Cannabis are the Cannabis cryptic Virus (CanCV), hemp streak virus (HSV) and hemp mosaic virus (HMV).

Examples of Viruses Known or Presumed to Affect Cannabis	
VIRUS NAME	SYMPTOMS
Beet Curly Top Virus (BCTV)	Stunted growth, yellowing leaves; Newly developed leaves narrower and pale green with slight sideways curl
Cannabis Cryptic Virus (CanCV)	Asymptomatic; transmitted through seeds, but not contact
Hemp Streak Virus (HSV)	Leaves turn pale green, followed by yellow streaks developing from veins
Hemp Mosaic Virus (HMV)	Discoloration, leaf mottling, stunted growth
Hop Latent Viroid (HLVd)	Brittle stems, horizontal growth, reduced flower mass, reduced trichome mass; can be transmitted through seeds

Another virus affecting Cannabis that was recently identified and characterized is the Hop Latent Viroid (HLVd), which caused a series of symptoms in Cannabis including "brittle stems, an outwardly horizontal plant structure and reduced flower mass and trichomes", although hops plants infected with HLVd often exhibit no symptoms (Bektas et al, 2019). The symptoms presented in infected Cannabis plants are often referred to colloquially as "dudding".

One of the most recent viruses to be found to infect Cannabis plants is the Beet Curly Top Virus (BCTV), reported in Cannabis for the first time in 2019 (Giladi et al, 2019). BCTV

Insects may carry viruses from one plant to another as they feed. Symptoms of viral infections of Cannabis often include discoloring and curling of leaves. Despite numerous reports by cultivators for decades, Tobacco Mosaic Virus (TMV) has not been identified on Cannabis in any peer-reviewed published scientific literature, though some private companies claim to have identified it.

DIFFERENTIATING PLANT DISEASE FROM MALNUTRITION OR ENVIRONMENTAL STRESS

The symptoms of disease in plants can often resemble the symptoms of nutrient deficiency or stress response. It is important to properly diagnose symptoms to determine the severity of the condition and take appropriate action. Symptoms such as discoloration, leaf spotting, and leaf curling could be indicative of one of many different problems including pest infestation, disease, or nutrient imbalance.

To learn more about Cannabis plant pathogens, I recommend:
Hemp Diseases and Pests: Management and Biological Control by John McPartland, Robert Clarke, and DP Watson (2000) and *Marijuana Horticulture: The Indoor/Outdoor Medical Grower's Bible* by Jorge Cervantes.

Enduring Understandings

- Common insect pests affecting Cannabis are aphids, spider mites, whiteflies, russet mites, broad mites, fungus gnats, and caterpillars.
- Common fungal pests affecting Cannabis include those responsible for gray mold, powdery mildew, and root rot.
- Viruses in Cannabis plants can be difficult to recognize and identify definitively.
- Some viruses thought to affect Cannabis plants are things like Cannabis Cryptic Virus, Hop Latent Virus, Curly Beet Top Virus, Hemp Streak Virus, and Hemp Mosaic Virus.
- When pathogens affect a Cannabis plant, the symptoms can sometimes mimic nutrient deficiencies, and cultivators must take care to rule out nutrient deficiencies when having a difficult time identifying why a plant is exhibiting problematic symptoms.

Chapter 6:
CANNABIS CONTAMINANTS

"Alle Dinge sind Gift und nichts ist ohne Gift, allein die Dosis macht es, dass ein Ding kein Gift ist."

"All things are poison, and nothing is without poison; only the dose makes a thing not a poison."

Paracelsus

Learning Questions
- What makes something toxic?
- What contaminants are commonly found in Cannabis or Cannabis products?
- What are the major classes of pesticides and how do they differ in their modes of action?
- What additives are sometimes found in Cannabis products?

WHAT IS A TOXIN?

Paracelsus (1493 – 1541) was one of the original founders of toxicology and studied a variety of subjects including physiology, botany, alchemy, and astrology. He has become popular for coining the above phrase, which is often shortened to "The dose makes the poison." It is important to keep this phrase in mind any time the subject of poisons, toxins, or contaminants is at hand. Something's toxicity is relative and depends on the length of time or frequency of exposure, the dose or level of exposure, and the nuances of an organism's individual internal systems. Water is toxic if consumed in too large of an amount in too short amount of a time, no matter how healthy you are!

When studying toxins, it is important to do research about both acute and chronic exposure health effects at various dosages to get an idea of how a compound might affect the body. Some pesticides, for instance, are relatively nontoxic at low dose acute exposures, whereas the same compounds might lead to neurotoxicity with increased exposure for prolonged periods of time. Some things, like mycotoxins, can be either acutely or chronically toxic depending on a person's immune system.

FUNGI: MOLDS/MILDEW AND YEASTS

Molds, mildews, and yeasts are all fungi. **Molds** are multicellular and produce strands of hyphae, giving them a fuzzy stringy appearance. **Yeasts** are unicellular and reproduce through "budding," creating a smooth appearance. They can cause a variety of negative health effects when ingested such as sinus infections, coughing, headaches, sneezing, and allergic reactions. Usually when a Cannabis product is smoked, the heat kills much of the microorganisms and spores present in the material, although it is still possible for viable spores to pass into the smoke and be inhaled into the lungs.

Some fungi are polyphenic and can change between different fungal forms such as mold or yeast. One example of this type of fungus is *Candida albicans*, the fungus responsible for the typical yeast infection in humans as well as Thrush, a fungal condition affecting the tongue, mouth, and throat. Chronic Cannabis consumers might house higher populations of *C. albicans* than acute or abstinent users of Cannabis (Darling et al, 1990).

Some spores of fungi can cause illness in humans. One example of this is found in the dark mold, *Aspergillus niger*. The spores of certain species of *Aspergillus* can enter the lungs and grow into a mass in the lungs which can cause internal bleeding and become fatal. This condition is called **Aspergillosis**. There is a recorded death due to Aspergillosis associated with Cannabis use by an immunocompromised 34-year-old man (Hamadeh et al, 1988).

Examples of Species of Aspergillus That Can Cause Aspergillosis
Aspergillus flavus
Aspergillus fumigatus
Aspergillus nidulans
Aspergillus niger
Aspergillus terreus

FIGURE 12: EXAMPLES OF ASPERGILLOSIS-CAUSING SPECIES OF ASPERGILLUS

MYCOTOXINS

Mycotoxins are the toxic byproducts of some types of fungi. You could think of them as a mold's personalized pesticide. Mycotoxins are quite persistent and will remain on a material after the mold that produced it has died. A sample may appear clean in any other way, or perhaps the material was sterilized, but it could still contain dangerous levels of mycotoxins. Some mycotoxins are highly carcinogenic and can be dangerous even when smoked.

Aflatoxin is an example of one of these dangerous mycotoxins. Aflatoxin is produced primarily by the mold *Aspergillus flavus* and is not only highly carcinogenic but is produced in copious amounts. Aflatoxin has been linked to liver cancer (Bhatnagar-Mathur *et al.*, 2015). Another common type of mycotoxin is Ochratoxin, such as Ochratoxin A. Ochratoxin A can cause substantial damage to the brain and is classified as "potentially carcinogenic" by the International Agency for Research on Cancer (IARC). There are a variety of other types of mold that are commonly detected in Cannabis flowers that can also produce mycotoxins, like Penicillium and Cladosporium.

It is important to understand that when we talk about mycotoxins, we are often actually referring to groups of compounds. Each type of mycotoxin has a myriad of variations. For instance, of the Aflatoxins there is Aflatoxin B1, B2, G1, G2, M1, M2, AFL, and Q1. Of the Ochratoxins there is Ochratoxin A, B, C, and TA.

E. COLI, SALMONELLA, PSEUDOMONAS

There are a wide variety of potential pathogenic bacteria that could be found on Cannabis. Primarily, the bacteria that are generally considered of most concern are shiga toxin-producing strains of *E. coli, Salmonella,* and certain species and strains of *Pseudomonas. E coli* and *Salmonella* are bacteria that share the same biological family, Enterobacteriaceae, and exposure to certain species of each can lead to gastrointestinal disease, like food poisoning. Shiga toxin is the toxin responsible for causing dysentery, for instance. Salmonella is commonly associated with food poisonings. While the source of *E. coli* and *Salmonella* outbreaks is usually thought to be meats and egg products, more attention has recently been brought to plant products like ready to eat herbs as a threat for Salmonella contamination (Zweifel and Stephan, 2012). Typically, *E. coli* and/or *Salmonella* contaminations in Cannabis occur during post-harvest handling.

Pseudomonas is in a family unto itself, separate from *E. coli* or *Salmonella*, but certain species of *Pseudomonas*, namely *P. aeruginosa*, can cause significant infections in the body and can quickly adapt to resist antibiotic drugs. Like E. coli and Salmonella, Pseudomonas can also be found in the environment, and many species and strains of the bacteria are not actually harmful. Rather, it is a small group of particular species and strains that infect the body or produce bacterial endotoxins, causing someone to feel sick.

Ruchlemer et al (2014) found that Cannabis can be plasma sterilized to ensure the absence of microbiological contaminants while only decreasing the potency of THC by approximately 12.6 percent, which in the study resulted in a potency reduction of approximately two percentage points. The Cannabis can then be vaporized using a temperature controlled herbal vaporizer to deliver the drug to the body more safely. Of course, the question remains, *how are the multitude of chemical constituents of Cannabis other than THC affected by sterilization techniques?*

BACTERIAL ENDOTOXINS

Endotoxins are toxic compounds that are embedded in the cell membranes of certain kinds of bacteria. When the cell is disturbed or destroyed, the toxins are released into the surrounding environment. In the human body endotoxins typically initiate a response from the immune system leading to inflammation. In rare cases the inflammation can become so bad that the individual enters septic shock and can be fatal.

AGROCHEMICALS

Agrochemicals like pesticides or herbicides are primarily used to control insect damage and fungal contamination of crops, or to suppress the growth of undesirable, or "weedy", plants. However, some agrochemicals, like fertilizers or plant hormones, may be used to manipulate the growth of a plant or the resin yield of a Cannabis crop.

Many pesticides are active by disrupting the central nervous system in animals, rendering them paralyzed and eventually killing them. As a potential or current Cannabis consumer, you may be wondering, "Okay, sure pesticides may be found in Cannabis, but will those pesticides actually pass through into the smoke?" The answer is yes. Pesticides have been recovered in Cannabis smoke (Sullivan et al., 2013). Extended exposure to some of these compounds can result in serious health effects in humans.

Common Agrochemicals Found in Cannabis Products	
Malathion	Myclobutanil
Carbaryl	Imidacloprid
Propoxur	Abamectin
Bifenthrin	Bifenazate
Permethrin	Azadirachtin
Piperonyl Butoxide	Spinosad
Paclobutrazol	Pyrethrins I and II

FIGURE 13: COMMON AGROCHEMICALS FOUND IN CANNABIS

COMMON PESTICIDE CLASSES

PYRETHROIDS

Pyrethroids are insecticides that mimic natural pyrethrins in some flowers like chrysanthemums. These chemicals are toxic to many organisms that feed and support many food chains like pollinators and aquatic organisms. Cyanide can be found in some Pyrethroids leading to health risks with repeated exposure. Exposure to some pyrethroids has been linked to an increase risk of prostate cancer (Alavanja et al, 2003).

Pyrethroid Examples: Allethrin, Bifenthrin, permethrin

CARBAMATES

Carbamates, like organophosphates, can disrupt the nervous systems of animals. High-level exposure can lead to central nervous system damage, nausea, vomiting, muscle weakness, changes in heart rate, convulsions, and coma (Alavanja et al, 2004). Chronic exposure to carbamates has also been linked to an increased risk for Parkinson's Disease (Seidler et al, 1996).

Carbamate Examples: Carbofuran, carbaryl, methomyl

ORGANOCHLORIDES (ORGANOCHLORINES)

Organochlorides, or organochlorines, include pesticides like DDT, the pesticide that was the subject of Rachel Carson's famous writing, *Silent Spring*, which breathed new life into the environmental movement in the 1960s.

These chemicals cling to tissue for very long periods of time, giving these pesticides a high potential to accumulate in water supplies and organisms for long periods of time after exposure to the chemical has ended. Some organochlorides exhibit very serious negative health effects, particularly in individuals with compromised immune systems. Organochlorines have been linked to non-Hodgkin's lymphoma and neurotoxicity (Blair and Zahm, 1991; Blair and Zahm, 1995; Keifer and Mahurin, 1997)

Organochlorine Examples: DDT, Aldrin, chlordane, lindane

ORGANOPHOSPHATES

Organophosphates, like Carbamates, can disrupt the nervous systems of animals, causing central nervous system damage. Organophosphates can be carcinogenic. Although organophosphates can be highly toxic, they do not last in the environment very long, breaking down quickly when exposed to air and light.

Both organophosphates and organochlorides have been linked to Non-Hodgkin's lymphoma (Blair and Zahm, 1991). Organophosphates and carbamates have both been linked to chronic lymphocytic leukemia (Nanni et al, 1996). Organophosphate exposure can also lead to a condition called organophosphate-induced delayed polyneuropathy (OPIDP), which is a condition consisting of muscle cramps, lethargy, changes to the senses, and possibly paralysis (Alavanja et al, 2004).

Organophosphate Examples: diazinon, malathion, chlorpyrifos, parathion, diazinon, isofenphos

OTHER AGROCHEMICALS IN CANNABIS

Some fungicides, like **myclobutanil**, can disrupt hormone signaling in organisms. This prevents fungi from producing a critical steroid needed to build their cell walls. In humans, chronic exposure to these types of fungicides can disrupt the endocrine system causing hormonal problems in the human such as high or low levels of various estrogens.

Spinosad is a commonly used organic pesticide which is toxic to pollinators and other small organisms. **Pyrethrum**, an organic pesticide containing pyrethrin I and II extracted from chrysanthemum flowers is moderately to highly toxic to many other organisms than insect pests (Pesticide Properties Database - PPD). There is little known about the level of toxicity that pyrethrins exhibit in humans. **Abamectin** is an acaricide, or miticide. Abamectin is a compound synthesized from a particular bacterium and exhibits broad toxicity toward many kinds of organisms including fish and mammals. **Bifenazate** is another pesticide compound commonly found in Cannabis products. Bifenazate is used to treat mites. Bifenazate is not approved for food crop use, so *there are no required chronic toxicity studies available,* meaning that it is not known what health effects repeated exposure to bifenazate would cause. Acute exposure toxicity studies show that it exhibits fairly low toxicity in humans but exhibits moderate or high toxicity in aquatic animals, honeybees, and earthworms (PPD).

Fumigants are sometimes used to sterilize grow rooms, drying rooms, storage rooms, and even soils and plants. Fumigants often contain various pesticides like Pyrethroids and organophosphates. Residues of these pesticides can hang around for prolonged periods of time if used in an enclosed space, potentially leading to contamination if plant material is brought into the area too soon. These fumigants often also contain synergistic compounds to enhance the effects of the pesticide such as piperonyl butoxide (PBO). PBO has been found to be nearly ubiquitous among Cannabis products, being found in approximately 60% of samples according to the results presented in a white paper published by the Cannabis Safety Institute (Voelker and Holmes, 2014). PBO is not only added to pyrethroid products, but some pyrethrin products as well as a variety of other pesticide products containing carbamates.

Certain **plant growth regulators** (PGRs) like paclobutrazol or daminozide, which are only approved for use on ornamental plants, *not* food crops meant for consumption, find their way into Cannabis plants. PGRs are typically used in indoor hydroponic growing to enhance Cannabis flower density and are sometimes unlisted ingredients in various products. These compounds have been banned for use on food crops by the EPA since 1989 due to proposed cancer and cytotoxicity (cell damage) risks to humans.

THINKING CRITICALLY ABOUT PESTICIDE TOXICITY

It is important to take a moment to point out that exposure rates and dose are critical variables when determining how toxic something is. Many pesticides are not thought to be harmful in acute exposures at low dosages. However, if someone is exposed to pesticides frequently at low dosages, it could become a problem. Likewise, if someone is exposed to pesticides one time, but at a high dose, it could be a problem. The dose and frequency of exposure make the poison, in this case.

When determining how to think about pesticide exposure, one would have to examine the toxicology information for each pesticide individually, and identify the risks associated with both acute and chronic exposure, and at what dosages that exposure becomes dangerous. When handling any agrochemical, it is important to wear appropriate personal protective equipment to shield the eyes, ears, airways, and skin from exposure. For consumers, it is generally best to be cautious and discerning of the Cannabis they are purchasing. Generally consumers should only purchase Cannabis that has been tested to be free of major pesticides of concern, though this is not always possible, particularly in regions that have not yet legalized medical or adult use Cannabis.

PESTICIDE PERSISTENCE AND MOBILITY

There are many other distinct types of pesticides with varying degrees of toxicity and persistence. Most pesticides act by either suppressing or overexciting an animal's central nervous system. Because of this, chronic exposure to some pesticides can result in neurological damage.

Persistence is a compound's ability to resist breaking down in the environment. Persistence is measured using half-life. A **half-life** is the amount of time it takes for half of the original amount of a compound to break down. Organochlorine pesticides like DDT are highly persistent (DDT has a half-life of 2 – 15 years!) and can remain in soil and water for a very long time. Other pesticides like Pyrethroids and Carbamates are typically not persistent.

Persistence in soil is directly influenced by a compounds soil adsorption coefficient and its half-life. The **soil adsorption coefficient** is a number which represents how likely the compound is to become mobile, or leach away from the application area. The smaller the soil adsorption coefficient, the more likely a compound is to become mobile. A compound's soil adsorption coefficient and half-life can help you get an idea of how persistent a compound might be. If a compound has a low soil adsorption coefficient and a high half-life, the compound is likely to migrate out and contaminate surrounding water and soil without breaking down for an extended period of time.

MODES OF ACTION:
CONTACT VS. SYSTEMIC VS. TRANSLAMINAR PESTICIDES

Not all pesticides affect plants equally or act the same way to kill insects. The way in which pesticides behave can influence whether pesticide residues may be present on harvested Cannabis. Generally, pesticides can be broken down into three primary modes of action – contact, systemic, and translaminar.

Contact pesticides are pesticides which kill insects upon contact. A common household example would be wasp spray. The pesticides in wasp spray will only kill a wasp if the spray contacts the wasp. Likewise, some pesticides applied to plants are only affective if they make direct contact with pests. Contact pesticides are often applied thoroughly on the undersides and tops of leaves to ensure thorough coverage and contact with pests. Some examples of common contact pesticides used in Cannabis cultivation are carbaryl, bifenthrin, pyrethrins, and bifenazate.

Examples of Common Pesticides by Mode of Action		
Contact Pesticides (Kill on Contact)	**Translaminar Pesticides (Soak into Tissues)**	**Systemic Pesticides (Accumulate)**
Carbaryl	Spinosad	Azadirachtin
Bifenthrin	Abamectin	Imidacloprid
Pyrethrins	Acephate	Myclobutanil
Bifenazate	Chlorfenapyr	

FIGURE 14: PESTICIDES BY MODE OF ACTION

Systemic pesticides work by circulating through the inside of the plant throughout its vascular tissues. Over time, pesticides concentrate into tissues throughout the plant, killing pests that consume the plant material. **Systemic pesticides can linger for a very long time, in some cases months after application.** Examples of commonly used systemic pesticides in Cannabis cultivation include azadirachtin, imidacloprid, and myclobutanil.

Another type of pesticide, which lingers in plants for a long time, but acts more like a contact pesticide, are translaminar pesticides. These are pesticides which will soak through leaf and stem tissues to form small pockets of pesticide within the plant tissue. If an insect feeds on the plant material or attempts to drink water from plant tissues, the insect will contact the pesticide and potentially die. Because these pesticides can become trapped in leaf tissue, they can be present long after application. It is important that Cannabis treated with translaminar pesticides be very thoroughly trimmed to remove any potential contaminated leaf material. Examples of translaminar pesticides commonly used in Cannabis cultivation include spinosad, abamectin, acephate, and chlorfenapyr.

ENVIRONMENTAL IMPACT OF RESIDUAL PESTICIDES

Many pesticides are toxic to pollinators, aquatic organisms, and other critical components of the interconnected systems that keep natural processes and ecosystems functioning as we know them. If these organisms are negatively impacted, over time the entire system of which they are a part will feel the effects of their decline in some way. This presents environmental concern depending on the sites of pesticide contamination and the persistence of the particular contaminant.

Neonicotinoid pesticides have been in the press over recent years as a possible culprit for Colony Collapse Disorder among some bee populations. Pollinators are necessary for many types of food and seed production. Without pollination, food crops and many flowering plants would not reproduce and would steadily decline in number. Eventually humans and many other organisms would struggle to survive. Although some plants can rely on wind-assisted pollination, most plants also require assistance from animals, like insects, to ensure pollination occurs.

Aquatic organisms like microinvertebrates help recycle nutrients in water systems, boosting dissolved oxygen levels, making it easier for fish and other organisms to breathe, and keeping the water clean. As aquatic organism populations fall, water quality suffers, sometimes leading to microbiological pathogen contaminations which can ultimately poison animals (including humans) that drink the water. When biodiversity in a water system drops, other organisms begin to dominate, like algae. When algal blooms occur, oxygen in the water is reduced, making it even harder for other organisms to live. Light is prevented from reaching other plants that grow in the water which provide food to other organisms. A cascading effect is initiated which slowly reduces the biodiversity, and ultimately the quality, of the water system.

Nearly all pesticides, including those derived from natural sources like azadirachtin, are often moderately to highly toxic to soil organisms that are responsible for nutrient cycling in the soil, maintaining bacterial and fungal populations, while also sometimes serving as predators for potential pests. The environmental impacts of pesticide use can be minimized through integrated pest management, proper planning, and if necessary to apply pesticides, utilizing light and direct applications. It should be noted that **some cultivators have learned how to avoid using pesticides or synthetic fertilizers altogether in turn for a cultivation system involving no tilling of the soil, strategic interplanting of other plant species, and integrated pest management with success.**

To learn more about pesticide persistence, human health effects, and potential environmental effects, visit the Pesticide Properties Database website: http://sitem.herts.ac.uk/aeru/ppdb/en/atoz.htm

RESIDUAL SOLVENTS

Organic solvents are commonly used to produce high potency Cannabis extracts. Some examples of solvents used in Cannabis extractions are butane, propane, and hexane. Traces of these solvents can be left behind during the production process. Depending on the purity of the solvent, there could also be a variety of industrial contaminants present. Organic solvents can also be found in the environment such as in the air or water, particularly in industrial areas, which can end up being absorbed into the plant.

The toxicity of solvents is classified among three classes. Class 1 represents compounds which have been shown to be carcinogenic, damaging to the nervous system, or otherwise highly toxic. Benzene is a Class 1 solvent and is highly toxic. Class 2 represents compounds which have not been shown to be extremely toxic upon light exposure, but may be dangerous with repeated exposure or direct ingestion. Compounds like hexane and methanol are Class 2 solvents. Class 3 solvents are compounds which have relatively low toxic potential, like ethanol, butane, and propane.

Solvent Toxicity Classes

CLASS 1
Compounds which have been shown to be carcinogenic, damaging to the nervous system, or otherwise highly toxic. Example: Benzene
CLASS 2
Compounds which have not been shown to be extremely toxic upon light exposure, but may be dangerous with repeated exposure or direct ingestion. Examples: Hexane, Methanol
CLASS 3
Compounds with a relatively low toxic potential. Examples: Ethanol, Butane, Propane

FIGURE 15: SOLVENT TOXICITY CLASSES

OTHER CHEMICAL CONTAMINANTS

Most pesticides and many commercial solvents have varying amounts of other chemicals present besides the target chemicals which can carry over into natural products. One common example is **piperonyl butoxide**, a synergist agent added to many pesticides to keep them from breaking down quickly, thus making them more effective. Lower purity grades of solvents (<99% purity) may have a variety of other compounds present in them. Commercial laboratories testing for residual solvents in Cannabis products may be able to assist in uncovering hidden industrial contaminants in solvents.

It is also possible to get chemical contaminants in a Cannabis product if the product is not manufactured appropriately with adequate quality controls. For instance, if a manufacturer is synthesizing a particular cannabinoid, like delta-8-THC, from another cannabinoid, like CBD, it is very easy to produce a lot of non-target compounds in the process which may be difficult or impossible to identify. Some of these compounds may be miscellaneous cannabinoids or terpenoids that may be fairly innocuous, but some could be much more toxic, like benzene or various aldehyde compounds. These unintended chemical byproducts which are not present in the plant material must be considered contaminants or additives and should be treated as such.

HEAVY METALS

Cannabis is a great nutrient accumulator. Cannabis is so good at drawing things out of the ground that it can be used to help remove toxic metals out of a contaminated soil. Depending on where and how Cannabis is being grown, it is possible for Cannabis to absorb elevated levels of metals. Certain pesticides contain heavy metals that can become concentrated with repeated applications.

Cannabis accumulates heavy metals in all plant parts, although newer research indicates that the highest concentration of metals typically accumulates in the roots (Galic and Zgorelec, 2019). In some cases, it can concentrate nickel as much as 63 ppm in leaves, 33 ppm in seeds, and 7 ppm in fibers (Linger *et al.*, 2002). These metals can become distributed throughout food chains that involve Cannabis. Heavy metals can accumulate in the body leading to health risks after constant exposure.

In addition to heavy metal contaminant exposuring coming from the plant itself, heavy metals from contact surfaces and storage containers can also contaminate Cannabis products, like Cannabis extracts and tinctures, with heavy metals. For instance, heavy metals have been found in vaporizer components used in common Cannabis vaporizer pens (EVIO Labs, *viva voce*). It is very important for product manufacturers to conduct chemical compatibility tests on their materials prior to releasing products into the market to ensure that they are not leaching chemicals, like metals, from their equipment or storage containers into an otherwise clean Cannabis product.

Additionally heavy metals contamination can come from contaminated growth media. When I spoke with Dr. Anthony Smith for season one of the Curious About Cannabis™ Podcast, he explained that some growers are finding high levels of metals in their immature plants due to contaminated rock wool (Curious About Cannabis™ Podcast, Episode 2).

ADDITIVES IN INHALABLE CANNABIS PRODUCTS

As novel Cannabis products are developed, the issue of additives in Cannabis products become a growing concern. This is of particular concern in inhalable products, like "vape pens" because toxins that are inhaled can damage the lungs and enter the bloodstream without first being broken down by the liver as they would normally be if consumed orally.

In 2019, a series of lung infections and deaths attributed to vaping were identified, resulting in over 2000 injuries and 40 deaths nationwide. The phenomenon was called E-cigarette or Vaping Product Use-Associated Lung Injury, or EVALI. After testing tissue samples of affected individuals, the Centers for Disease Control (CDC) announced that they had identified an additive that was consistent in all the samples tested (CDC, 2019). The additive that was identified was tocopherol acetate, or Vitamin E acetate. Another contaminant that was later identified in some of these vaping solutions was a compound called Squalane, which is a derivative of a compound called Squalene which is known to cause lipoid pneumonia and other lung complications (Duffy et al, 2020). Vitamin E acetate and Squalane were being added to Cannabis oils, as well as nicotine oils for electronic cigarettes, as a thickening agent and a cheaper alternative to Vitamin E to reduce lung irritation and coughing. The consequence was that these thickeners could not be properly removed from the lungs after vaping, and the substance coated the lungs, making it difficult for the lungs to keep up with normal functioning.

Additionally, many Cannabis products are starting to be formulated with the additions of many different flavoring compounds and diluents. While many of these compounds, like common plant-derived terpenoids, have been used traditionally in foods and topicals for many years, these compounds have not been traditionally ingested through smoking or vaping – which means there is not a lot of health or safety information regarding the use of these compounds in this manner.

Foreign materials which are known to be hazardous to inhale, such as pine rosin, are being used to dilute Cannabis extracts (Meehan-Atrash and Strongin, 2020). This pine rosin adulterant seems to primarily show up in "shatter" extracts and are now referred to as "fake shatter". The consequences of smoking pine rosin can be very similar to the symptoms seen in EVALI patients. At the time that the study identifying pine rosin in Cannabis extracts was published, EVALI patient tissues had not been tested for some of the chemical markers of pine rosin.

It would be naïve to think that this adulteration is limited to legal Cannabis markets. Even in states that require Cannabis quality testing, labs cannot identify adulterants that they are not prepared to look for. For instance, now that pine rosin is a known adulterant in Cannabis extracts, laboratories can develop assays that look for some of the unique chemicals found in pine rosin, such as abietic acid, palustric acid, pimaric acid, communic acid, and pimarol (Meehan-Atrash and Strongin, 2020).

In the United States, the FDA has begun compiling a list of harmful or potentially harmful compounds (HPHCs) in tobacco products, which can help serve as a guide to Cannabis producers on what additives to definitely avoid using in products. In 2019, the FDA submitted to add several more compounds to the current list of HPHCs in response to unique compounds found in vaping devices and electronic nicotine delivery systems (ENDS). (FDA, 2019)

Proposed Additions to the FDA's List of Harmful or Potentially Harmful Compounds (HPHCs)		
Acetic Acid	Ethyl Acetate	Isobutyl Acetate
Acetoin	Ethyl Acetoacetate	Methyl Acetate
Acetyl Propionyl	Ethylene Glycol	n-butanol
Benzyl Acetate	Furfural	Propionic Acid
Butyraldehyde	Glycerol	Propylene Glycol
Diacetyl	Glycidol	
Diethylene Glycol	Isoamyl Acetate	

Figure 16: Proposed Additions to FDA List of Harmful Compounds

Common Additives Found in Cannabis Extracts			
Propylene Glycol (PG)	May irritate lungs in high doses; Formaldehyde is a degradation product; Turns into propylene oxide when burned, which is carcinogenic	**Squalane and Squalene**	Squalene can cause lipoid pneumonia when inhaled and is sometimes found as a contaminant in squalane.
Vegetable Glycerine (VG)	May irritate lungs in high doses; Formaldehyde is a degradation product	**Tocopherol (Vitamin E)**	May impair lung function
Terpenoids	May irritate lungs and cause inflammation in high concentrations, particularly if the terpenoids are oxidized	**Tocopherol Acetate (Vitamin E Acetate)**	May impair lung function
Medium Chain Triglycerides (MCT Oil)	May impair lung function and cause inflammation	**Pine Rosin**	More common in "shatter"; can cause severe lung dysfunction

FIGURE 17: COMMON ADDITIVES FOUND IN CANNABIS EXTRACTS

Enduring Understandings

- Something's toxicity is relative to the dose and rate of exposure ("the dose makes the poison").

- Some of the common contaminants found in Cannabis include fungi, like molds, mycotoxins, bacteria, pesticides, and metals.

- Common contaminants found in Cannabis extracts include mycotoxins, pesticides, metals, and residual solvents.

- Common contaminants found in finished Cannabis infused products typically include bacteria, like E. coli, Salmonella, or Pseudomonas.

- Various additives may also be found in Cannabis products, like propylene glycol, tocopherol acetate (vitamin E acetate), or squalene.

- More recently, pine rosin has been identified as an adulterant in Cannabis extracts, and primarily in "shatter" extracts

Pop Quiz!

What is the primary source of bacterial contamination of Cannabis?

Mycotoxins can pass into side stream smoke during Cannabis smoking.

TRUE   FALSE

In what parts of the Cannabis plant do metals accumulate?

a) Roots
b) Roots and Shoots
c) Leaves
d) All plant parts
e) No plant parts

Describe the concepts of pesticide persistence and mobility.

List at least four additives that may be found in Cannabis extracts.

Answers: Post harvest handling; True; d); persistence is the lifetime, mobility describes how likely a compound will move

101

Chapter 7:
ENVIRONMENTAL IMPACTS OF THE CANNABIS INDUSTRY

Learning Questions
- What are the environmental impacts of Cannabis cultivation?
- What are the environmental impacts of Cannabis extraction and processing?
- What are the environmental impacts of Cannabis packaging?
- How can the negative environmental impacts of the Cannabis industry be mitigated?

ENVIRONMENTAL IMPACTS OF CANNABIS CULTIVATION

Cannabis cultivation, like all forms of large-scale crop cultivation, presents a variety of environmental concerns and challenges depending on the scale of production, style of cultivation, and inputs used. Most energy consumption for indoor production comes from fossil fuel sources. Fertilizers and other chemical inputs are often also derived from fossil fuels. Water diversion for outdoor cultivation changes the flows of streams throughout watersheds which can have adverse effects both locally at the site of diversion as well as downstream due to reduced dissolved oxygen levels and increased water temperatures.

"The broad array of impacts from marijuana cultivation on aquatic and terrestrial wildlife in California has only recently been documented by law enforcement, wildlife agencies, and researchers. These impacts include loss and fragmentation of sensitive habitats via illegal land clearing and logging; grading and burying of streams; delivery of sediment, nutrients, petroleum products, and pesticides into streams; surface water diversions for irrigation resulting in reduced flows and completely dewatered streams." (Bauer et al, 2015)

ENERGY CONSUMPTION

One thing that makes Cannabis unique is that a substantial amount of its cultivation is done indoors, requiring energy inputs to control lighting and climate. A pound of indoor Cannabis flower takes approximately 2000 kWh of energy to produce according to some estimates (O'Hare et al, 2013). Because Cannabis has a relatively high value per weight, the energy costs of production can be manageable whereas in other industries the costs of production would make indoor growing cost prohibitive. Cannabis produced indoors can be more consistent, potent and produced multiple times a year, making it an attractive cultivation option.

It is estimated that approximately 3% of California's electricity is used for indoor Cannabis cultivation (Mills, 2012). The level of lighting required for indoor Cannabis cultivation is nearly the equivalent of the lighting needed for hospital operating rooms and air exchange rates six times as high as found in high-tech laboratories (Mills, 2012). Energy is not only used for lighting and air exchange, but also for humidification and dehumidification of the air to control mold growth. All in all, a typical "grow house" could contain 50,000 to 100,000 W of lighting power (Brady, 2004).

Another method used to cultivate Cannabis which uses much less energy than indoor growing is greenhouse cultivation. Usually most of the power for greenhouse cultivation is used to warm the greenhouse in winter, run fans, and power supplemental lighting. The shape of the greenhouse and the material used to cover it are two primary factors affecting the greenhouse's energy consumption. A greenhouse can be designed in such a way that it absorbs and stores sunlight efficiently so that the greenhouse can keep itself warm for longer periods of time without supplemental heating. Mechanical shades can be built into the greenhouse for manual control of ventilation, further reducing energy demands.

CARBON DIOXIDE EMISSIONS

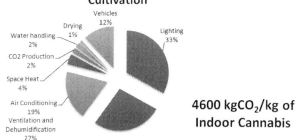

Sources of Carbon Emissions from Indoor Cannabis Cultivation

Vehicles 12%
Drying 1%
Water handling 2%
CO2 Production 2%
Space Heat 4%
Air Conditioning 19%
Ventilation and Dehumidification 27%
Lighting 33%

4600 kgCO$_2$/kg of Indoor Cannabis

DATA SOURCE: MILLS, 2012

FIGURE 18: CARBON EMISSIONS FROM INDOOR CANNABIS CULTIVATION

Besides the energy consumption used for indoor cultivation of Cannabis, the use of CO2 generators in indoor grows contribute to carbon emissions produced by indoor Cannabis cultivation. CO2 generators are used to pump CO2 into the grow room to help stimulate or enhance photosynthesis in the plant. The production of CO2 in this manner could be responsible for 2% of the total carbon emissions attributed to indoor Cannabis growing (Mills,

2012). Indoor CO2 levels are generally raised to levels twice to four times as high as the ambient levels to boost plant growth, although this effect might be less effective when plants are grown in shorter growth cycles (Mills, 2012). The use of vehicles associated with the production and distribution of the Cannabis material is responsible for approximately 15% of total carbon dioxide emissions associated with indoor grows (Mills, 2012).

AGROCHEMICAL INPUTS

Agrochemicals are chemicals used in agricultural production including things like pesticides, fungicides, growth hormones, and herbicides. Many of these compounds are toxic to a variety of organisms to different degrees. Some agrochemicals are very persistent and will linger in the environment for months or years before breaking down. Organisms can concentrate agrochemicals into various tissues, leading to toxic accumulations which can pass down to a predator of the contaminated organism. Cannabis is a particularly efficient hyperaccumulator with the ability to absorb compounds like heavy metals into its tissues very easily.

Many fungicides contain compounds which kill fungi by disrupting their hormone production. These compounds affect other organisms including humans. Hormone disruption can cause a variety of health conditions, including cancer. Most pesticides, whether organic or not, are toxic to soil organisms which are responsible for a variety of functions in the soil including nutrient cycling and aeration. Reduction in soil organism diversity often leads to increased demand for agrochemical inputs like fertilizers and pesticides.

Many agrochemical products are toxic to aquatic microinvertebrates and other organisms. Therefore, it is very important to keep any agricultural runoff from reaching major waterways. If microinvertebrates in the water die off, dissolved oxygen levels go down making it more difficult for larger organisms to get the oxygen needed for respiration. Aside from that, various macroinvertebrates, arthropods, and fish lose a food source when aquatic microinvertebrate populations decline. Over time, if dissolved oxygen levels are too low, other organisms will die off due to lack of oxygen. While this is all happening, the pH of the water is also changing. This leads to algal blooms which keep light from reaching other aquatic plants, diminishing the varieties of another food source for aquatic organisms. Dissolved oxygen levels continue to decline, and anaerobic bacteria populations begin to thrive, contaminating the water and potentially poisoning any organisms that then drink from the water. The water source is then contaminated and unavailable for consumption by most organisms.

Contaminated fresh water is a problem because there is relatively little of it around. Very little of the world's water is in a form that can be consumed by humans. 96.5% of water on Earth is found in the sea and cannot be consumed due to the mineral content. Sea water can be made potable, but the process is expensive and energy intensive. Approximately 2% of water on earth is bound in glaciers at the North and South Poles. Approximately 1% of water on earth is fresh water that can be used and consumed by humans. This makes any threat to fresh water a significant threat. Fresh water diversion is another threat facing water quality and the health of any organisms that are dependent on local streams.

PLASTIC SOIL MULCH

It has become commonplace in the Cannabis industry, particularly among large-scale outdoor hemp cultivators, to use plastic sheet mulch to suppress "weeds", which I prefer to call "undesirable opportunistic plants". There are various kinds of plastics that can be used, including "biodegradable" plastics, but none of them escape environmental concerns. Biodegradable plastics often contain more chemicals in them than typical plastics in order to expedite the breakdown process. These plastics tend to become very weak and brittle over the course of a growing season. When the plastic is removed, it often tears or breaks into smaller pieces -many of which will pollute the ground. These plastics can also leach microplastics into water, contaminating streams and water supplies.

"Compostable" plastic may be a better alternative, as "compostable" plastics are generally made of plant biomass that very quickly degrades, as opposed to "biodegradable" plastics which take a long time to break down *and* fracture more than regular plastic leading to possibly greater soil and water contamination in the short term compared to regular plastic. In general, though, it is best to avoid any type of plastic in the cultivation environment to avoid soil and water pollution. With proper spacing, timing, and the use of living ground cover, Cannabis can be cultivated in a manner that it ultimately suppresses any significant growth of undesirable opportunistic plants without the use of plastic mulches.

WATER DIVERSIONS

Cannabis uses a lot of water during growth. A recent research study examined the changes of several watersheds in northern California due to water diversion for Cannabis cultivation. It was estimated that the water demands for the cultivation of Cannabis in these areas ranged from 523,144 liters per day to 724,016 liters per day. Surface water diversions are supposed to be registered with the state, but this study found that many diversions used for Cannabis cultivation are not registered. Excessive water diversion primarily impacts organisms that live in aquatic or riparian environments. Riparian environments are the areas on the margins of a body of water.

As stream flows reduce, less species can survive, including fish species like salmon. Salmon require cold clean water with a lot of dissolved oxygen and particular water flow dynamics. If those conditions change, the salmon in the stream begin to struggle. As the flow reduces, the temperature of the water tends to increase (Moyle, 2002). As the temperature increases, dissolved oxygen levels go down. This reduces the growth rate of salmon which increases the risk that the salmon will be eaten by something else or fall susceptible to disease

106

(Marine, 2004). Reduced flows also negatively impact amphibians like salamanders and frogs. If flows are reduced in areas that already experience drought or high-water diversion for irrigation are even more susceptible to these adverse environmental effects. All in all, this leads to decreased biodiversity, compromising the ecosystem itself.

It should be noted that these water usage issues are not unique to Cannabis cultivation. All of agriculture faces the issue of how to properly acquire and use enough water to complete harvests each year. It is of greatest concern in areas that experience regular droughts. Water pollution is another ongoing major problem facing agriculture. Chemical and waste runoff can contaminate nearby waterways and groundwater. This is of extra concern in areas that experience flooding.

Cultivating Environmental Solutions

The key to cultivating Cannabis, or any other crop, in a manner that is more sustainable involves taking steps to tend to the ecology of the soil and the ecology of the garden or farm, which are interconnected. The ecology of the soil can be assisted using minimal soil disturbance techniques, the use of compost and compost teas, erosion control, and other soil building techniques. The ecology of the garden can be supported by using companion plants, beneficial organisms, and integrated pest management strategies.

Soil ecosystems are responsible for the efficiency of nutrient cycling, ultimately determining what nutrients are available for plant growth. A soil can be incredibly nutrient dense, and yet all those nutrients could be unavailable to a plant if the soil ecosystem, or soil microbiome, is not appropriate. The soil consists of any number of bacteria, fungi, algae, and animals that help to transform the chemical constituents of the soil and move nutrients around. All the organisms that live in the soil make up **the soil microbiome**. All the organisms that interact with the soil, above *and* below ground, such as grazing animals and birds, make up the **soil food web**.

One method of enhancing the biology of soil is to try to support diverse complex nutrient cycling pathways to, in theory, maximize the number of available nutrients in the soil that a plant can use, thus minimizing the need for external inputs like fertilizers or pesticides. Often this is done by introducing various soil bacteria as well as one or many different species of fungi to the soil. Nitrogen fixing bacteria are utilized to help capture nitrogen from the atmosphere and store it in the soil. Many plants form associations with nitrogen fixing bacteria, like legumes. Other types of bacteria interact with other bacteria and fungi to cycle nutrients in the soil.

Glomus is a genus of fungi that includes all the **arbuscular mycorrhizal fungi (AMF)**. These fungi penetrate root cells and exchange various nutrients and water with the plant in exchange for carbon (Redecker et al., 2000). This is in contrast with **ectomycorrhizal**

fungi which form sheaths around roots without penetrating the cells and are commonly found associated with bushes and trees rather than grasses or forbs (herbs and other flowering plants). Arbuscular mycorrhizal fungi produce a substance called **glomalin** which acts as a "soil glue" to hold nutrients and small soil particles together. Glomalin helps soil to stay in place and resist erosion.

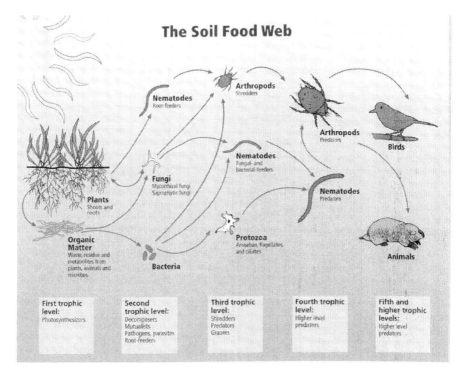

AN ILLUSTRATION OF THE SOIL FOOD WEB; IMAGE PUBLIC DOMAIN COURTESY OF USDA-NRCS

The use of fungal inoculants in Cannabis cultivation are quite common as a method of trying to enhance the biodiversity of soil microorganisms or enhance plant growth and yield. Though this concept seems straightforward, the use of mycorrhizal fungi in agriculture is not quite as simple.

Research has shown that a plant will resist a mycorrhizal symbiont if the relationship is not needed. One meta-analysis of field studies revealed that AMF root colonization reduces by over 30% after phosphorous fertilization (Treseder, 2004). So, nutrient availability, and particularly phosphorous availability, seems to be a factor influencing AMF colonization rates. If the plant is having trouble finding nutrients that are bioavailable, it might be more likely to accept a symbiosis with the AMF. If the plant is not struggling to feed itself, it might resist mycorrhizal associations. This is particularly important in the context of

Cannabis, given that Cannabis is an opportunistic plant that seems to take care of itself pretty well without inputs. More research on the ecological functions and effects of Cannabis are needed to better understand how Cannabis might affect fungal populations in the soil.

Despite widely held belief, **mycorrhizal associations are not always symbiotic** (Kiers and Heijden, 2006). As conditions change, fungi can begin to take more resources out of the relationship than the plant receives, potentially leading to a situation where the fungus is limiting plant growth and yield. AMF have been shown to counter-intuitively *restrict* root and shoot growth in some plants (Desserud and Naeth, 2012). It has also been shown that 5%-20% of a plant's photosynthetically fixed carbon may be used *just* to maintain the fungal relationship (Douds et al., 2000).

The point is that, although these fungi have exciting potential to expedite nutrient cycling and store water, carbon and other materials in the soil, there are yet complexities to these biological systems that are not well understood. Enhancing the biological activity of the soil does not *necessarily* mean that the plant will grow more vigorous or yield more than usual, for instance. In fact, the opposite might occur if conditions are not appropriate.

Beyond mycorrhizal fungi, sometimes microbiological inoculants for soils include the spores of **saprophytic fungi**. Saprophytic fungi are fungi that obtain energy by breaking down organic matter. These are the fungi responsible for the molds that appear on the top layer of soil that is often found in indoor Cannabis cultivation. This is *NOT* mycorrhizal fungus. This mold is usually not harmful to the plant, but it *does* indicate that conditions are ripe for the growth of other less desirable fungal species due to excess moisture content and excess organic matter in the soil. This also attracts fungus feeding insects which might also feed on plant material or roots and attract other insects that could be pests. Some pests like broad mites or russet mites travel on the backs of other insects, like ants or white flies, to find a new plant host.

Typically, a well-balanced soil microbiome will naturally limit soil pests. When soil pests are a problem, one way of handling them is by introducing predatory soil animals, like certain species of nematodes. Nematodes are a diverse group of organisms that have specialized to feed on roots, fungi, bacteria, and small insects. **When a strong soil microbiome is built up through careful cultivation methods and minimal soil disturbance, the need for agrochemical inputs can be drastically reduced or eliminated.**

No-till cultivation helps nurture soil micro-organism communities by minimizing soil disturbance. Instead of tilling the soil, time is spent building a rich series of deep soil horizons, or layers, home to a diverse community of soil organisms. No-tillage cultivation methods tend to result in enhanced soil moisture at greater soil depths compared to conventional tillage cultivation techniques (Blevins et al, 1971). No-tillage methods have also been shown to decrease nutrient mobility in the soil, meaning that the nutrients present in the soil remain in place rather than washing away (Hendrix et al, 2014). Additionally, minimizing soil disturbance also minimizes the growth of unwanted opportunistic plants (aka "weeds") by not digging up and exposing their seeds to things like water and light which will cause the seeds to germinate and grow.

Conventional and no-tillage systems have unique soil ecosystems. Bacteria have an upper hand in conventional tillage methods and are the dominant type of organism breaking down the organic matter (Hendrix et al, 2014). The frequent disturbance of the soil limits the ability of fungi to thrive. Nematodes, protozoa, and small worms feed on bacteria in soil. Fungi, on the other hand, are more common in no-tillage systems (Hendrix et al, 2014). Fungi are often fed on by insects, nematodes, small mammals, and worms.

> *No-tillage cultivation methods tend to result in enhanced soil moisture at greater soil depths compared to conventional tillage cultivation techniques (Blevins et al, 1971).*

To deal with environmental water concerns, some cultivators have developed methods to maximize the efficiency of water use in farming by **slowing** water down, **spreading** it throughout an area, **sinking** it deep into the ground, and keeping it in the ground using mulch and **cover crops** to minimize evaporation. **Drought tolerant varieties** of Cannabis may be chosen for cultivation to further minimize water use. Thick mulches of organic material can act as a sponge to help retain water, while also working to suppress the growth of unwanted opportunistic plants.

Companion plants and other crops may be planted in the garden to provide functions like soil building or attracting predatory insects, to support the ecosystem of the garden itself. Companion plants can also help fill in space in the garden or farm to reduce the presence of unwanted opportunistic plants. **Compost** and **compost teas** are used to boost soil nutrient availability and introduce various bacteria and fungi to the soil which help break down organic matter and release nutrients to the soil. Rather than spending resources keeping low-performing plants alive, poor performing plants are allowed to die off, leaving plants that are better adapted to their particular environment. This method of cultivation, sometimes referred to as biodynamic (or ecodynamic) no-till cultivation, can be both productive and economical while minimizing environmental impacts and in some cases enhancing the environment.

Cannabis and sunflowers serving as companion plants for one another.

Comfrey and other companion plants in the Cannabis garden

Compost tea is aerated to limit growth of anaerobic bacteria.

This cultivation site utilized mulching and companion planting to absorb and trap water, reducing watering requirements. This mulch was inoculated with edible mushroom species to build soil while also producing food for the farmer.

This root ball of a harvested Cannabis plant has been colonized by saprophytic fungi. Fungi break down organic matter in the soil, assisting nutrient cycling, building soil, and providing food for local wildlife, including humans.

King Stropharia mushrooms cultivate easily in mulch beds and are edible.

A broad fork can be used to turn soil, rather than using a tiller. A broad fork reduces gas or electricity costs, disturbs the biology of the soil less than rototilling and results in less overall nutrient loss from the soil.

One way of reducing water usage in cultivation is by using "hügelkultur" style raised beds. Hügelkultur beds consist of wood which is buried. The wood absorbs and slowly releases water, reducing water input requirements, while decomposing and contributing to the generation of soil.

As pathways for the hügelkultur beds are carved out, the dirt is piled on top of the wood, burying it.

As seasons pass, the wood decomposes, and the raised bed flattens out and sinks

After establishing a cultivation area, it is important for all gardeners and farmers to consider designing ways in which the area may still support the life of nearby native wildlife to minimize the negative impacts of disturbing and clearing habitat. One suggestion is to **create wildlife "corridors"** throughout the gardening or farming landscape which include interconnected areas of native plant life and habitat to support native insects, birds, and other native wildlife that are critical for the support of the ecosystems present around the cultivation area. Accommodating wildlife in the garden or farm can bring other benefits, like enhanced pest control and food crop yield.

CANNABIS AS A BIOREMEDIATION TOOL

Although Cannabis cultivation can present environmental risks, as all forms of farming can, it can also present potential environmental remedies. Cannabis can tolerate absorbing many different compounds from the soil including potentially toxic compounds like heavy metals. Because of this, researchers have been looking at whether Cannabis could be used to extract excess levels of metals or other toxins from contaminated soils.

While there is relatively little information available about Cannabis' abilities to uptake and tolerate metals, it has been found that Cannabis accumulates nickel more than lead, and lead more than cadmium (Linger, 2002). During one study, cultivated hemp could extract 126g of cadmium from contaminated soil within one vegetative period without sacrificing the fiber quality (Linger, 2002). Metals can be distributed into every tissue in the plant, although they are most accumulated in the roots.

In one study researchers inoculated Cannabis with the arbuscular mycorrhizal fungus *Glomus mosseae* and measured the degree of metal uptake. They found that the inoculation of the fungus caused reduced plant growth and changes in the ways that metals are stored in the plant. After colonization of roots by mycorrhizal fungi, Cannabis translocated metals from the roots to the shoots (Citterio et al, 2004).

Bioremediation is a topic that is growing in popularity. **Not only can plants like Cannabis be used to extract potentially toxic compounds from the environment, but other hyperaccumulating organisms like fungi, lichen, and bacteria (as well as many other types of plants) can also be utilized in a collaborative effort against soil contaminants.**

Pop Quiz!

Approximately how many kilograms of CO_2 is released to produce one (1) kilogram, or 2.2 pounds, of indoor grown Cannabis?

What makes Cannabis a bioremediation tool candidate?

What are some techniques that can be used to reduce the environmental impact of Cannabis cultivation (or any type of cultivation, for that matter)?

What cultivation techniques can be used to better tend the ecology of the soil?

What cultivation techniques can be used to better tend the ecology of the garden?

ENVIRONMENTAL IMPACTS OF CANNABIS PROCESSING AND EXTRACTION

The environmental impacts of Cannabis processing can be challenging to assess because there are many ways to process Cannabis. The primary issues to take note of regarding the environmental impacts of Cannabis processing are: energy usage, solvent use, storage methods, and waste disposal methods.

Extracting Cannabis can sometimes require a lot of energy, depending on the method. Cannabis extractions can take place entirely without electricity, as in the case of ethanol macerations, or Cannabis extractions can use quite a bit of electricity when using large electrically controlled pumps, digital control systems, water chillers, water heaters, digital temperature and pressure gauges, and atmospheric monitors, as is common with things like CO_2 or hydrocarbon extraction (see Chapter 19 for more information about Cannabis extraction technologies).

The manner in which a laboratory handles solvent can substantially affect their environmental impact. A laboratory must first ensure that all of their solvents are of a known purity, as contaminants or impurities in solvents can affect how dangerous the solvent could be to the environment. Secondly, a laboratory must ensure that solvents are always properly labeled and stored so that they do not become environmental risks. Additionally, when a lab is using a solvent, it is best to implement ways in which to keep the solvent from being exposed to the atmosphere. Systems which contain the extraction solvent throughout the entire extraction process are often referred to as "closed loop systems." It is important that extraction systems are checked for leaks on a regular basis to ensure that solvents are not being expelled into the atmosphere unnecessarily.

Cannabis extraction processes can sometimes result in increased fire risks, which can present risks to the environment in the form of wildfires. This risk is most associated with laboratories performing extraction methods that utilize flammable solvents under pressure, such as ethanol or alkane extraction (hexane, butane, pentane, etc). By contrast, supercritical fluid CO_2 extraction does not present this same risk since CO_2 is not flammable. Additionally, mechanical forms of extraction such as dry sift hash production or rosin pressing do not present these same fire risks.

The manner in which a laboratory stores its chemicals is critical for minimizing environmental impact. Laboratories must take steps to ensure that chemicals will not make their way into nearby water ways or public lands where they could poison wildlife. Proper chemical storage usually involves the use of special lockable storage cabinets that are completely enclosed and fire-proof so that the cabinet can contain any spillage and prevent the spread of fire. Additionally, these cabinets are often stored in designated locations within a laboratory where they will be best shielded from accidents.

Finally, it is critical that extraction laboratories properly dispose of their waste in order to minimize their environmental impact. Solvents and other industrial waste is often considered "hazardous waste" and must be disposed of in a special manner to ensure that the material does not present harm to the public or the environment. Hazardous waste is typically collected in designated containers with appropriate "hazardous waste" labels present to ensure that the material will be handled with care. Waste disposal companies typically dedicate certain times of the year to pick up industrial waste for a reasonable fee, or at times even free, to ensure that the material is properly managed. Solvents and other waste should never be dumped down drains or in areas where they could be washed into storm drains.

ENVIRONMENTAL IMPACTS OF CANNABIS PACKAGING

The stringent rules and regulations that often get passed once Cannabis becomes legal in a new state or country usually results in a significant unforeseen negative consequence – trash, and lots of it. Cannabis products are often required to feature any number of warnings, test results, and batch information on the labels of each product. Additionally, most places with legal Cannabis require that Cannabis be sold in tamper-proof, or child proof, packaging. These factors end up coming together to result in Cannabis being sold in plastic bottles, akin to traditional pill bottles, as well as thick resealable plastic and mylar bags, excess boxes, and more. In some places it is even required to then place Cannabis products into a secondary container when travelling. This has led to a major problem.

The good news is that there are companies springing up to tackle this problem head-on by providing recycling services for used Cannabis packaging, such as plastic bottles and bags. However, not all packaging can be recycled. For instance, it has been reported that smaller containers, often used to hold single Cannabis joints, or Cannabis cigarettes, are too small for recycling machines to process. Additionally, labels must be removed from packaging before it can be accepted for recycling.

In 2018 The Washington Post reported on this issue in Washington State in an article entitled, "Garbage from Washington state's booming pot industry clogs gutters, sewers and landfills." The article points out that, while companies are beginning to attempt to fill a niche by providing recyclable and compostable packaging solutions for the Cannabis industry, it has proven challenging for many Cannabis producers to rationalize paying the premium that it takes to invest in more ecologically-friendly packaging when their margins are already very tight due to the cost of operating within a highly regulated environment.

There is also another issue that is quickly becoming a major environmental concern, and that is the use of vaporizer pens, or vape pens. Many vape pens are designed in such a way that consumers cannot, with ease, refill the cartridges that hold the Cannabis extract. Additionally, the batteries to vape pens are cheap and often lost, leading to these batteries making their way into landfills. Some vape pens are even designed to be disposable, with the battery and cartridge impossible to separate. This problem is substantially more problematic than the use of plastic bottles or bags, because the waste cannot be simply recycled. Vaporizer pen cartridges vary in their materials and are complex in their designs – making them challenging to break down and recycle. At a time when more and more Cannabis users are turning to vaporizer pens due to their convenience, it is critical that careful consideration is made regarding the environmental impacts that these devices could have. When possible, it is recommended to use refillable cartridges and avoid disposable cartridges altogether. Vape pen batteries should be disposed in special disposal bins approved for collecting batteries.

It seems like the issue of Cannabis packaging filling up landfills will continue to be a problem for years to come until creative solutions are employed to improve the designs of Cannabis products to minimize environmental impacts and regulatory environments loosen up regarding product labeling and packaging – if that ever happens. In the meantime, producers and retailers can work to find companies that provide recyclable or compostable packaging and encourage consumers to re-use packaging or deliver used packaging to designated pick-up spots so that less of these items make their way onto city streets, landfills, and water ways. Consumers can choose to support companies and retailers that demonstrate a commitment to environmental stewardship, and avoid problematic products, like disposable vape pens.

Enduring Understandings

- Some of the environmental problems facing Cannabis cultivation primarily relate to energy consumption, carbon dioxide emissions, the use of agrochemical inputs, water contamination and natural waterway diversions.
- Cannabis extraction activities can result in the release of greenhouse gases into the atmosphere, contamination of water systems with hazardous materials, increased fire risk, and energy consumption.
- Cannabis laws typically require child-resistant packaging for Cannabis products, leading to excess plastic waste in the form of pill-bottle style plastic tubes, thick mylar-lined plastic bags, and other waste that is often discarded quickly after use.

Chapter 8:   CANNABIS GENETICS

Learning Questions
- What is the difference between filial generations (F1, F2, etc) of Cannabis plants?
- How do genes determine how cannabinoids are produced in the Cannabis plant?
- How are feminized seeds produced?

This chapter is meant to provide a basic introduction to plant genetics and how genetics influence attributes in the Cannabis plant, such as cannabinoid production. However, this chapter barely scrapes the surface of the depth of this highly nuanced topic. Genetics is a complicated topic in just about any context. In the context of Cannabis and cannabinoid science, it is especially complicated. This is compounded by the fact that researchers keep learning more and more about the Cannabis genome and the mechanisms responsible for cannabinoid and terpenoid production in the plant. Let's start with some basics.

WHAT ARE GENES?

All living organisms contain **DNA** in the nucleus of all their cells which contain **genes**. A gene is a bit of DNA that codes for one or more **proteins** in an organism. A protein is a broad term used to describe a molecular machine that does some sort of work in an organism. So basically, genes are the codes embedded in DNA which tell a cell what chemical machines to build and when to build them. These chemical machines then go on to form tissues, organelles, organs, and organisms!

By examining an organism's genes, it can be possible to determine characteristics of the organism as well as potential characteristics of an organism's offspring such as sex, disease susceptibility, paternity and more.

To examine and better understand the genes of various organisms, scientists have begun to map the **genomes** of organisms of interest. A genome is simply the complete (or mostly complete) genetic code of an organism. It is a map of all the genes of an organism.

The Human Genome Project, the world's largest collaborative scientific effort which was conceived in the late 1980s and completed by the early 2000s, was an attempt to map the entire human genome in order to better understand and treat diseases. This was an immense project. Genetic variation among individuals meant that it was not enough to just map all the genetic information of one individual, but rather the project required a very large sample size to map the differing genetic variations that may be present in the human population. One problem that arose from this project was that clinicians discovered that seeing the genetic code of a human is not very helpful if you don't understand how to interpret it. Mapping a genome is only one piece of a bigger puzzle to understanding how to utilize genetic information in a meaningful way.

Today, a new effort is underway to conduct much the same sort of genome mapping, but with Cannabis. There are a variety of groups throughout the world and the US which are attempting to catalog the genetic information of as many strains of Cannabis as possible as an attempt to better understand the plant, develop plants with very specific chemical and physical profiles, secure strain data for protection against patenting, and more.

GENETIC INHERITANCE AND HYBRIDIZATION

Organisms change over time in response to various selection pressures, whether it be natural selection or artificial selection. **Natural selection** is the concept of genetic traits being influenced by the natural environment over time. **Artificial selection** is the concept of genetic traits being influenced by other means, like human manipulation through domestication and breeding. Some scientists argue that artificial selection is really a misnomer since humans are very much inescapably a part of nature, but alas…

Cannabis genetics have been influenced both naturally and artificially for thousands of years as the plant has coevolved with humans. Cannabis cultivators have been working diligently for thousands of years to breed different Cannabis varieties for different desirable characteristics such as resin yield, fiber quality, or seed crop. Because Cannabis has been coevolving alongside humans for so long, the plant has undergone a massive amount of hybridization, or mixing, between varieties. The result is that there is now a seemingly endless array of Cannabis varieties to satisfy most any desire.

However, this sense of diversity is somewhat of an illusion because intensive hybridization and artificial selection ultimately results in a loss of "native" genes that served functions or produced traits which were not selected for. In ecological science, there is a predictable model by which we can see how intensive hybridization leads to losses in a genome, which may ultimately set up future offspring to be less adaptable to ecological conditions, leading to a potential extinction event. It is for this reason that it is critical that native organisms, or in the case of Cannabis, naturalized "landrace" cultivars, be preserved.

We are already experiencing intensive hybridization of Cannabis varieties across the planet. Even landrace cultivars are largely contaminated, having been intentionally or unintentionally crossed with other landrace varieties (McPartland and Small, 2020). Let's assume all of these landrace varieties were now extinct, and all that exists are the cannabinoid resin-rich cultivars currently present in the commercial Cannabis market. Through the intensive hybridization and selection for resin-rich production, perhaps a handful of genes which once belonged to the ancient landrace varieties from which the plant descended was lost in the process.

In this scenario, what would happen if some previously unnoticed viral disease started wiping out commercial Cannabis crops across the world? The landrace cultivars that were naturally resistant to the virus would have had those very genes that were lost in the commercial Cannabis varieties due to intensive breeding for cannabinoids and terpenes. If the purer landrace varieties were still accessible, they could be crossed once again into the modern commercial Cannabis gene pool to give plants the resistance and adaptability needed to survive. However, in this worst-case scenario those landrace varieties would *not* be available, and the only hope would be to rely on external controls like pesticides or invasive genetic modification. And with those external controls come other considerations, like consumer health and safety.

This is a very simple thought experiment, but it demonstrates the risks to an organism's population if distinct varieties are allowed to hybridize without any preservation of the native genome. You might be asking, "How does someone preserve a genome?" The answer is simple – seeds. Seed banks have been established for many native and non-native plants to ensure that, should we ever need access to a genome from the past, whether for research purposes, restoration, or breeding – it is available. Another way that genomes are preserved is by tissue culturing plants, creating a callus which can be turned into a synthetic seed. Tissue culturing allows a genetically identical copy of a plant to be preserved for future reference, rather than the offspring as in seed collection.

Genetic breeding affects the predictability of inherited traits of child Cannabis plants from parent Cannabis plants. The first hybrid generation of an organism is referred to as the F1, or first **filial**, generation. This generation of organisms will contain genes from both parents and, thus, will display mixed traits of each. For example, mules are F1 hybrids of horses and donkeys; peppermint is an F1 hybrid of watermint and spearmint. Generally, F1 organisms will end up being consistent if the same parent organisms are used for crossing/breeding. This means that you will always end up with a mule if you breed a horse and donkey; likewise, if you cross a watermint and spearmint, you will always end up with peppermint. These characteristics generally make F1 organisms more desirable for professional breeders or nurseries – they are predictable.

F2 organisms, the offspring of two F1 parents, can exhibit a wide variety of phenotypes due to the advanced genetic mixing that has occurred between the different hybrids. Because of the high variability of F2 organisms, these organisms are generally less desired by professional breeders because they are unpredictable.

Parent A x Parent B = F1 Hybrid

- Stable phenotype expressing dominant traits

F1 x F1 = F2 Hybrid

- Unstable phenotype expressing dominant *and* recessive traits

Review the differences between genotypes, phenotypes, and chemotypes below.

Genotype	Phenotype	Chemotype
Genetic characteristics of an organism	Physical characteristics of an organism (what you see, feel, etc)	Chemical characteristics of an organism (chemical phenotype)
Controlled by genetic transcription	Controlled by genes and environment	Controlled by genes and environment
Examples: B_T alleles present in DNA of Cannabis plant, promoting THCA production	Examples: plant's size, shape, color, etc	Examples: THC/CBD ratio, terpene profile

FIGURE 19: GENOTYPE VS PHENOTYPE VS CHEMOTYPE

CANNABINOID AND TERPENOID PRODUCTION IN CANNABIS

To understand the genetics behind cannabinoid and terpenoid production, we must first talk about the chemical pathways involved in producing cannabinoids and terpenoids in the Cannabis plant. There are elaborate series of chemical pathways that lead to the formation of terpenes and cannabinoids in Cannabis, and not all of these pathways are well understood. Monoterpenoids, sesquiterpenoids, the olivetolic acid-based cannabinoids (CBGA, THCA, CBDA, CBCA), and the divarinic acid based cannabinoids (CBGVA, THCVA, CBDVA, CBCVA), all stem from a common chemical pathway, called the deoxyxylulose synthetic pathway. This pathway begins with the combination of **DMAPP** (Dimethylallyl pyrophosphate/diphosphate) and **IPP** (Isopentenyl pyrophosphate/diphosphate) to form geranyl-pyrophosphate, or **GPP**.

Geranyl-pyrophosphate then either binds with olivetolic acid or divarinic acid to form the unique pathways toward the various phytocannabinoids (Fellermeier *et al.*, 2001; de

Meijer *et al.*, 2003). If GPP binds with **olivetolic acid**, the synthetic pathway leads toward CBGA which can then be synthesized into either THCA, CBDA, or CBCA. If GPP binds with **divarinic acid**, the pathway leads toward THCV, CBDV, etc (Russo, 2011).

Through a particular enzymatic process, GPP could instead transition toward other terpenoids, like the monoterpenoids or sesquiterpenoids. If GPP does not acquire any extra isoprene units, it might encounter an enzyme which rearranges the GPP molecule into what we now know as the monoterpene limonene. If GPP *does* acquire an extra isoprene unit and then encounters certain enzymes, it might be transformed into a sesquiterpenoid.

How Cannabinoids and Terpenes Are Produced in Cannabis
The Deoxyxylulose Synthetic Pathway of Cannabinoids and Terpenoids in Cannabis

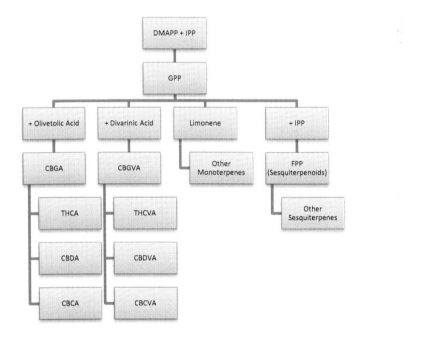

FIGURE 20: DEOXYXYLULOSE PATHWAY FOR CANNABINOID AND TERPENOID SYNTHESIS

Data Sources: Russo, 2011; Fellermeier et al., 2001; de Meijer et al., 2003

DMAPP	Dimethylallyl pyrophosphate	CBDA	Cannabidiolic acid
IPP	Isopentenyl pyrophosphate	CBCA	Cannabichromenic acid
GPP	Geranyl pyrophosphate	CBGVA	Cannabigerivarinic acid
FPP	Farnesyl pyrophosphate	THCVA	Tetrahydrocannabivarinic acid
CBGA	Cannabigerolic Acid	CBDVA	Cannabidivarinic acid
THCA	Delta-9-tetrahydrocannabinolic acid	CBCVA	Cannabichromivarinic acid

Note that decarboxylated cannabinoids like THC, CBD, THCv, etc are not actually synthesized by Cannabis. Instead the plant synthesizes cannabinoid acids such as THCA, CBDA, THCVA, etc.

WHY DOES CANNABIS PRODUCE TERPENOIDS AND CANNABINOIDS?

Terpenoids are hypothesized to serve a variety of functions in the Cannabis plant, but no one really knows exactly why the Cannabis plant produces the compounds that it does. Some primary functions of terpenoids are thought to be: **protection from desiccation (drying), insect predation, and UV radiation**. Since cannabinoids are oily, they can serve as good barriers to water loss in surrounding plant tissues (Pate, 1994). In THC chemotype Cannabis plants, THC concentration tends to increase with increased UV-B radiation, potentially producing a protective effect for the plant. This effect does not exist for other cannabinoids like CBD, lending a particular evolutionary advantage to THC dominant Cannabis plants in higher elevation areas (Pate, 1994). The cannabinoid acids present in growing Cannabis have demonstrated insecticidal properties that could discourage insect predation.

Ethan Russo points out that **the Cannabis plant expresses a "phytochemical polymorphism"**, meaning that **the plant produces varying concentrations of terpenoids in varying parts of the plant** (2011). For instance, the bottom portion of the plant typically produces higher concentrations of bitter sesquiterpenoids that discourage herbivory from grazing animals (Russo, 2011; Franz and Novak, 2010; Nerio et al, 2010). Plants typically produce excess terpenes in response to environmental stresses to attract predatory insects and repel herbivorous insect predators. Terpene concentrations are influenced by poor soil nutrition as well, as one research project demonstrated that terpene concentrations were higher in plants that experienced reduced nitrogen prior to harvest (Potter, 2004; Russo, 2011).

In Michael Pollan's book turned PBS documentary, *Botany of Desire,* Pollan remarks on how smells and intoxication effects have influenced humans to help the plant spread its geographical reach, reproduce and express itself in countless physical and chemical varieties. By artificially selecting plant varieties based on how they meet various human desires such as intoxication, smell, and taste, humans have drastically affected the evolution of the Cannabis plant and have bred out a huge variety of cannabinoid and terpene profiles.

GENETICS AND CANNABINOID PRODUCTION

So far, researchers are under the assumption that there are three primary dominant cannabinoid phenotypes present in Cannabis: THC dominant, CBD dominant, and CBG dominant. To be more accurate in accounting for carboxylic acids, it would be THCA dominant, CBDA dominant, and CBGA dominant. Among these dominant cannabinoid phenotypes there are intermediaries, forming a spectrum of possible phenotypes. Other chemotypes have been identified and/or developed such as the CBCA dominant chemotype, but these are considered rare, for now.

The ratios of cannabinoids in the Cannabis plant are primarily controlled by genetics and generally affected little by the environment, though little is understood about potential epigenetic effects in Cannabis. However, the *concentrations* of compounds in Cannabis can be influenced heavily by the environment.

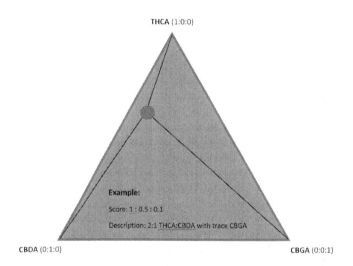

FIGURE 21: VISUALIZATION OF THCA:CBDA:CBGA CHEMOTYPE SPECTRUM

Cannabis is typically a **diploid** organism with each Cannabis plant containing two (di-) separate sets of genes (-ploid), one from each parent. However modern breeding has produced tetraploid Cannabis plants, containing two sets of genes from each parent, which have then been bred with diploid plants to produce triploid Cannabis plants containing two sets of genes from one parent and one set of genes from another parent. (Oregon CBD, 2020).

These genes are present as tightly wound bunches of DNA that are coiled into structures called chromosomes. Cannabis plants contain 20 chromosomes total – 10 from each parent. Throughout these chromosomes are certain sections, or **loci** (locations), responsible for providing genetic instructions for building particular proteins, like an enzyme responsible for making THCA, for example. The different variations of a gene at a single location on a chromosome are called **alleles**.

In many cases, some alleles are considered "dominant", while others are considered "recessive". When different alleles for a genetic trait are mixed in a progeny, the dominant alleles will be expressed unless two recessive alleles are paired together. In the case of THC and CBD production in Cannabis, the associated alleles for THC and CBD production are "codominant", meaning that the presence of one does not override the other. If the B_D allele (CBD allele at the "B" locus) is present, the plant will produce CBD. If the B_T allele (THC allele at the "B" locus) is present, the plant will produce THC. If both the B_D and B_T allele are present, the plant will produce a mix of CBD and THC.

A variety of genetic models describing cannabinoid production exist. One proposed mechanism consists of four genetic loci on Cannabis chromosomes that affect the cannabinoid chemotype of a Cannabis plant.

Proposed Genetic Loci Associated with Cannabinoid Production in Cannabis

Locus	Traits Affected	Notes
Locus O	Will cannabinoid precursors be formed?	Resorcinolic acids are either formed or not formed, leading to the production of geranylpyrophosphate (GPP), one of the primary precursors for cannabinoids.
Locus A	How much olivetolic acid and divarinic acid will be made?	These alleles are thought to control production of divarinic and olivetolic acid, or somehow control how GPP joins with either DA or OA to produce CBGA or CBGVA.
Locus B	How efficiently will CBGA/CBGVA convert to THCA/THCVA, CBDA/CBDVA, etc?	B_T alleles control THCA production, B_D alleles control CBDA production. B_T/B_T = high THC plant. B_D/B_D = high CBD plant. B_D/B_T plants responsible for intermediate THC:CBD ratio chemotypes. Mutant alleles (B_0) produce excess CBGA or CBGVA in the plant
Locus C	CBCA production?	Fixed, not allelic

FIGURE 22: GENETIC LOCI FOR CBGA, CBCA, AND THCA CANNABINOID PRODUCTION IN CANNABIS

Data source: de Meijer E. 2015. The Chemical Phenotypes (Chemotypes) of Cannabis. Chapter five. Handbook of Cannabis. Oxford University Press. 89-110

One thing that is very interesting about the genetics that control cannabinoid production, is that a Cannabis lineage could be bred to eliminate the THCA synthase gene, which would mean that, in theory, the THCA synthase *enzyme* should not be produced in the plant, and thus THCA itself should not be produced in the plant - and yet the plant could still produce trace amounts of THCA. This is because, simply put, genes are not perfect. They behave in different ways depending on a variety of factors. It may be possible for the CBDA synthase gene, for instance, to occasionally build THCA synthase enzymes instead of CBDA synthase enzymes (McKernan et al, 2020).

Additionally, genes that control for traits like cannabinoid expression, may also be associated with other characteristics like pathogen resistance (McKernan et al, 2020). Breeding that is targeted at specific cannabinoids could potentially end up breeding out pathogen resistance, putting the crop at greater risk of attack or infection (remember that worst-case example we went through earlier in regard to preserving landrace varieties of Cannabis?).

GENETICS AND TERPENOID PRODUCTION

Terpene production in plants is made possible because of enzymes called terpene synthases, or TPS. Terpene synthase genes, or TPS genes, control the production of these critical enzymes. When terpenoids are being produced in the Cannabis plant, they are formed from a common precursor shared with cannabinoids – geranyl pyrophosphate. Only, instead of pairing with olivetolic acid or divarinic acid to form CBGA or CBGVA – terpene synthases can change geranyl pyrophosphate into any number of monoterpenoids, or it can bring in other compounds like isopentenyl pyrophosphate, which provides enough isoprene units to form larger terpenoids like sesquiterpenoids.

There are various subfamilies of TPS genes – names TPS-a, TPS-b, and TPS-g. TPS-a genes are typically associated with sesquiterpenoid production. TPS-b genes are typically associated with monoterpenoid production, although it has been shown that these genes can sometimes also contribute to the production of sesquiterpenoids. TPS-g genes form certain acyclic monoterpenoids.

TPS gene subfamily	Description
TPS-a	Mostly sesquiterpenoids
TPS-b	Mostly monoterpenoids, but also contributes to sesquiterpenoid production
TPS-g	Acyclic monoterpenoids

Research into understanding the genes behind terpene synthase production is still relatively early. Currently 30 unique TPS genes have been characterized, isolated from only 14 cultivars. This highlights the immense research opportunity available to understand how terpene profiles vary on a genetic level between cultivars. In a recent 2020 study, one TPS gene, CsTPS9, which is responsible for producing the enzyme that produces beta-caryophyllene and alpha-humulene, was found in all of the cultivars studied (Booth et al, 2020). This study also verified that the TPS genes in Cannabis are very similar to those found in hops (*Humulus lupulus*) and much of the terpenoid diversity we see in Cannabis today is likely a result of "relatively recent multiplications of a few ancestral CsTPSs." When examining the variation of terpenoid profiles between cultivars of different and identical names, they found that **"...there was as much variation among plants that were named as the same cultivar as there was variation between plants that were labeled as different cultivars."** (Booth et al, 2020)

EPIGENETICS AND FEMINIZED SEEDS

The genetic story of an organism does not end at its conception when its parents' genetic information mixes to produce the offspring's DNA. Genetics are not entirely determined but also influenced throughout the life of the organism. Environmental conditions can affect how cells read genes and what genes are turned on and off. This means that a cell's ability to perform its function in a tissue, organelle, or organ can become altered or compromised at various times throughout its life based on environmental stress or other factors. The study of how DNA is altered by environmental factors rather than direct DNA manipulation is called **epigenetics**. Epigenetic factors affecting Cannabis are not well understood at this time but are the target of genomic research currently being done with Cannabis.

An example of epigenetic effects in Cannabis can be found in "feminized seeds". An otherwise female Cannabis plant can undergo environmental stresses which can cause the plant's genes to signal the production of different sexual hormones, leading to the production of male sexual structures, potentially causing self-fertilization. Hermaphroditism is at the heart of developing "feminized seeds." **"Feminized seeds"** are seeds which have been developed to produce approximately 80 - 98%+ female plants upon germination, on average. This is contrasted with the roughly 50% chance of getting a female from non-feminized seeds. Generally feminized seeds are marketed as an advantage for cultivators because it takes some of the guesswork out of the process of growing for resin production and results in a greater number of desired plants while using less seeds, and thus less money – in theory.

The process of producing feminized seeds is fairly straightforward. A female Cannabis plant is first stressed, sometimes using exposure to colloidal silver, to exhibit hermaphroditic tendencies. Once the stressed female plant produces male flowers and pollen, the pollen is collected and distributed to other female plants of the same variety which have not been stressed. The pollen then fertilizes the female plants to produce seeds. The resulting seeds often have a higher potential of growing into female seeds. Unfortunately, it is often the case that these resulting seeds often produce plants which are more sensitive to environmental stress and may become hermaphrodites more easily than other plants grown from traditional seeds. It should be noted that there are other ways to produce feminized seeds other than the method mentioned in this example. Modern breeding practices are utilizing DNA and RNA analytical technology to understand genetic changes in plants, allowing for the production of seeds that tend to produce females which cannot produce seed or male pollen should they revert to hermaphroditism (Oregon CBD, 2020).

Enduring Understandings

- Intensive hybridization without preservation of "native" or "naturalized" germplasm can leave a population at risk for extinction should environmental conditions or pest pressure change in an unfavorable way.
- A filial generation is a generation of plants produced through hybridization.
- An F1 generation produces stable phenotypes.
- F2 generations produce very unstable phenotypes.
- The Cannabis plant is diploid and its DNA consists of 20 chromosomes (10 pairs)
- Cannabinoids and terpenes are produced in Cannabis through a biosynthetic pathway called the deoxyxylulose pathway.
- The ultimate precursor to cannabinoids and terpenes is a compound called geranyl pyrophosphate (GPP).
- When geranyl pyrophosphate (GPP) is bound with Olivetolic Acid, CBGA is formed, which is the precursor to THCA, CBDA, and CBCA.
- When geranyl pyrophosphate (GPP) is bound to Divarinic Acid, CBGVA is formed, which is the precursor to THCVA, CBDVA, etc.
- When geranyl pyrophosphate (GPP) is bound to Isopentenyl Pyrophosphate (IPP), Farnesyl Pyrophosphate (FPP) is formed, which is the precursor to most sesquiterpenoids.
- Geranyl pyrophosphate (GPP) can itself form into a monoterpenoid, like limonene, when the phosphate group is removed from the molecule.
- Cannabinoid ratios are genetically controlled by cannabinoid synthase genes.
- Cannabinoid synthase genes can be promiscuous, sometimes producing other cannabinoid synthases than expected. For instance, CBCA and CBDA synthase genes can also produce THCA synthase under certain conditions.
- Cannabinoid genetics can be affected by the environment in certain ways. For instance, when a plant is stressed, it's DNA may go through epigenetic changes that lead to the expression of sexual organs of the opposite sex.
- Terpenoid production is moderated by terpene synthase (TPS) genes

PART II

THE CHEMISTRY OF CANNABIS

Essential Questions

What are the primary chemical compounds found in the oils of the Cannabis flower?

Are cannabinoids polar (water loving) or non-polar (oil loving)?

What is the difference between monoterpenoids and sesquiterpenoids?

How are the resins of Cannabis commonly extracted from the Cannabis plant?

Chapter 9:
CANNABIS CHEMISTRY INTRODUCTION

Learning Questions
- What is chemical polarity? Are cannabinoids polar or nonpolar?
- What is a chemical functional group?
- What are some common chemical functional groups that are likely to show up in Cannabis compounds?
- What chemical compounds are found in the Cannabis plant?

In some of the upcoming chapters we will be exploring the chemistry of the Cannabis plant. However, before diving into the chemistry of Cannabis, it is important to brush up on some basic chemistry terms and concepts like chemical polarity and functional groups. If you are already familiar with these terms, you might like to skip ahead to the next chapter.

INTRODUCTION TO KEY CHEMISTRY CONCEPTS

CHEMICAL POLARITY

Oil and water do not mix. The reason for this is chemical polarity. **Polarity is a description of how the bonds in a molecule are sharing electrons.** Even further, it refers to whether electrons are shared equally between atoms. Electrons carry a negative charge. If there are unpaired electrons present, a negative charge is present. If all electrons are paired up, no electrical charge is generated. If an electron is removed, a positive charge is generated. This is the core principle of polarity.

If the electrons in the bond are equally shared, the molecule is considered nonpolar. Nonpolar compounds are typically made of lots of carbons and hydrogens. Propane, which is made of 3 carbons and 5 hydrogens, is nonpolar. An example of a nonpolar compound would be vegetable oil. Nonpolar compounds are considered **hydrophobic** because they do not dissolve in water. They are, however, **lipophilic** because they dissolve easily in lipids, fats, and oils.

If the electrons in the bond are shared unequally, the molecule is considered polar. An example of a polar compound is water. Polar compounds are **hydrophilic**, meaning they dissolve in water. Polar compounds are **lipophobic** meaning they do not dissolve in lipids.

Polarity	Hydro-	Lipo-	Description	Examples
Polar	Hydrophilic	Lipophobic	Dissolve in water; Oxygen, nitrogen, etc often present	Water, Caffeine, Flavonoids
Nonpolar	Hydrophobic	Lipophilic	Dissolve in lipids; Primarily made of hydrogen and carbon	Cannabinoids, Terpenes, Vegetable Oil

If a polar compound like water and a nonpolar compound like oil are mixed, the two substances will eventually separate and form two layers due to the nonpolar compound's hydrophobic characteristic and the polar compound's lipophobic characteristic which repel each other.

There is a third category of polarity called a hybrid. This usually occurs in larger molecules where one side of the molecule is more polar while another side is more nonpolar, allowing it to have an affinity for both polar and nonpolar compounds. Many compounds exhibit hybrid polarity to some level. Additionally polarity can be manipulated by things like temperature and pH.

Cannabinoids and terpenes in Cannabis are nonpolar. Because of this, cannabinoids and terpenes mix well with other nonpolar compounds like oils and fats. **Organic solvents** like butane and propane are also nonpolar, which is why they are used in Cannabis extract production (the term "**organic**" refers to compounds with carbon in them). The polarity of Cannabis compounds also explains why cannabinoids tend to cling to fatty tissues in the body.

READING CHEMICAL DIAGRAMS

There are a variety of ways to draw a molecule. The two most common methods are shown in the following figure. These are line diagrams that represent the same compound, butane. The first diagram has every atom labeled with lines showing the bonds between each atom.

Both of these diagrams represent butane, C4H10

In the second diagram, the carbon and hydrogen atoms are not drawn but implied. This is common in diagrams of *organic* compounds. **Organic compounds contain carbon.** Each end of a line in these diagrams represents a carbon atom and each carbon atom is implied to be surrounded by hydrogen unless otherwise noted. Each end of a line represents a carbon atom. If there is a line above one of these lines, it represents a double bond.

As for the inorganic parts of a molecule, the bonds are represented by small lines connecting one element to another. If there are two lines, then it represents a double bond. If it has a "-" next to an atom, that means that it gained an electron, and thus has a *negative* charge (because electrons are negatively charged). If it has a "+" next to an atom, it lost an electron (which is negatively charged) and has become *positively* charged.

CHEMICAL FUNCTIONAL GROUPS

Functional groups are molecules that attach to compounds and give them certain characteristics. For instance, **-OH is an alcohol** functional group. Any compound with an –OH group attached is considered an alcohol and will have the "–ol" suffix. The functional group that is responsible for the behavior or cannabinoid acids is **–COOH, or the carboxylic acid functional group**. As the compound is exposed to heat, the -COOH functional group pops off in a process called decarboxylation, leaving behind the neutral cannabinoid.

There are many different functional groups and each one changes the behavior of the molecule it is attached to in some way. When reading a functional group diagram, the "R" refers to the rest of the molecule that the group is attached to.

CARBOXYLIC ACID
FUNCTIONAL GROUP

ALCOHOL FUNCTIONAL
GROUP

Examples of Common Functional Groups		
Functional Group	**Description**	**Example**
Carboxylic Acid	Carbon featuring a double bonded oxygen and a hydroxyl group R-COOH	
Alcohol (Hydroxyl)	Simple bonded oxygen and hydrogen (-OH) R-OH	
Ester	Results when a hydroxyl (-OH) group is replaced with an oxygen attached to another organic molecule – often derived from carboxylic acids and alcohols.	
Ketone	Double bonded oxygen connecting two organic molecules R – C (=O) - R Acetone is a simple ketone 	
Aldehyde	Carbon with a single bonded hydrogen and a double bonded oxygen R – C (= O) - H	
Phenyl	Aromatic ring with a functional group. **Phenols** are phenyls bonded to a hydroxyl group (-OH)	

FIGURE 23: EXAMPLES OF COMMON FUNCTIONAL GROUPS

NUMBERING CARBONS IN A MOLECULE

You may notice that many chemicals, including the formal name for THC, delta-9-tetrahydrocannabinol, feature a number within the name. This number typically represents the location of a significant functional group or bond.

The way that the carbon atoms in a molecule are numbered starts with finding the longest carbon chain in the molecule. This is referred to as the "parent chain". The next step involves identifying the "highest priority" functional group in the molecule. This ultimately dictates where you start numbering, because the highest priority functional group must have the smallest number in the carbon numbering sequence. There are tables of functional group priorities that you can look up that explain which functional groups are considered higher priority than others for the purposes of numbering carbons and naming molecules. Once the highest priority functional group has been identified, you start counting carbons, one by one, following the longest path of the carbon chain. If there is a bond or functional group somewhere along that chain, you would indicate that in the chemical name by using a number that represents the location of the carbon atom where the bond or functional group is located.

For instance, the "9" in delta-9-THC represents the location of a double bond within a carbon ring. The difference between delta-8-THC vs delta-9-THC lies in the location of the double bond.

DELTA-9-THC MOLECULE WITH CARBON NUMBERING

Molecule diagram image source: Karas et al. 2020. The Antimicrobial Activity of Cannabinoids. Antibiotics. 9:406. doi:10.3390/antibiotics9070406. Figure 1.

DELTA-8-THC

DELTA-9-THC

OVERVIEW OF CANNABIS CHEMICAL CONSTITUENTS

Over 400 compounds have been described in the Cannabis plant and approximately 200 more in Cannabis smoke (McPartland *et al.*, 2001). Among these compounds there are around 85 – 100, if not more, **phytocannabinoids** that have been identified (Brenneisen, 2007; Mehmedic *et al.*, 2010), and over 200 **phytoterpenoids** have been identified (Hendriks *et al.*, 1975; 1977; Malingre *et al.*, 1975; Davalos *et al.*, 1977; Ross and ElSohly, 1996; Mediavilla and Steinemann, 1997; Rothschild *et al.*, 2005; Brenneisen, 2007). Cannabis also consists of approximately twenty different **flavonoids** (Turner et al. 1980). It is estimated that Cannabis leaves consist of approximately 1% flavonoids (Paris *et al.*, 1976). There are also other compounds in Cannabis like glycoproteins and alkaloids, with relatively unknown pharmacological effects. Cannabis also contains various carotenoids, which are orange-yellow pigment compounds, and vitamin K (Brenneisen, 2007).

Some of these compounds are either **phenolic** or **polyphenolic** compounds. A **phenol** is a series of carbons in an aromatic ring with an –OH group attached, making it essentially an "aromatic alcohol." A **polyphenol** is simply a compound that is made of multiple phenol groups.

Notable Cannabis Chemical Constituents	
Cannabinoids	>100 described in Cannabis; found in trichomes of Cannabis
Terpenoids	>200 described in Cannabis; primary essential oil fraction of Cannabis; triterpenoids found in Cannabis roots
Flavonoids	~20 described in Cannabis; pigment compounds in Cannabis leaf tissues
Esters	Hexyl acetate, linalyl acetate, methyl anthranilate
Ketones	2-methyl-4-heptanone, 2-methyl-3-heptanone, methylisohexenyl ketone, 1-chloroacetophenone
Aldehydes	Benzaldehyde, Decanal, Heptanal, Octanal, Hexanal, Isobutyraldehyde
Sterols	Campesterene, Stigmasterol, Beta-Sitosterol
Stilbenoids	Denbinobin, Canniprene
Alkaloids	Cannabisativine, annhydrocannabisativine found in Cannabis roots (HL Latter et al, 1975)
Glycoproteins (sugar proteins)	Galactose, xylose, glucose, mannose, arabinose, rhamnose, galacturonic acid from Cannabis leaves (A Hillestad et al, 1977)
Vitamins	Vitamin K; Vitamin E found in seeds
Lignanamides	Cannabisin A; found in Cannabis seeds (Sakakibara et al, 1991)

FIGURE 24: NOTABLE CANNABIS CHEMICAL CONSTITUENTS

Enduring Understandings

- When the electrons in a molecule are equally shared, the molecule is considered nonpolar. Nonpolar compounds typically contain primarily only carbon and hydrogen and are often not soluble in water (i.e. vegetable oils, cannabinoids, etc)

- When the electrons in a molecule are not equally shared, the molecule is considered polar. Polar compounds typically contain elements like oxygen, nitrogen, etc and are often soluble in water. (i.e. caffeine, flavonoids)

- Functional groups affect the behavior of a molecule.

- Numbers in a chemical name indicate the location of a significant chemical bond or functional group.

- Numbering carbons begins with identifying the parent chain, then identifying the functional group of highest priority before numbering each carbon along the parent chain.

- To date, Cannabis is thought to produce well over 500 chemicals, and it is likely that the plant produces thousands of chemical compounds.

- Over 200 unique compounds have been identified in Cannabis smoke.

- Some of the most common chemical compounds found in Cannabis include cannabinoids, terpenoids, flavonoids, esters, sterols, alkaloids, glycoproteins, and vitamins.

Chapter 10:
CANNABINOIDS

Learning Questions

- How many cannabinoids have been identified in Cannabis?
- How are cannabinoids and terpenoids related?
- What is decarboxylation?
- What are some of the common cannabinoids found in the Cannabis plant?
- What are some of the common degradation products of phytocannabinoids?
- What are some of the common metabolites of phytocannabinoids?

INTRODUCTION TO CANNABINOIDS

Many of the most sought-after chemical compounds in Cannabis, including CBD and THC, are phytocannabinoids, or "plant cannabinoids". At the time of this writing, there are approximately 550 chemical compounds that have been identified in Cannabis. Of these chemical compounds, approximately 105 are cannabinoids (Pertwee, 2014, pg 3). Currently the most sophisticated commercial Cannabis testing laboratories in the United States test for approximately 10 – 15 different cannabinoids.

Cannabinoids are **terpenophenolic** (terpene + phenol group) meroterpenoid compounds produced in secretory cells in glandular trichomes primarily in unfertilized female flowers, often referred to as "sensimilla", or "seedless" (Potter, 2004; Potter, 2009). The ratios of primary cannabinoids such as THCA and CBDA are predetermined genetically (AHP, 2013). However, the environment significantly influences the concentrations of cannabinoids present as well as what cannabinoid degradation products may be present in the plant resins.

What does it mean for cannabinoids to be "meroterpenoids"? Are cannabinoids terpenes? Well, sort of. Terpenoids are **isoprenoids**, meaning that they are compounds made of variously arranged isoprene units. An isoprene is a simple five carbon compound with two double bonds, as pictured here.

ISOPRENE UNIT

PHENOL STRUCTURE

Remember that cannabinoids are considered terpenophenolic compounds, meaning that they are terpenoids featuring a phenol group…

Isoprene Units (Terpenoid)   +   Phenol   =   Terpenophenolic Compound

…but cannabinoids are also sometimes thought of as **polyketide terpenoids**. This is because cannabinoids are formed through the combination of a geranyl pyrophosphate, which lends two isoprene units (a simple monoterpene), and olivetolic acid, which lends a polyketide structure with a carbon tail. Polyketides are compounds that feature alternating oxygen bonds. Although olivetolic acid features many oxygens in its structure, making it a more obvious polyketide compound, only two of those oxygens remain when it is bound with the remaining isoprene units of geranyl pyrophosphate.

OLIVETOLIC ACID

GERANYL PYROPHOSPHATE (GPP)

Cannabinoids are synthesized through a chemical pathway called the deoxyxylulose pathway (Russo, 2011). This pathway is responsible for both the production of cannabinoids as well as mono and sesquiterpenoids. And for each cannabinoid found in the Cannabis plant, there are minor variations and degradation products that form an entire class of compounds. For instance, there are at least 18 or more compounds that belong to the "delta-9 THC type" chemical class (Pertwee, 2014, pg 4).

DECARBOXYLATION

THCA   HEAT   THC

In the plant, Cannabinoids are typically found in their carboxylic acid forms. Carboxylic acid cannabinoids, like THCA, are cannabinoids that have a carbon dioxide, or CO_2, group attached to it. When the molecule is heated up or receives enough energy, the CO_2 group breaks off, leaving behind the "neutral cannabinoid", such as THC. The process of heating a carboxylic acid so that a carboxyl group breaks off the molecule is called **decarboxylation**. For example, CBGA is a cannabinoid acid that the plant can synthesize into THCA, CBDA, or CBCA which could then be heated to leave behind THC, CBD, and CBC. Alternatively, CBGA could be decarboxylated to CBG.

Cannabinoid acids have not been shown to be psychoactive or intoxicating, although there is some evidence supporting a variety of pharmacological effects. Cannabinoid acids can exhibit anti-inflammatory behavior (Starks, 1990; Ruhaak et al., 2011). There is also evidence that THCA and CBDA can act as anti-vomiting agents (Moldzio et al., 2012; Bolognini et al, 2013; Rock et al., 2013). There is even evidence that some of the cannabinoid acids can inhibit prostate cancer cell growth *in vivo* and *in vitro* (De Petrocellis et al., 2013).

Despite common assumption, cannabinoids are not unique to the Cannabis plant, but have been found in a variety of other organisms. As cannabinoids are researched further, it is likely that our definition of what constitutes a cannabinoid will expand, encompassing more compounds. For instance, the terpenoid beta-caryophyllene is now considered to be a cannabinoid because it interacts with cannabinoid chemical receptors in the body. Beta-caryophyllene is an essential oil component found in a wide array of plants including vegetables like corn!

TRUE OR FALSE? Cannabinoids are polar compounds and mix easily with water.

Circle One: TRUE   FALSE

Answer: False

Delta-9-Tetrahydrocannabinol (THC)

THC is the primary **psychoactive** and intoxicating component of Cannabis. Its carboxylic acid form, THCA, is the most common cannabinoid found in Cannabis. THC has been reported as being an effective **painkiller** and **muscle relaxant** (Pacher et al., 2006). THC has been shown to act as a **bronchodilator**, decreasing resistance in the airways and increasing airflow into the lungs (Williams et al., 1976). THC has also been reported as having 20x the **anti-inflammatory** power of aspirin and twice the anti-inflammatory power of hydrocortisone (Evans, 1991).

Examples of Other Members of the Delta-9 THC Type Chemical Class	Examples of Degradation Products of THC	Examples of THC Metabolites
THC acid A	Cannabinol (CBN)	11-OH-THC
THC-C4	Delta-8 THC	11-COOH-THC
Delta-9 Tetrahydrocannabiorcolic Acid	Delta-10 THC	
THC acid B		
THCA-C4		
Delta-9 Tetrahydrocannabiorcol		

CANNABIDIOL (CBD)

In its carboxylic acid form, CBDa is the second most common cannabinoid in medical Cannabis and is the most common cannabinoid present in fibre hemp Cannabis plants (Russo, 2011). CBD has a unique ability to **reduce the effects of THC** by quieting the CB1 receptor while THC is binding to it (Thomas *et al.,* 2007). CBD has been shown to display a wide variety of medicinally beneficial effects in animal and *in vitro* models. CBD has been reported to exhibit **anti-anxiety and anticonvulsant effects** as well as the ability to **reduce acne bacteria** (Russo *et al.* 2005; Jones *et al.*, 2010; Biro *et al.* 2009). For ~~more information about CBD, see the next chapter.~~

Examples of Other Members of the CBD Type Chemical Class	Examples of Degradation Products of CBD	Examples of CBD Metabolites
CBDM	Cannabinodiol (CBND)	7-OH-CBD
CBD-C1	Delta-9-Tetrahydrocannabinol (d9-THC) and derivatives may form under acidic conditions	7-COOH-CBD
CBDV Acid		Cannabielsoin (CBE)
CBDP		
Cannabimovone		
CBD-C4 (aka CBDB)		
CBDV		

Note: While 33 or more metabolites of CBD have been identified, very few have been characterized.

CANNABIGEROL (CBG)

It is thought of as the "parent" phytocannabinoid because CBGa goes on to synthesize into THCa, CBDa, and CBCa. **CBG** has been shown to be an **anti-fungal** (ElSohly *et al.*, 1982), **antidepressant** (Musty and Deyo, 2006; Cascio *et al.*, 2010), and **painkiller** (Cascio *et al.*, 2010). CBG has also been indicated as a potential treatment for skin conditions, glaucoma, sex hormonal dysregulations, eating disorders, irritable bowel syndromes and bone disease (Deiana, 2017).

Examples of other members of the CBG Type Chemical Class:

CBG Acid	CBG-C5
Cannabigerolic Acid Monomethyl Ether	Cannabigerol Monomethyl Ether
(CBGAM)	(CBGM)
CBGV Acid	CBGV

CANNABICHROMENE (CBC)

CBC exhibits potential to **reduce THC intoxication** (Hatoum *et al.*, 1981), like CBD. It has also displayed **anti-inflammatory** (Wirth *et al.*, 1980) and **painkilling** properties (Davis and Hatoum, 1983). CBC has been shown to produce powerful **antidepressant** effects in rodent models (Deyo and Musty, 2003). CBC is also a noted **antifungal** and **antibiotic** (ElSohly *et al.*, 1982).

Examples of other members of the CBC Type Chemical Class:

CBC Acid	CBC-C3
CBCV Acid	CBCV

Example of a degradation product of CBC: Cannabicyclol (CBL)

DELTA-9-TETRAHYDROCANNABIVARIN (THCV)

    The divarinic cannabinoids, or propyl chain cannabinoids, such as THCV and CBDv feature shorter carbon tails extending from the phenol group in the molecule as seen above. **THCV** is psychoactive and potentially intoxicating at certain dosages, but less so than delta-9 THC, although the effects come on more quickly (Hollister, 1974; Gill *et al.*, 1970). THCV can **suppresses the appetite at certain dosages** (Hollister, 1974; Cawthorne *et al.*, 2007; Riedel *et al.*, 2009). In rodent models, THCV showed **anticonvulsant** effects as well (Hill *et al.*, 2010).

CANNABIDIVARIN (CBDV)

CBDV has become a compound of interest lately due to its anticonvulsant effects both observed in animal models and *in vitro* (Hill et al, 2013; Amada et al, 2013). CBDV is currently being studied in human clinical trials for the treatment of epilepsy under the name GWP42006.

CANNABIVARIN (CBV)

Cannabivarin, or **CBV**, is an oxidation product of THCv, much like CBN is an oxidation product of THC. Any pharmacological effects are currently unknown.

DELTA-9-TETRAHYDROCANNABUTOL (THCB, THC-C4)

THCB is a version of THC that features one less carbon in the carbon tail of the molecule compared to THC. THCB has exhibited similar potency as THC in cannabinoid receptor binding assays. THCB is also known as delta-9-THC-C4.

CANNABIDIBUTOL (CBDB, CBD-C4)

CBDB is a version of CBD that features one less carbon in the carbon tail of the molecule compared to CBD. The cannabinoid receptor binding activity of CBDB is, as of the time of this writing, unknown. CBDB has been discovered as an impurity in CBD extracts of hemp (Citti et al, 2019). CBDB is also known as CBD-C4.

DELTA-9-TETRAHYDROCANNABIPHOROL (THCP, THC-C7)

THCP is a version of THC that features a couple of extra carbon atoms in the molecule's carbon tail, which in turn makes THCP exhibit an affinity for CB1 receptors that is 30 times that of THC! While it is unclear exactly how this difference relates to differences in psychoactivity, the discovery of THCP and other similar cannabinoids, has helped researchers better understand how the molecular structure of a cannabinoid correlates with cannabinoid receptor activity, which may in turn help researchers develop tools for predicting how a cannabinoid may interact with cannabinoid receptors.

In addition to its enhanced activity at CB1 receptors, THCP is five to ten times more active at CB2 receptors compared to THC. THCP may appear in concentrations as high as 5% in refined ethanol extracts of Cannabis. (Citti et al, 2019)

CANNABIDIPHOROL (CBDP, CBD-C7)

Like THCP, CBDP is a version of CBD featuring an extra-long carbon tail. At the time of this writing, very little is known about CBDP and no chemical receptor binding assays or pharmacological data was available.

Number of Carbons in Tail	Molecule Abbreviation	Molecule Name
3	THCV	Delta-9-tetrahydrocannabivarin
4	THCB	Delta-9-tetrahydrocannabutol
5	THC	Delta-9-tetrahydrocannabinol
7	THCP	Delta-9-tetrahydrocannabiphorol

CANNABIMOVONE (CBM)

Cannabimovone is a cannabinoid that was discovered in 2010 from hemp (Taglialatela-Scafati et al, 2010). It is an interesting cannabinoid because, unlike many other cannabinoids, it is polar, due to the abundance of oxygen in the molecule. CBM has not demonstrated much affinity for CB1 or CB2 receptors, but has demonstrated mild affinity for TRPV1 receptors, similar to CBD's activity. There is currently very little other information available about CBM at the time of this writing.

WHAT HAPPENS TO CANNABIS AS IT AGES?

Over time, the chemical compounds in Cannabis change as they react to things like heat, oxygen, and light. Terpenoids are often most impacted by degradation over time. Pure monoterpenes quickly oxidize, forming terpenoid alcohols. For instance, Myrcene oxidizes to become other terpenoids like geraniol or linalool. In addition, terpenes are more volatile than cannabinoids, leaving behind heavier sesquiterpenes and cannabinoids. As a result, the smell of the Cannabis changes. Cannabinoids do not tend to volatize out of Cannabis, but they do react to heat and light to form various degradation products. Little is known about the pharmacological activity of many of these photodegradation and oxidation products. When compounds are ingested, they change again. If consumed orally, compounds will be changed into metabolic products in the liver and gut. While some information is known about THC metabolites, little is known about other metabolites.

Starting Compound	Decarboxylation Product	
THCA	THC	**Degradation Product(s)**
		CBN
		Delta-8 THC
		Metabolic Product(s)
		11-OH-THC
		11-nor-9-COOH-THC
CBDA	CBD	**Degradation Product(s)**
		CBND, CBE
		Metabolic Product(s)
		7-OH-CBD
		7-COOH-CBD
CBCA	CBC	**Degradation Product(s)**
		CBL
		Metabolic Product(s)
		Hydroxylated Metabolites
THCVA	THCV	**Degradation Product(s)**
		CBV
		Delta-8 THCV
		Metabolic Product(s)
		11-OH-THCV
		11 nor-9-COOH-THCV
CBDVA	CBDV	**Degradation Product(s)**
		CBV
		Metabolic Product(s)
		11-OH-CBDV
		11-nor-9-COOH-CBDV

FIGURE 25: METABOLIC PRODUCTS OF PHYTOCANNABINOIDS

COMMON CANNABINOID DEGRADATION PRODUCTS

CANNABINOL (CBN)

CBN is a breakdown product of THC and is commonly found in higher quantities in older Cannabis samples (Merzouki and Mesa, 2002). It has been indicated as a **sedative** and seems to only be active in the presence of THC (Musty *et al.*, 1976). CBN, like CBD, has also demonstrated **anticonvulsant** effects (Turner *et al.*, 1980). And, like THC, it has demonstrated **anti-inflammatory** effects (Evans, 1991).

Examples of other members of the CBN Type Chemical Class:

CBN Acid	CBN-C3	CBN-C4
Cannabiorcol	Cannabinol Methyl Ether	CBN-C2

CANNABINODIOL (CBND)

CBND is the result of the photochemical transformation of cannabinol (CBN) and cannabidiol (CBD). Any pharmacological effects are unknown. (ElSohly and Slade, 2005)

DELTA-8-TETRAHYDROCANNABINOL (D8-THC)

Delta-8 THC is almost the same as delta-9 THC, structurally, except that the location of a double bong has changed. It is psychoactive and intoxicating but less so than delta-9 THC (Hollister, 1974). In a study focusing on children ages 2 – 13 undergoing chemotherapy treatments, delta-8 THC displayed no psychoactive effects in the children and effectively **reduced nausea** at the doses administered of 18mg per square meter of body surface area. (Abrahamov and Mechoulam, 1995).

CANNABICYCLOL (CBL)

CBL is the result of the photochemical transformation of cannabichromene (CBC). **Cannabicyclolic acid** (CBLa) results from the irradiation of CBCa. There is no pharmacological information available.

CANNABINOQUINOIDS

QUINONE STRUCTURE   **CANNABIDIOLQUINONE (CBDQ, AKA HU-331)**

Once cannabinoids have been decarboxylated they can degrade into a class of compounds called cannabinoquinoids, which are compounds that contain the structure of quinone, containing two double bonded oxygens on an aromatic ring. All phenolic compounds are sensitive to this kind of degradation. Little is currently known about the pharmacological activity of many cannabinoquinoids, but cannabinoquinoids have been used to produce semi-synthetic cannabinoid drugs, like the semi-synthetic form of cannabidiolquinone, or CBDQ, called VCE-004.8. Cannabinoquinoids may be responsible for some of the colors present in Cannabis extracts, such as deep red colors. (Caprioglio et al, 2020)

COMMON CANNABINOID METABOLITES

11-HYDROXY-THC

11-Hydroxy-THC is not actually a phytocannabinoid but is a highly potent psychoactive primary metabolite of the phytocannabinoid THC, produced in the liver after ingestion (Johnson, 1984). It is the compound primarily responsible for the unique effects attributed to Cannabis infused edibles. 11-Hydroxy-THC is thought to be 4x as potent as THC.

11-NOR-9-CARBOXY-THC
(THC-COOH; 11-COOH-THC)

11-COOH-THC is a *secondary metabolite* of THC formed in the liver through the oxidation of 11-OH-THC. This compound is not psychoactive but has a long half-life, making it the target of urinalysis drug tests to identify Cannabis use. This compound has the ability to reduce the effects of THC by antagonizing cannabinoid receptors (Burstein et al, 1986). It may exhibit some anti-inflammatory and analgesic effects (Burstein et al, 1988). Some researchers speculate that THC might be a **pro-drug** for 11-COOH-THC (Ujvary and Grotenhermen, 2014).

7-OH-CBD AND 7-COOH-CBD

Little is known about the metabolites of CBD. There are over 100 metabolites of CBD that have been identified among different animals, but the two most well-known are 7-OH-CBD and 7-COOH-CBD (Ujvary and Hanus, 2016). 7-OH-CBD inhibits FAAH, the enzyme that breaks down anandamide, although 7-COOH-CBD does not exhibit this activity (Ujvary and Hanus, 2016).

CANNABIELSOIN (CBE)

Cannabielsoin is a metabolite of cannabidiol (CBD) formed in the liver after oral ingestion of CBD (Yamamoto et al, 1991). There is currently little pharmacological information available about cannabielsoin. Cannabielsoin may reduce intraocular pressure (Ujvary and Hanus, 2016).

11-OH-CBN, 8-OH-CBN

The metabolites of the cannabinoid Cannabinol are not very well studied, although there are a handful of in vitro metabolite studies that have examined CBN's common degradation products. Two of the primary metabolites of CBN are 11-OH-CBN and 8-OH-CBN (Watanabe et al, 2006). Very little is known about the pharmacology of these CBN metabolites, presenting an area ripe for research as the cannabinoid grows in popularity.

11-OH-THCV, THCV-11-OIC ACID

The metabolites of divarinic cannabinoids like THCV and CBDV are not well studied, although the metabolites 11-hydroxy-THCV (or 11-OH-THCV) and delta-9-THCV-11-oic Acid have been identified. Additionally, there are likely other THCV derivatives that are formed during metabolism such as 8a-OH-THCV and 8B-OH-THCV (Tinto et al, 2020). Likewise, there are certainly comparable metabolites of CBDV present after metabolism as well.

Enduring Understandings

- Cannabis produces well over 100 cannabinoids.
- Cannabinoids produced by a plant are called "phytocannabinoids".
- Cannabinoids like THC or CBD are initially produced in the Cannabis plant as cannabinoid acids, like THCA or CBDA, which feature a carboxylic acid functional group.
- The process of removing the carboxylic acid functional group from a cannabinoid acid is called decarboxylation and is often achieved by applying heat to Cannabis.
- Many of the degradation and metabolic products of cannabinoids are not well understood.

Chapter 11: CANNABIDIOL (CBD) – HYPE OR HERO?

Learning Questions
- What is CBD and how is it different than THC?
- How has CBD been studied throughout history?
- How does CBD affect the body?
- What contraindications and safety issues are associated with CBD?

CBD vs. THC

Cannabidiol (CBD)   Delta-9-Tetrahydrocannabinol (THC)

CBD is markedly different than THC, although they look similar. To start, CBD does not cause intoxicating or euphoric effects like THC does (Russo, 2011). This feature has gotten the attention of a lot of people, ranging from medical researchers looking to unlock the therapeutic potential of Cannabis without the risk of abuse to consumers interested in Cannabis but not looking to get high. Although CBD is not intoxicating, it *is* psychoactive, meaning that it elicits effects on neurons. This is a common misunderstanding about CBD.

CBD also affects the body in very different ways. While THC is a partial agonist, or stimulator, of CB1 and CB2 receptors in the body, CBD barely has any affinity for these chemical receptors at all. Instead, CBD stimulates the production of the endocannabinoid Anandamide, which then stimulates CB1 and CB2 receptors. In this way, CBD could be thought of as encouraging the body to do what it does naturally, stimulating the ECS indirectly, while THC could be seen as hijacking the endocannabinoid system and stimulating it directly. Additionally, CBD interacts with a host of other receptor types in the body, including serotonin, adenosine, transient receptor potential ion channels, PPAR-gamma receptors, and miscellaneous g-protein coupled receptors.

A BRIEF SCIENTIFIC HISTORY OF CBD

The story of CBD goes back thousands of years – as cultures across time have used non-psychoactive varieties of Cannabis for different uses. But the most relevant part of CBD's story really starts in 1940, when researchers Roger Adams, Madison Hunt and JH Clark published a report indicating the structure of a compound that they extracted and isolated from wild hemp in Minnesota (Adams et al, 1940). These researchers named this compound, Cannabidiol, or CBD as it would become commonly known. CBD was only the second cannabinoid found in Cannabis at the time, the first reportedly being Cannabinol, or CBN – a degradation product of THC. However later it would be discovered that what researchers reported as CBN in the late 1800s and early 1900s was likely THC (Scialdone, *viva voce*).

In 1944 it was discovered that the effects of barbiturates could be extended if administered with CBD, but not with CBN or THC (Loewe S, 1944). Their answer to why CBD had this effect would come almost 30 years later.

For a moment in 1963, scientists in Israel would shine light on CBD once again, before announcing their discovery of THC as the intoxicating components of Cannabis – a year later in 1964 (Mechoulam and Shvo, 1963). CBD would become a bit more ignored once again until around the 1970s and 80s when research into CBD really began to pick up steam.

In 1972 it would be discovered that CBD inhibited certain enzymes in the body, which affects how the body metabolizes certain foods and drugs (Paton and Pertwee, 1972). This helped begin to complete the puzzle that stemmed from the barbiturate study three decades prior. In 1981 researchers were able to demonstrate anticonvulsant effects in humans – indicating that it might be an effective treatment for certain forms of epilepsy and spasticity (Carlini and Cunha, 1981). In 1982 CBD was found to exhibit anti-anxiety effects, which would later be reconfirmed in 1993 (Zuardi et al, 1982; Zuardi et al, 1993). In 1995 it was discovered that CBD improves symptoms of psychosis (Zuardi et al, 1995). In 1998 the United States government filed a patent on the antioxidant and neuroprotective effects of CBD, as well as THC (Patent #: US6630507B1).

The 2000s would become the decade of elucidating the activity of CBD. In 2001, researchers began to finally understand more about how CBD actually works in the body by revealing that CBD targets non-cannabinoid receptors in the body, stimulates the production of at least one endocannabinoid, Anandamide, and inhibits an enzyme responsible for breaking down Anandamide, effectively allowing it to linger in the body longer. (Bisogno et al, 2001)

In 2002 researchers would confirm that CBD exhibits anti-nausea effects, which had already been reported as far back as the 1800s when systematic Cannabis research really began to take shape (Parker et al, 2002). In 2004 it was discovered that at certain dosages CBD can increase wakefulness and counteract THC induced sedation (Nicholson et al, 2004). So if you are feeling sleepy after using THC-rich Cannabis, a little bit of CBD might wake you back up! However, be careful, because CBD exhibits what is known as biphasic activity, meaning it acts differently in low doses versus high doses. At high doses, CBD can actually be sedating (Zuardi et al, 1993).

In 2005 it was discovered that CBD interacts with certain serotonin receptors in the body (Russo et al, 2005). In 2006 researchers would go on to discover that CBD also enhances adenosine receptor signaling, which is associated with heart health, blood pressure, and body temperature regulation (Carrier et al, 2006). It was also in 2006 that researchers discovered that CBD can kill breast cancer cells – bringing significant attention to the compound as a potential anti-cancer drug (Ligresti et al, 2006).

In 2007 researchers began to understand why CBD reduced the effects of THC in some of their prior research. It turns out that CBD changes the shape and activity of CB1 receptors, even though it does not exhibit much affinity for them directly (Thomas et al, 2007). In this way, it changes the way that THC binds to the CB1 receptor, modulating its activity. This kind of activity is called allosteric modulation, and CBD is considered an allosteric modulator of the CB1 receptor. This is why CBD is able to reduce the high associated with THC – it essentially deforms the CB1 receptor so that THC cannot stimulate the receptor as well as it normally would.

In 2008 it was discovered that CBD was a potent antibiotic against MRSA – a powerful infection that is commonly picked up in hospitals and often resists treatment (Appendino et al, 2008). In 2012 researchers discovered that CBD may be as effective as standard antipsychotics (Leweke et al, 2012). In 2014 it was discovered that CBD might be able to effectively treat acne in the skin by reducing inflammation, fighting bacteria on the skin, and changing the way that the skin produces oil (Olah et al, 2014).

IS CBD SAFE?

In general CBD has been demonstrated to be a very safe compound when consumed in oral dosages less than 1500mg/day (Epidiolex SDS, Greenwich Biosciences). At high dosages above 15-20mg of CBD per kg of body weight per day, liver damage could begin to occur, although it is uncommon for most consumers to encounter dosages this high (Ewing et al, 2019). The most common adverse effects of CBD that have been demonstrated in clinical trials are lethargy, gastrointestinal upset, and changes to appetite (Iffland and Grotenhermen, 2017). It should be noted that some of these side effects may be attributable to other drugs taken at the same time as CBD during these clinical trials.

The biggest safety issue related to CBD is how it interacts with other drugs. CBD inhibits the activity of cytochrome p450 enzymes in the liver which are responsible for breaking down all sorts of medications. This effect is often referred to as the "grapefruit effect" because grapefruits are notorious for causing drug interactions through suppression of liver enzymes. The effect is so common that many medications now feature "grapefruit warnings" on them.

By taking CBD with other medications, the risk for adverse effects associated with elevated levels of other medications may increase. This risk is even more serious if someone is using a CBD product that has been manipulated in a way that enhances CBD's bioavailability and absorption in the body, such as through pico- or nano-emulsification, where the CBD oil is split into droplets the size of picometers or nanometers before being surrounded by a water-loving, or hydrophilic, shell. This keeps the oil droplets from coming back together when in an aqueous solution, thus increasing surface area and allowing the body to process more of the CBD, faster.

There was a recent report of a fatality associated with the use of nanoemulsified CBD (Yin et al, 2020). The patient had been using CBD products with no problems for some time before she suddenly developed Stevens Johnson syndrome after trying a liposomal CBD product. Her skin began breaking out in severe rashes before starting to peel off. The reaction was a side effect of one of the medications, meloxicam, that the patient was taking at the time, although the patient had tolerated Meloxicam well. It is possible that, due to the enhanced bioavailability of CBD in the emulsified product, levels of the patient's medications were elevated to dangerous levels. However, at the time of this writing, the exact cause of the reaction could not be determined.

This kind of incident, regardless of whether it was definitively caused by CBD-drug interactions or not, highlights the need for consumers to be aware of the potential serious adverse reactions that can happen when CBD is mixed with other medications. It also highlights the need for doctors and other health care professionals to be educated on the liver enzyme altering effects of CBD. In general, one should always consult with a licensed healthcare professional that is educated in cannabinoids prior to mixing CBD or any other cannabinoid therapy with other medications.

Enduring Understandings

- CBD is not intoxicating, but it *is* psychoactive, meaning that it has effects on neurons in the brain.

- CBD was first isolated and characterized in 1940.

- Most relevant CBD research kicked off in the 1970s and 1980s.

- CBD's mechanisms of action began to be understood in the early 2000s, but are still not properly understood.

- CBD has demonstrated a host of potential therapeutic application sin pre-clinical research, but more clinical research is needed to understand how to utilize CBD as a medicine more effectively.

- CBD is generally safe and well tolerated by most people at dosages up to 1500mg per day, however CBD can interact with medications and possibly contribute to serious, potentially life-threatening, drug interactions due to the way CBD can inhibit certain enzymes in the liver that would normally break down common drugs.

Chapter 12:
CANNABIS TERPENOIDS

Learning Questions
- What are terpenes?
- How do terpene concentrations change over time after Cannabis has been harvested?
- What are the most common terpenes found in Cannabis?

INTRODUCTION

Terpenes are essential oil components of plants and other organisms, imparting some of their aromas and flavors, and at one time were considered the fifth element alongside earth, wind, water, and fire (Schmidt, 2010). **Terpenoids** make up the largest group of plant chemicals consisting of approximately twenty thousand terpenes that have currently been scientifically described. There are several different classifications of terpenes based on the size of the molecule. **Monoterpenoids** and **Sesquiterpenoids** are the most common types of terpenoids encountered. Monoterpenoids are very simple terpenoids consisting of two isoprene units and a molecular formula of $C_{10}H_{16}$. Sesquiterpenoids contain three isoprene units and maintain a molecular formula of $C_{15}H_{24}$, making them heavier and less volatile. Cannabinoids are considered **meroterpenoids**, a term used for compounds that contain partial terpenoid structures.

Terpenoid Classification	Number of Carbon Atoms	Common Examples in Cannabis
Monoterpenoid	10	Myrcene, Limonene, Linalool
Sesquiterpenoid	15	Beta-Caryophyllene, Humulene
Diterpenoid	20	Phytol
Triterpenoid	30	Friedelin, Epifriedelanol

FIGURE 26: TERPENE CLASSIFICATIONS

The terpenes of Cannabis have largely already been discovered and researched in other plants, although the diversity and density of these compounds in Cannabis varieties are only recently being explored. Monoterpenoids are highly volatile due to their very simple structure (see Limonene below) and dissipate quite a bit after the drying of Cannabis (Turner *et al.*, 1980; Ross and ElSohly, 1996).

Terpenes undergo a lot of changes from the time a Cannabis plant is harvested to the time the material makes its way to a user. One research study found that if not kept in an airtight container, 31% of terpenes were lost in Cannabis material after 1 week of drying at room temperature; 44.8% of terpenes were lost in material that was dried for 1 week and then stored in a paper bag for 1 month; 55.2% of terpenes were lost in material that had been dried at room temperature for 1 week and then stored in a paper bag for 3 months. (AHP, 2013).

The concentration of monoterpenes in this study went from being 92.48% of the terpene fraction in fresh Cannabis, to 85.54% in material that had been dried for 1 week at room temperature. It dropped further to 67.60% in material that was stored for 3 months in a paper bag. (Ross and ElSohly, 1995)

This results in a greater proportion of sesquiterpenoids, with beta-caryophyllene usually being the most dominant. Sesquiterpene concentration can increase approximately six times the original content over three months of storage (AHP, 2013). Contrary to cannabinoid yield, phytoterpenoid yield occurs best in soils with reduced fertility (Langenheim, 1994).

Many terpenes oxidize into a variety of other terpenes during aging while other terpenes quickly volatize off from the plant material, making test results difficult to meaningfully interpret. Oxidized terpenes include things like linalool, geraniol, and terpinol. The non-oxidized terpenes, or terpenes lacking any oxygen atoms, are often referred to as "true terpenes". Examples of true terpenes include limonene, myrcene, and terpinolene.

The high degree of volatility and variability of terpenes makes them a sort of moving target for Cannabis testing labs. For instance, the true terpene myrcene can oxidize and turn into linalool. When a testing lab finds linalool in a sample, is it because linalool was present or did the lab improperly store the sample, causing oxidation and degradation of myrcene and other true terpenes, resulting in a greater proportion of sesquiterpenes and oxygen containing terpenes?

Recent research has focused on whether terpenes might be responsible for some of the reported effects of Cannabis and whether these compounds might have synergistic effects with cannabinoids. Animal studies seem to support this idea of the "entourage effect" (Buchbauer *et al.*, 1993).

Most terpenes are not very acutely toxic if ingested directly in small amounts but can act as respiratory irritants when inhaled. There is little toxicity information available about persistent long-term exposure to terpene compounds when inhaled. **There is currently little or no research on the health effects of directly smoking large concentrations of terpenes, as are found in some terpene enriched Cannabis extracts.** Terpenes interact with molecules in the air such as NO_3, OH, and others to form oxidative products. These secondary organic aerosols can cause lung irritation and gastrointestinal problems. There have been no studies on mammalian health effects of chronic exposures to elevated levels of secondary organic aerosols from terpene oxidation products that would be found in Cannabis or Cannabis products.

AVERAGE CONCENTRATION RANGES OF COMMON TERPENOIDS IN CANNABIS FLOWERS

Compound	% Content
a-Pinene	0.1 – 0.75
b-Myrcene	0.1 - 2.0
d-Limonene	0.1 – 1.5
Terpinolene	0.1 – 1.25
Linalool	0.1 – 0.5
b-Caryophyllene	0.1 – 1.5

FIGURE 27: AVERAGE TERPENOID CONCENTRATIONS IN CANNABIS

Data Source: *viva voce* Kenevir Research, Oregon, USA, 2015

Note: Terpenoid concentrations of 0.05% or greater are of pharmacological interest. (Russo E, 2011)

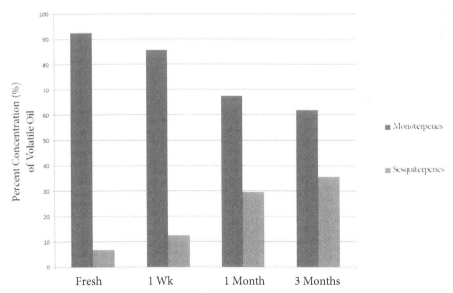

How Do Terpene Concentrations Change Over Time?

FIGURE 28: HOW DO TERPENE CONCENTRATIONS CHANGE OVER TIME?

Data from Ross and ElSohly, 1996 – "The Volatile Oil Composition of Fresh and Air-Dried Buds of Cannabis sativa"

WHICH TERPENE? A NOTE ABOUT CHIRALITY

There is a glaring problem facing Cannabis terpenoid data, currently – and that is that most analytical laboratories performing Cannabis testing do not test for something call enantiomers. Enantiomers are molecules that have the same exact chemical structure but are mirror opposites of one another – similar to your left hand and right hand. They are built the same, with the same components, and they look the same – only they are mirror opposites of one another. Enantiomers are examples of a concept called chirality. Chirality is property that describes asymmetry in something, and in chemistry a set of compounds are chiral if they are the same structure but cannot be superposed upon one another no matter what way the molecule is manipulated.

The implications for not understanding the enantiomers of Cannabis compounds are quite significant. Although enantiomers may seem to be essentially the same molecule, the way they interact with chemical receptors in the body, and thus the physiological effects they promote, can be very different.

Because the enantiomers of Cannabis terpenoids are not well understood, and the data provided by Cannabis testing labs is largely inadequate, often improperly validating the identification of specific terpenoid enantiomers, I stress caution when attempting to interpret terpene results of Cannabis products. This issue also highlights one of several reasons why terpene profiles are unreliable for predicting the effects a Cannabis product may have on a consumer.

DO TERPENOIDS DETERMINE EFFECTS?

There is a prevailing notion throughout the Cannabis community that terpenoids produce unique effects among Cannabis varieties. This then often leads people to jump to the conclusion that if they study the effects of individual terpenes, and then recognize the dominant terpenes in a Cannabis product, that they might be able to predict how the Cannabis product with affect them. This is a problematic idea for several reasons.

First, there is the issue around enantiomers that we just covered. When a lab reports limonene concentration in Cannabis, is that d-Limonene, or l-Limonene? When a lab reports linalool, is that S-linalool or R-linalool? Evidence suggests that this really matters in terms of therapeutic activity.

Next there is the problem that terpenoids have been shown to elicit different effects depending on the context in which they are administered. This is tied into the concept of "set and setting." Set and setting describes the physical environmental and psychological mindset involved in the administration of a drug. Going back to research around linalool, it has been

168

shown that different enantiomers of linalool perform differently when administered under different circumstances. While linalool might be calming in one environment, it might precipitate feelings of irritation in another setting (Hofer et al, 2006).

Finally, the effect of a medication or drug is not just dependent on the chemistry of that product, but also the physiology and psychology of the consumer. The chemistry is just one piece of a bigger puzzle. Even if you know the chemistry of a product, and the psychological component (set and setting) are controlled, there is still the fact that different people feature different biochemistry that influences how that product will behave in the body once consumed. To make things even more complicated, your biochemistry is not static. Drugs affect the body differently depending on the time of day, your age, your diet, and many other factors.

Despite these nuances, there are many companies – both well intentioned and not – that try to capitalize on a narrative that someone can learn what Cannabis varieties are best for different conditions by understanding the terpene content of the plant or cannabinoid product. The "science" offered for this approach is generally based on research around isolated terpenoids, and often times without references to specific enantiomers. The ironic thing about this approach is that it ignores the concept of the "entourage effect" which informs us that compounds may produce unique activities that are greater than the sum of their parts. Given that we already acknowledge the entourage effect and its importance in the therapeutic activity of Cannabis, why would someone assume that the activity of an isolated terpenoid will produce a certain effect when it is administered in the presence of hundreds of other terpenoids and cannabinoids?

To summarize the point, terpenoids certainly contribute to the effects elicited by Cannabis. But it is currently impossible to determine to what degree these effects occur, and what meaningful conclusions we can draw from knowing the concentrations of terpenoids in a Cannabis product. Even if we had a perfect understanding of the chemistry of a Cannabis product, which we certainly do not, we would still have difficulty predicting the effects that a Cannabis product will have. A Cannabis product that has a lot of linalool in it is not necessarily going to help with sleep. In fact, it could have the opposite effect in certain situations. A Cannabis variety dominant in terpinolene or limonene is not necessarily going to cause excitability or give someone energy, as is often commonly thought.

The picture is much more complex, and we must be careful not to let our minds oversimplify the dynamics involved. It is okay to admit that we do not yet properly understand how terpenoids influence the effects of Cannabis, and there is a lot of research needed to begin to tackle that question.

COMMON MONOTERPENOIDS FOUND IN CANNABIS

BETA-MYRCENE

Beta-myrcene is commonly found in fresh Cannabis and exhibits anti-inflammatory effects (Lorenzetti *et al.,* 1991). It has also been shown to fight cancer caused by the mycotoxin, aflatoxin (DeOliveira *et al.*, 1997).

Myrcene is found in hops and acts as a sedative (Bisset and Wichtl, 2004). In rodent studies, myrcene has been demonstrated to act as a muscle relaxant (Russo, 2011). Myrcene's sedative and muscle relaxant properties combined with other terpenoids might be responsible for the "couch lock" effect (Russo, 2011).

LIMONENE

Limonene is a terpene that is common to citrus fruits and is the second most common terpenoid in nature (Noma and Asakawa, 2010). Studies suggest it to have significant anti-anxiety effects (Carvalho-Freitas and Costa, 2002; Pultrini Ade *et al.*, 2006). Throughout history, lemons have been thought of as an antidote to Cannabis intoxication or hang over (Christison, 1851). Limonene has also exhibited potent antioxidant effects (Choi et al, 2000). Some data suggests that it might also be a treatment of gastro-esophageal reflux (Harris, 2010).

Although it's called "Limon"-ene, it is actually reported to smell like oranges, though the enantiomer l-limonene is reported to have a more piney scent compared to the dominant citrus scent of d-limonene.

TERPINOLENE

One research group found that the concentration of **a-terpinolene** was a key distinguisher between Cannabis varieties from two different geographical regions (Novak et al, 2001). It is described as having a woody, citrusy, and piney odor. The odor is also said to resemble lilac. Terpinolene has demonstrated **antioxidant** and **sedative** properties in recent studies (Turkez et al, 2015; Ito and Ito, 2013). Terpinolene has also been cited as an effective skin penetration enhancer for trans-dermal drug delivery (Aqil et al, 2007).

ALPHA-PINENE

alpha-Pinene is the most widely encountered terpenoid in nature (Noma and Asakawa, 2010). It can be found in conifers and many other plant essential oils and it seems to serve an insect-repellent role (Russo, 2011). It is an anti-inflammatory (Gil *et al.*, 1989), a bronchodilator in humans at low exposure levels (Falk *et al.*, 1990), and a broad-spectrum antibiotic (Nissen *et al.*, 2010). It can also aid memory, possibly offsetting some of the memory loss effects of THC (Perry *et al.*, 2000; Russo, 2011).

ALPHA-TERPINEOL

Terpineol is a monoterpene found in Cannabis which exhibits some affinity for CB1 and CB2 receptors, making it a non-traditional cannabinoid of sorts, along with other terpenes like beta-caryophyllene and humulene (Mehmedic et al, 2014). Alpha-terpineol has a pleasant aroma and is often used in perfumes. It is commonly sourced in nature, as well as being manufactured using alpha-pinene as a precursor. Terpinoeol is said to have a piney lilac aroma.

Linalool

Delta-Linalool is a monoterpene that is common in Lavender (Russo, 2001). In rodent models, linalool has been shown to act as a sedative when inhaled (Buchbauer *et al.*, 1991; Jirovetz *et al.*, 1992). It is thought to be a compound responsible for healing burns with reduced scarring (Gattefosse, 1993). It has been shown to have anesthetic effects similar to procaine and menthol (Ghelardini *et al.*, 1999). It has also demonstrated anticonvulsant activity (Ismail, 2006).

Eucalyptol (aka cineol, cineole, cajeputol)

Eucalyptol has demonstrated anti-inflammatory effects in asthma patients (Juergens et al, 2003). As the name implies, this compound is a dominate compound in eucalyptus oil and smells strongly of eucalyptus. It is an ingredient in many types of mouthwash and cough suppressant.

Borneol

Borneol is a terpene derivative found in Cannabis and many other plants, which exhibits a piney-woody odor. This compound has been utilized in traditional Chinese herbal medicine for many years to help other therapeutic agents reach the central nervous system. It is now known that borneol has a unique ability to open the blood brain barrier, allowing greater concentrations of drugs to enter the brain (Yu et al, 2013).

ALPHA-THUJENE

Alpha-thujene is an often under recognized monoterpenoid found in Cannabis which has been found to be unique enough among certain Cannabis varieties that it could be used for chemotaxonomical purposes (Jacqueline von Salm, *viva voce*). It is a primary component of the essential oil of Boswellia (Indian Frankincense) and in high concentrations, alpha-thujene may exhibit anti-inflammatory and antimicrobial properties (Mothana et al, 2011; Siddiqui, 2011).

COMMON SESQUITERPENOIDS FOUND IN CANNABIS

BETA-CARYOPHYLLENE

beta-Caryophyllene is usually the most common sesquiterpenoid found in Cannabis samples (Mediavilla and Steinemann, 1997). The Cannabis plant uses this terpene to attract predatory lacewings which feed on Cannabis pests (Langenheim, 1994). It is the predominant terpenoid in Cannabis extracts or other products that have been decarboxylated under heat for long periods of time. Beta-Caryophyllene is an anti-inflammatory (Basile *et al.*, 1988), gastric cytoprotective (Tambe *et al.*, 1996), and is a full CB2 agonist (Gertsch *et al.*, 2008). Because of its affinity for a cannabinoid receptor, it is now considered a "dietary cannabinoid" by some researchers. Beta-caryophyllene has a spicy, clove-like odor.

CARYOPHYLLENE OXIDE

Caryophyllene oxide is commonly found in lemon balm and eucalyptus (Farag *et al.*, 2004). It seems to exhibit insecticidal, anti-feedant, and antifungal properties for plant defense (Bettarini *et al.*, 1993; Langenheim, 1994). It is also the component in Cannabis responsible for identification by drug sniffing dogs (Stahl and Kunde, 1973).

HUMULENE

Humulene is a terpene commonly found in hops and has some affinity for CB1 and CB2 receptors, making it a non-traditional cannabinoid, in some sense (Mehmedic et al, 2014). It has been shown to exhibit anti-cancer activity which is enhanced with the combination of beta-caryophyllene (Legault and Pichette, 2010). Humulene has been demonstrated to show anti-inflammatory effects (Fernandes *et al.*, 2007).

NEROLIDOL

Nerolidol is a low-level compound in citrus peels. It acts as a skin penetration enhancer (Cornwell and Barry, 1994) as well as an antifungal (Langeheim, 1994). There is evidence that Nerolidol has the ability to control parasites and malaria (Lopes *et al.*, 1999; Goulart *et al.*, 2004).

174

B-Eudesmol

B-Eudesmol has demonstrated antiangiogenic effects both *in vitro* and *in vivo* (Tsuneki et al, 2005). Angiogenesis is a term referring to the formation of new blood vessels. An antiangiogenic drug slows down or limits the production of new blood vessels. This can be useful in slowing the growth of cancer cells by limiting the blood flow to the cancer cells. This hypothesis was tested in a 2008 study when researchers suppressed the growth of cancer cells on mouse tumors *in vivo* (Ma et al, 2008). Eudesmol has a woody odor.

Guaiol

Guaiol is a terpene that is more commonly found in wide leaflet drug varieties of Cannabis of Afghani origin (Hillig, 2003). These are usually plants typically thought of as "Cannabis indica." This terpene is usually also found in relatively high ratios along with Eudesmol (Hillig, 2003). It is described as having an odor like that of tea roses or violets.

Trans-B-farnesene

Trans-beta-farnesene is a scent compound that acts as an aphid repellent. This terpene has been found to be correlated with narrow leaflet drug varieties of Cannabis, conventionally referred to as "Cannabis sativa" (Hillig, 2003). It is described as having a sweet woody odor.

COMMON DITERPENOIDS FOUND IN CANNABIS

PHYTOL

Phytol is a diterpene (20 carbon terpene) breakdown product of chlorophyll and is usually present in Cannabis extracts (McGinty *et al.*, 2010). Phytol can exhibit relaxing effects (Bang *et al.*, 2002). It is reported to have little to no smell.

COMMON TRITERPENOIDS FOUND IN CANNABIS

FRIEDELIN

Friedelin is a triterpenoid (30 carbon terpene) found in Cannabis roots. Prior research on Friedelin from other plant sources reveals it may be an effective anti-inflammatory, analgesic (pain reliever), and antipyretic (anti-fever). (Antonisamy et al, 2011)

EPIFRIEDELANOL

Epifriedelanol is another triterpenoid found in Cannabis roots. There is some research indicating that it could be a therapeutic target due to its demonstrated anti-tumor and cytoprotective (cell protective) effects among others (Russo and Marcu, 2017).

Terpene	Common Source	Notes
Limonene	Oranges, Lemons	Reduces acne bacteria Stimulates the immune system when inhaled Modulates psychoactive effects of THC
a-Pinene	Pine Needles	Assists memory
b-Myrcene	Hops	Sedative effects Possibly primary culprit in the "couch lock" phenomenon
Linalool	Lavender	Anti-anxiety Anticonvulsant
b-Caryophyllene	Black Pepper	Attracts predatory insects while discouraging herbivory while the plant is growing May hold promise in treating gastric ulcers
Caryophyllene oxide	Lemon Balm	Serves as an insecticidal anti-feedant and broad-spectrum antifungal May be the compound responsible for identification by drug sniffing dogs
Nerolidol	Orange Peel	Sedative Potent antimalarial
Phytol	Tea	Relaxant Results from the breakdown of chlorophyll

FIGURE 29: COMMON TERPENES IN CANNABIS

SOURCE: RUSSO E. 2011. TAMING THC: POTENTIAL CANNABIS SYNERGY AND PHYTOCANNABINOID-TERPENOID ENTOURAGE EFFECTS. BRITISH JOURNAL OF PHARMACOLOGY. 163(7): 1344-1364.

Reported Boiling Points of Common Cannabinoids and Terpenoids in Cannabis

Boiling Point °C*	Boiling Point °F*	Compound
119°C	246°F[1]	β-caryophyllene
156°C	312°F[1]	α-pinene
157°C or 200°C?	315°F[1] or 392°F[3]	Δ9-THC Δ9-Tetrahydrocannabinol
160-180°C	320-356°F[1]	CBD Cannabidiol
166-168°C	330-334°F[1]	β-myrcene
168°C	334°F[1]	Δ3-carene
175-178°C	347-352°F[1]	Δ8-THC Δ8-Tetrahydrocannabinol
176°C	349°F[2]	eucalyptol
177°C	350°F[1]	d-limonene
177°C	350°F[1]	p-cymene
185°C	365°F[1]	CBN Cannabinol
198°C	388°F[1]	linalool
209°C	408°F[1]	terpineol-4-ol
210°C	410°F[1]	borneol
217-218°C	422-424°F[1]	α-terpineol
220°C	428°F[1]	CBC Cannabichromene
~220°C	~428°F[1]	THCV Tetrahydrocannabivarin

FIGURE 30: CANNABINOID AND TERPENOID BOILING POINT CHART

Note: These are *reported* boiling points at atmospheric pressure unless otherwise noted. Other reports may vary (see d9-THC for an example)

(1) McPartland, John M. and E. Russo. "Cannabis and cannabis extracts: greater than the sum of their parts?" Journal of Cannabis Therapeutics. 2001. Vol. 1. No. 3/4. pp. 103-132; (2) Downs, David Victor, et al. "Extraction of pharmaceutically active components from plant materials." U.S. Patent No. 7,344,736. 18 Mar. 2008.; (3) PubChem (pubchem.ncbi.nlm.nih.gov) – measured at 0.02 mm Hg pressure

BEYOND STRAIN NAMES: IDENTIFYING TERPENE PATTERNS AMONG THC-RICH CANNABIS CULTIVARS

In 2018, Cannabis terpenoid researcher Dr. Justin Fischedick published a paper presenting results of terpene tests on over 200 samples across 30 cultivars (aka "strains"). In this study, Fischedick proposes a classification system by which a cultivar is categorized based on its dominant terpenoids, ratios of major terpenes, the presence of unique terpenes, and the presence of any other characteristic terpenes. After reviewing the resulting data, Fischedick found that 5 primary groups of terpene chemotypes could be easily identified among the samples tested, with unique classes under each of those 5 groups, comprising a total of 13 unique terpene chemotype classes. Identifying patterns in terpene profiles across cultivars is critical for establishing a new nomenclature that does not rely on strain names or indica/sativa designations.

The following figure (Figure 25) summarizes the 5 primary groups and 13 total classes of terpene profiles that Fischedick identified among the samples tested for this particular study. If this classification system is applied to larger data sets, it is plausible that other groups and classes would be identified, which would begin to construct a more meaningful and reliable system of classifying Cannabis cultivars. This classification system would then provide a framework from which researchers and clinicians can begin to better study the unique properties and effects associated with each of these chemotype clusters – taking Cannabis and cannabinoid therapeutics to a new level of sophistication.

It is important to note that this model is not the end all be all model of differentiating Cannabis varieties by terpenoid content. Instead, the work presented by Fischedick should be considered the beginning of the exercising of this technique which will gain sophistication over time as other researchers analyze more Cannabis samples and examine more chemical constituents of Cannabis.

As an example, in 2020, ElSohly Award winner Jacqueline von Salm, PhD announced that her work examining the chemical variation of Cannabis cultivars revealed the unique presence of a terpenoid rarely measured by most Cannabis testing laboratories, alpha-thujene, which may be an important differentiator between certain cultivars (*viva voce*). This highlights how much more work needs to be done before jumping to conclusions about how we should differentiate cultivars based on their chemical profiles.

Group	Characteristics	Class	Cultivars (Strain Names)
Terpinolene Dominant	a-Phellandrene, b-phellandrene 3-carene, a-terpinene	Terpinoloene	Trainwreck, Jack Herer, Ace of Spades, Sage
Beta-Caryophyllene Dominant	1:1 Limonene : Humulene	Cookie	Animal Cookies, Blue Cookies, Fortune Cookies, Girl Scout Cookies, Thin Mints, Cookie, Phantom Cookies
	2:1 Limonene : Humulene linalool, endo-fenchyl-alcohol, and a-terpineol	Sherbert	Sherbert, Sunset Sherbert
	1:1 Limonene : Myrcene	Glue	Gorilla Glue #4, Super Glue
Limonene / Myrcene Dominant	1:1 Limonene : Myrcene	OG Kush	Crown Og, Gas, Og Kush, Skywalker Og Kush, Superman Og Kush, Tahoe Og Kush, Hardcore Og, Louis XIII Og Kush, Milky Way Og Kush, Wifi Og Kush
	2:1 Limonene: Myrcene	Limonene OG Kush	Miami White Kush, Triple O, Headband
	3:1 Limonene : Linalool Endo-fenchyl-aclohol, alpha terpineol, geranyl acetate	Gelato	Gelato
Limonene / Myrcene / Beta-Caryophyllene Dominant with alpha-Bisabolol	2:2:1 Limonene : Beta-Caryophyllene : Myrcene	Kush	Bubba Kush, Master Kush
	1:1:1 Limonene : Myrcene : Beta-caryophyllene	Mr. Nice	Mr. Nice
Myrcene Dominant	4:1 myrcene : alpha-pinene Alpha-pinene > trans-ocimene	Purple	Grape Ape, Purple Cream, Purple Princess, Purple Urkle, Blue Mazaar, Granddaddy Purple, Purple Max, Watermelon
	2:1:4 alpha-pinene : beta-pinene : myrcene	Blue Dream	Blue Dream
	Trans-ocimene > limonene	Strawberry	Strawberry Haze, Strawberry Cough
	Alpha-pinene > limonene Low in beta-caryophyllene and humulene	High Myrcene	Godfather, AK-47

FIGURE 31: TERPENE CHEMOTYPE GROUPS AMONG COMMON CANNABIS CULTIVARS

Source: Fischedick JT (2017) Identification of terpenoid chemotypes among high ()-trans-D9 -tetrahydrocannabinol-producing Cannabis sativa L. cultivars, Cannabis and Cannabinoid Research 2:1, 34–47, DOI: 10.1089/can.2016.0040

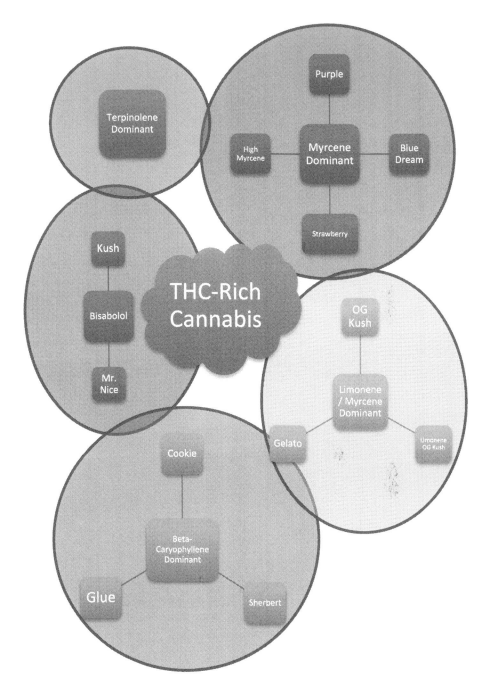

Visualization of Terpene Chemotype Groups and Classes from Fischedick 2017

TERPENOIDS AS SKIN PENETRATION ENHANCERS

Terpenes have been used with varying degrees of success to enhance the drug delivery of compounds through the skin. Terpenes can be used with cannabinoids to increase the efficiency of drug delivery for epicutaneous and transdermal drug delivery systems through the skin. There are a variety of characteristics that affect a terpene's potential to serve as a potent skin penetration enhancer.

A terpene's **lipophilicity** (its affinity for lipids) is a major characteristic that influences its ability to help other lipophilic compounds, like cannabinoids, pass through the skin.

A terpene's **boiling point** is inversely related to its level of skin penetration (Aqil et al, 2007). Low boiling point terpenes can serve as better skin penetration enhancers than higher boiling point terpenes. Likewise, smaller terpene compounds serve as better skin penetration enhancers than larger terpene compounds. The following are some terpenes that are also found in Cannabis that have been studied for their effects of assisting in skin penetration:

Terpene	Type	Permeant	Description
Limonene	Monoterpene	Butyl paraben, mannitol	Limonene enhances permeation of lipophilic drugs but ineffective for hydrophilic drugs
Linalool	Monoterpene alcohol	Haloperidol	Linalool reported as the potent enhancer for transdermal delivery of Haloperidol, an antipsychotic medication used to treat schizophrenia.
Nerolidol	Sesquiterpene alcohol	Nicardipine hydrochloride, hydrocortisone, carbamazepine, tramoxifen	Nerolidol is found to be good candidate for the enhancement of hydrophilic drugs rather than lipophilic drugs
Terpinolene	Monoterpene	Dapiprazole	Terpinolene is found to be effective enhancer for the transdermal delivery of Dapiprazole through mouse skin.
Geraniol	Monoterpene alcohol	Caffeine	Geraniol provided a 16x increase in permeation of caffeine

FIGURE 32: SKIN PENETRATION EFFECTS OF COMMON TERPENES IN CANNABIS

Data Source: Aqil et al, 2007

Many terpenes can serve as effective skin penetration enhancers for nonpolar compounds like cannabinoids due to their lipophilic structures. Terpene alcohols can often serve as carriers for both polar and nonpolar compounds due to the addition of oxygen atoms to the molecular structure. For instance, Nerolidol and Geraniol, two terpene alcohols, have both been demonstrated as permeation enhancers for more water-soluble compounds like caffeine (Aqil et al, 2007).

TERPENE TOXICOLOGY

Many terpenes found in Cannabis are classified as GRAS, or "generally recognized as safe", when consumed in low concentrations *orally*, or when exposed to low concentrations on the skin. There is very little information available regarding how safe any terpenes are to inhale, and it is very important to acknowledge that something that may be safe to consume orally may not be safe to consume through other methods.

Low molecular weight terpenoids, like those found in Cannabis, can act as allergens in some people. Many terpenes oxidize very easily, resulting in compounds which may be more irritating to the skin or to tissues in the body. A good example of this is Limonene. Limonene is typically well tolerated, but when it oxidizes, it can become very irritating.

Additionally, when heated terpenes can actually form some fairly toxic byproducts, presenting unique health risks for Cannabis smokers. When smoking Cannabis extracts, often referred to as "dabbing", terpenes can breakdown and form new chemical compounds which can be much more toxic than any of the terpenes initially present in the extract. Primarily, terpenes like myrcene, limonene, and linalool can form products like benzene, which is very carcinogenic, and methacrolein, which is a potent lung irritant (Meehan Atrash, et al, 2017).

As the smoking of Cannabis extracts continues to grow in popularity, researchers will surely be further examining the health effects of terpene and terpene byproduct inhalation, to determine what, if any, additional health risks may be associated with Cannabis extract smoking.

AROMA IS ABOUT MORE THAN TERPENOIDS

While it is true that terpenes impart a lot of the aromas and flavors of unique Cannabis varieties, terpenes are only part of the picture. As we will cover in the next chapter, there are other chemicals at play that are also affecting the aromas and flavors of Cannabis, including terpenoid esters, aldehydes, and flavonoids – to name a few. A recent study examining the chemicals responsible for the aroma of Cannabis found that,

"The compounds found to be responsible for the overall aroma of dry marijuana … are 1) Benzaldehyde, 2) Myrcene, 3) Decanal, 4) Heptanal, 5) Methyl anthranilate, 6) Octanal, 7) Hexanal, 8) Methylisohexenyl ketone, 9) Linalool, 10) β-Caryophyllene, 11) α-Humelene, and 12) Acetic acid. Highly odorous compounds…from fresh marijuana…are A) Nonanal, B) Decanol, C) o-Cymene, D) Isobutyraldehyde, E) 1-

Chloroacetophenone, F) Nerol, G) Propylamine, H) o-Guaiacol, I) Linalyl acetate, J) Methyl anthranilate, K) Benzaldehyde, L) Limonene." (Rice and Koziel, 2015)

You may notice that many of the compounds listed in this study are *not* terpenoids. This is very important because many consumers and producers rely on organoleptic properties, like aroma, to make purchasing decisions. There are cultural memes that claim to relate Cannabis aromas to therapeutic profiles, largely relying on clinical research about terpenoids. This focus on associated aroma with terpenoids could be leading many to miss the forest for the trees.

Enduring Understandings

- Cannabis produces over 200 different terpenoids.
- Lightweight terpenes are often somewhat responsible for the aromas and flavors of the Cannabis plant.
- Terpenes are highly influenced by the environment and are used as a way for the plant to communicate and react to its environment such as attracting predatory insects, repelling pests, changing the flavor of leaves to discourage herbivory, and more.
- Researchers have attempted to categorize Cannabis varieties based on terpenoid variation.
- Terpenes can act as skin penetration enhancers in topical formulas.
- At high temperatures, terpenes can form carcinogenic and irritating byproducts, like benzene.
- Although terpenes have been used safely in foods and cosmetics, there is little information available about the health effects of inhaling terpenes.
- Terpenes are only a piece of the Cannabis aroma puzzle. Research has shown that there are many other chemical types influencing the overall aroma of Cannabis besides terpenes.

Chapter 13:

OTHER CANNABIS COMPOUNDS

Learning Questions
- What are flavonoids? What are some unique flavonoids found in Cannabis?
- What are esters? What are some common cannabinoid derived esters found in Cannabis?
- What are stilbenoids? What stilbenoids are commonly found in Cannabis?
- What essential fatty acids are found in the Cannabis plant?
- What other chemical compounds may be found in Cannabis?

FLAVONOIDS

Flavonoids are polyphenolic compounds found in plants that are responsible for various color pigments. They are responsible for giving fruit skins their color, for example. Flavonoids are responsible for all sorts of color pigments in plants, including hues of blue, red, purple, yellow, and even some shades of green.

Cannabis produces approximately twenty different flavonoids either as free flavonoids or as conjugated glycosides (Turner et al. 1980). There are several flavonoids that are thought to be unique to Cannabis, like **Cannflavin** A, B, and C. During extractions in the laboratory, some flavonoids like **anthocyanins** and **anthocyandidins** leave a rosy or purple color in the solvent. Many flavonoids, like **kaempferol** and **quercetin** have a yellow tint.

There are some flavonoids that have been shown to easily penetrate cell membranes and maintain their pharmacological activity in Cannabis smoke (Sauer et al. 1983). Flavonoids might have chemoprotective properties by inhibiting certain enzymes responsible for the activation of carcinogens, including some carcinogens thought to exist in Cannabis smoke (Fuhr, 1998; Offord et al., 1997; McPartland and Pruitt, 1997). Flavonoids have demonstrated antioxidant and anti-inflammatory effects in a variety of research models. Many flavonoids elicit effects from the body by interacting with estrogen receptors.

Yellow-Green

Pink

Violet-Red

In this example, three different cannabis flower varieties produce varying colors of polar extracts, possibly indicating varying flavonoid or quinoid content

In addition, it has been shown that some of the anthocyanin flavonoids in cannabis exhibit affinity for CB1 and CB2 receptors. Particularly, cyanidin and delphinidin have shown moderate affinity for CB1 receptors, and cyanidin, delphinidin, and peonidin exhibit moderate affinity for CB2 receptors. This means that these flavonoids could be interacting with the endocannabinoid system directly to promote other pharmacological effects in the body other than the typical antioxidant and neuroprotective effects often associated with flavonoids. (Korte et al, 2009)

Some flavonoids, like kaempferol and hydroxyflavone, can inhibit the enzyme fatty acid amide hydrolase (FAAH), which is responsible for breaking down the endocannabinoid anandamide (Thors et al, 2008; Thors et al, 2007). This in turn can mean that anandamide will circulate in the body longer, interacting with cannabinoid receptors in the body longer.

Anthocyanidin flavonoids are responsible for many of the purple colors of Cannabis.

Cannabis can exhibit many different pigments.

TRY THIS! PIGMENT EXTRACTIONS AT HOME

You can extract flavonoids and other pigments from Cannabis or other colorful plants at home (assuming your home resides in a state or country where Cannabis is legal). Simply find a Cannabis "bud" that has purple, blue, or red hues, grind it up, put it in a tea bag, and soak in water. Within minutes the pigment compounds will transfer to the water. This water is now infused with antioxidant bioflavonoids!

Materials

Cannabis Inflorescence (Flower)	Herb Grinder	Cheesecloth, coffee filter, or tea bag
Glass Cup	Water	

Procedures

1. Ensure the Cannabis inflorescence is dry to facilitate grinding
2. Grind the plant material up using a hand grinder or other grinding method. The material does not need to be a powder – this is about increasing surface area, but it doesn't have to be perfect.
3. Fill a glass with water.
4. Option 1:
   a. Pour the ground plant matter into the water.
   b. Stir and let sit for approximately 5 to 10 minutes.
   c. Pour the water over a cheesecloth or strainer to remove the plant matter
5. Option 2:
   a. Place the ground plant matter in a tea bag and place into water. Note: a coffee filter can be stapled or otherwise sealed together to make an impromptu tea bag, if needed.
   b. Stir and let sit for approximately 5 to 10 minutes.
   c. Remove the teabag from the water.
6. Evaluate the pigments of the water! I recommend shining light through the water to better see the pigments present.

Congratulations! You just extracted pigments, including flavonoids, from Cannabis! What colors did you notice?

Cannflavin A, B and C

CANNFLAVIN A

CANNFLAVIN B

Cannflavin A, B, and C are thought to be unique to Cannabis, as they have not been discovered or described in any other organism, so far. These compounds are potent anti-inflammatory agents and exhibit antioxidant and analgesic effects. An isomer of Cannflavin B, known as FBL-03G or Caflanone, is currently being studied for its potential to treat pancreatic cancer (Moreau et al, 2019).

LUTEOLIN

➤ Anti-inflammatory; inhibits pro-inflammatory immune system signaling
➤ Some anti-cancer effects demonstrated *in vitro*.
➤ Yellow pigment

QUERCETIN

> More potent antioxidant than ascorbic acid (Vitamin C). (McPartland, 2000)
> Prevents immune cells from releasing histamine *in vitro*. May exhibit anti-inflammatory effects (UMM)
> Anti-cancer effects *in vitro*. (UMM)

KAEMPFEROL

> Wide range of proposed pharmacological actions including antioxidant, anti-inflammatory, antimicrobial, anticancer, cardioprotective, neuroprotective effects and more. (Calderon-Montano et al, 2011)
> Can induce apoptosis in breast cancer cells
> Can inhibit FAAH, an enzyme that breaks down the endocannabinoid anandamide

APIGENIN

> Potent anti-prostaglandin activity
> Inhibits tumor necrosis factor induced inflammation
> Potent inhibitor of Cytochrome P450 2C9 liver enzyme that is responsible for breaking down many drugs.
> Yellow pigment

CHRYSOERIOL

➤ May have vasorelaxant and hypotensive properties (Gorzalczany et al, 2013)
➤ Exhibits bronchodilation effects when administered in tea (Khan and Gilani, 2006)
➤ Exhibits antioxidant activity (Mishra et al, 2003)
➤ Yellow pigment

VITEXIN AND ISOVITEXIN

Commonly found in passionflower and a variety of other medicinal plants, vitexin is a flavonoid derived from apigenin. It is a glycoside, meaning that it contains a sugar (glucose/glucoside) in the molecule. Vitexin, and it's related molecular family member isovitexin, are commonly used in traditional Chinese medicine. Vitexin is recognized as having antioxidant, anti-cancer, anti-inflammatory, anti-hyperalgesia, and neuroprotective effects (He et al, 2016).

FBL-03G (Caflanone)

CAFLANONE (FBL-03G)

CANNFLAVIN B

In 2019, a paper was published identifying the potential therapeutic applications of a flavonoid derivative of Cannabis called FBL-03G, also known as caflanone. This compound is not actually naturally occurring in Cannabis, but rather is a synthetic isomer of Cannflavin B, which *is* a naturally occurring flavonoid in Cannabis.

Specifically, this compound has been identified as being a potential treatment for pancreatic cancer (Moreau et al, 2019). Orphan drug status was granted to caflanone in 2019, and the drug is due to enter clinical trials (Flavocure press release, Oct. 3, 2019). It should be noted that the designation of orphan drug does not indicate whether the drug actually holds promise for treating pancreatic cancer. Rather, this status allows researchers a seven-year window to exclusively research the drug for the treatment of pancreatic cancer. Time will tell whether this flavonoid compound of Cannabis holds clinically significant therapeutic value.

MISCELLANEOUS PIGMENT COMPOUNDS

There are a variety of pigment compounds, other than flavonoids, that produce some of the various colorations in the Cannabis plant. These include compounds like chlorophyll, which is responsible for the green color of plants, and carotenoids, which typically provide orange and yellow colors to plants. Xanthophylls are a type of carotenoid found in Cannabis that produces yellow pigments in leaves. Many of these pigment compounds exhibit antioxidant properties. Additionally, oxidative products of Cannabis compounds, such as the quinone derivatives of cannabinoids, can produce color in Cannabis extracts.

ESTERS

Esters are compounds that are formed by joining together an alcohol and a carboxylic acid with an oxygen atom. These compounds are widespread throughout nature and are responsible for giving many fruits and vegetables their characteristic aromas and flavors. Some esters are even used as perfumes. While terpenes are the compounds that are often most discussed when thinking about essential oils and plant aromas, esters compliment terpenes in critical ways to provide the smells and tastes of plants that we are familiar with.

Very few esters have been characterized in Cannabis so far. In 1995, hexyl acetate was discovered in the volatile components of Cannabis (Ross and ElSohly, 1996). In 2008, two esters of CBGA were discovered as well as an assortment of THCA esters (Ahmed et al, 2008). The table below lists most of the esters that have been characterized in Cannabis so far.

THCA Esters		CBGA Esters
B-fenchyl-delta-9-tetrahydrocannbinolate	a-terpenyl-delta-9-tetrahydrocannbinolate	y-eudesmyl cannabigerolate
a-fenchyl-delta-9-tetrahydrocannbinolate	4-terpenyl-delta-9-tetrahydrocannabinolate	a-cadinyl cannabigerolate
Epi-bornyl-delta-9-tetrahydrocannbinolate	a-cadinyl-delta-9-tetrahydrocannabinolate	
Bornyl-delta-9-tetrahydrocannabinolate	y-eudesmyl-delta-9-tetrahydrocannbinolate	
Volatile Esters		
hexyl acetate	methyl anthranilate	linalyl acetate

FIGURE 33: COMMON CANNABIS ESTERS

A synthetic cannabinoid that is gaining popularity among limited circles of Cannabis users seeking a more psychedelic high is a compound called THC-O-Acetate. THC-O-Acetate is a cannabinoid ester formed by replacing the -OH group on THCA with an acetate group. This leads to several distinct changes in effects. THC-O-Acetate is said to be as much as three times as potent as THC, however it takes as much as 30 minutes for the effects to set in. This is because the body must perform extra work to metabolize this compound before enabling the drug to take effect. Technically, THC-O-Acetate could be thought of as a prodrug for THC.

KETONES

Ketones are compounds which consist of two different carbon containing compounds are joined together by a double bonded oxygen. Very few ketones have been characterized in Cannabis so far. A review of the volatile components of Cannabis revealed two ketones: 2-methyl-4-heptanone and 2-methyl-3-heptanone (Ross and ElSohly, 1995). One of

those compounds, 2-methyl-4-heptanone, is also present in bananas and has been speculatated to be responsible for contributing to the flavor profile of Cannabis in some way (Sirius J, 2016). The ketones methylisohexenyl ketone and 1-chloroacetophenone were reported as a volatile ketone contributing to the characteristic aroma of dry Cannabis (Rice and Koziel, 2015).

STILBENOIDS

Stilbenoids are phenolic compounds, technically phenylpropanoids, that are derivatives of the compound stilbene. One of the most popular stilbenoids is resveratrol, found in the skin of grapes, among other plant products. In plants, stilbenoids play an important role in plant defense responses to stresses like fungal or bacterial infections, insect attacks, or herbivory. The presence and abundance of stilbenoids in plants is often associated with disease and pest resistance in plants.

Examples of Isomers of Stilbene

There are a variety of stilbenoids found in Cannabis, detectable in the stems, leaves, resins, and flowers. There are three primary categories of stilbenoids found in Cannabis, including phenanthrenes, dihydrostilbenes, and spiroindans.

Stilbenoid Class	Examples Found in Cannabis
Phenanthrenes	Denbinobin
Dihydrostilbenes	Canniprene, Cannabistilbene I, Cannabistilbene IIa, Cannabistilbene IIb
Spiroindans	Cannabispirone, Cannabispiradienone, Beta-Cannabispiranol

FIGURE 34: EXAMPLES OF STILBENOIDS IN CANNABIS

DENBINOBIN

Denbinobin is one of the most understood stilbenoids found in Cannabis. It is an interesting stilbenoid because it is not terpenoid derived, like many other stilbenoids. In research that has been done with denbinobin, it has been discovered that this compound can induce apoptosis in cells, with implications for cancer treatment (Sanchez-Duffhues et al, 2009). In one study, denbinobin was shown to have significant anti-cancer effects on leukaemia cells through inhibition of the NF-kB pathway. It may also be an inhibitor of the HIV-1-lentiviral promotor, with implications for treating HIV (Sanchez-Duffhues et al, 2008). It may be worth noting as well that denbinobin is also a quinone compound.

CANNIPRENE

Canniprene has been isolated from the leaves of the Cannabis plant and has been found to be a potent inhibitor of inflammatory signaling compounds in the body (Allegrone et al, 2017).

PHYTOSTEROLS

Phytosterols are plant-derived steroid alcohols. Steroids are organic compounds that all share a common four ring structure, as seen in the following examples for campesterol, stigmasterol, and beta-sitosterol. Phytosterols are formed in the plant from the precursor cycloartenol, which is derived from a triterpene called squalene.

Phytosterols can modulate the way the body absorbs cholesterol, primarily by competing with cholesterol in the body, effectively lowering cholesterol over time. In one human study, "the consumption of 1.5 – 1.8 g/day of plant sterols or stanols reduced cholesterol absorption by 30 – 40%" (Ogbe et al, 2015; Normen et al, 2000). It should be noted, however, that phytosterols are not absorbed readily in the body. Usually less than 5%

of consumed phytosterols are absorbed into the blood. In contrast, the body absorbs approximately 40% of cholesterol that is consumed.

In general, the consumption of phytosterols is considered safe and even health promoting, possibly reducing the risk of heart disease, however there are some people that possess a rare genetic disorder called phytosterolemia, or sterolemia, that can cause the body to absorb far too many sterols, leading to a number of symptoms including elevated cholesterol levels, accumulation of fatty deposits in blood vessels, development of small growths called xanthomas which can cause pain and difficulty moving, and sometimes blood abnormalities, including a shortage of red blood cells, also called anemia. (Berge, 2003; Kidambi and Patel, 2008; Salen et al, 2002)

CAMPESTEROL

Campesterol is a common steroid alcohol (sterol) found in plants. While it is found in all sorts of vegetables, fruits, nuts, and seeds, it is found in greater concentrations in concentrated plant oils, including Cannabis oils (Fenselau and Hermann, 1972). Campesterol and other sterols have been found in refined Cannabis ethanol extracts (Fenselau and Hermann, 1972) as well as the Cannabis smoke (Adams and Jones, 1975).

STIGMASTEROL

Stigmasterol is one of the most abundant phytosterols and is commonly used as a food additive in an attempt to lower LDL cholesterol. It is often used as a precursor to progesterone (Sundararaman and Djerassi, 1977) and vitamin D3 (Kametani and Furuyama, 1987).

196

B-sitosterol

Beta-sitosterol is another very common sterol found in plants, including Cannabis. Higher levels of beta-sitosterol in the blood may be correlated with increase heart attack risk in men that have already had a previous heart attack, although research is conflicting on this issue (Assmann et al, 2006).

ALDEHYDES

Volatile aldehydes are responsible for the aromas of Cannabis arguably just as much as terpenes. An aldehyde functional group consists of a carbon with a double bond to an oxygen and a single bond to a hydrogen. Examples of volatile aldehydes found in Cannabis include Benzaldehyde, Decanal, Heptanal, Octanal, Hexanal, and Isobutyraldehyde (Rice and Koziel, 2015).

FATTY ACIDS IN SEED OIL

33 fatty acids have been found in Cannabis seed oil. Most of these fatty acids are unsaturated fatty acids (Brenneisen, 2006). The fatty acid variety in Cannabis seed oil does not differ substantially between different types of Cannabis (Ross et al., 1996). Some of the fatty acids contained in Cannabis seed oil are essential fatty acids required by the body which the body cannot produce. These include omega-3 and omega-6 fatty acids.

OTHER CANNABIS COMPOUNDS

All plants are rich sources of polyphenols, like flavonoids. Polyphenols are just compounds made up of multiple phenol units, which are simply aromatic rings with an –OH group, or alcohol group, attached. Various polyphenols display some binding affinity for CB1 and CB2 receptors, though this action is not greatly understood (Gertsch et al., 2010). Researchers are exploring whether diets high in polyphenols might enhance cardiovascular health (Habauzit and Morand, 2011). More research needs to be conducted to determine what polyphenols, other than the known flavonoids, might be found among various strains of Cannabis.

Cannabis seeds contain a novel lignanamide called Cannabisin A, which has been identified as a potential inhibitor of an enzyme involved in the infection of SARS-CoV-2 (COVID-19) (Ngo et al, 2020). There are also a variety of mono and polysaccharides found in Cannabis. Vitamin K has been found in the Cannabis plant (Turner et al, 1980). Vitamin # has been found in the plant's seeds. There are also a number of nitrogenous compounds (amines), amino acids, proteins, other alcohols, and other steroids that have been described of Cannabis.

Reported Boiling Points of Other Cannabis Compounds

Boiling Point °C*	Boiling Point °F*	Compound	Class
134	273	B-sitosterol[1]	Phytosterol
170	338	Stigmasterol[2]	Phytosterol
178	352-353	Apigenin[1]	Flavonoid
182	360	Cannflavin A[1]	Flavonoid
250	482	Quercetin[1]	Flavonoid

FIGURE 35 BOILING POINTS OF MISC CANNABINOID COMPOUNDS

Data Sources:

1 McPartland, John M. and E. Russo. "Cannabis and cannabis extracts: greater than the sum of their parts?" Journal of Cannabis Therapeutics. 2001. Vol. 1. No. 3/4. pp. 103-132

2 PubChem (pubchem.ncbi.nlm.nih.gov)

Enduring Understandings

- Flavonoids are a class of polyphenol compounds which are often pigment compounds that give plants their various colors.

- Cannflavin A, B and C are flavonoids thought to be unique to Cannabis – although it is possible that they may be found in other plants in the future.

- Esters are another set of compounds, like terpenes, that are often responsible for the aromas and flavors of plants.

- Very few ketones have been studied in Cannabis, although one ketone found in Cannabis is also found in bananas and may contribute to the flavor of some Cannabis varieties.

- Aldehydes are as responsible for the aromas of Cannabis as terpenes.

- Stilbenoids are commonly associated with pest resistance in plants.

- Cannabis seeds are rich sources of essential fatty acids including Omega-3 and Omega-6 fatty acids. They also contain Cannabisin A which may be a drug target for treating SARS-CoV-2 (COVID-19)

Review

Which cannabinoid is considered to be the parent compound of THCA, CBDA, and CBCA?

_____

True or False: Monoterpenes are lighter compounds than Sesquiterpenes, and are more likely to volatize quickly.   TRUE   FALSE

What compound does GPP have to bind with to begin the synthetic pathway to CBGV, THCV, CBDV, and CBCV?

_____

Chapter 14:
HEMP

- How has the term "hemp" been used throughout history?
- What is the difference between "hemp" and "marijuana"?
- What are some of the ways in which Cannabis can be used industrially?

WHAT IS HEMP?

Cannabis plants that are low in the intoxicating component THC are often referred to as "hemp". The word "hemp" has been used to refer to all kinds of plants, not just Cannabis. In Ernest Small and David Marcus' paper *Hemp: A New Crop with New Uses for North America*, they point out that "the term has been applied to dozens of species representing at least 22 genera, often prominent fiber crops." By that reasoning, it would seem apt to say that **"hemp" is a generic term referring to any plant that serves as a particularly good fiber crop**, and *Cannabis sativa* certainly fits that bill.

Cannabis that is labeled as hemp is often used for a wide variety of things ranging from fiber and fuel to food, medicine and more. The fiber from Cannabis makes very durable roping and paper. It can also be pressed into composite boards and used like traditional composite wood. Cannabis "hemp" seeds can be found in many birdseed mixes as well as breakfast cereals. One way that Cannabis may have spread

During World War II, US farmers were encouraged to grow hemp with incentives in the form of "special tax stamps" to produce it, as seen above.

throughout the world is through seed distribution as humans brought the nutritious food with them when travelling. Hemp can even be used as a source of carbon sheets used for supercapacitors to store and move electricity!

Traditionally "industrial hemp" is thought of as varieties of Cannabis that are suitable for fiber, but today the term hemp has everything to do with its chemical profile rather than its intended use. Instead of THC, hemp plants often have much higher levels of a different cannabinoid - cannabidiol (CBD). CBD is extracted from hemp type Cannabis to produce CBD-based products like tinctures, topicals, and dietary supplements. Additionally, at the time of this writing, hemp farmers are also starting to grow hemp crops featuring resin rich in Cannabigerol, or CBG. **Today, hemp is legally defined in most places as a *Cannabis sativa* plant with trace levels of delta-9 tetrahydrocannabinol (THC), often at 0.3% or lower concentration by weight** depending on the country or state.

At the time of this writing in the United States, the THC in hemp is legally defined as THC "post-decarboxylation", meaning the total theoretical concentration of THC after THCA has decarboxylated. This has confused many hemp farmers operating under the assumption or misinterpretation that THC is defined as delta-9-THC alone. The practical impact that this definition has is substantial – as it makes it much more challenging to cultivate cannabinoid rich resin Cannabis crops while staying within the legally allowed concentration of THC.

The actual text of the 2018 United States Agricultural Improvement Act of 2018 aka the 2018 Farm Bill states on section 297B "State and Tribal Plans" that *"A State or Tribal plan...shall only be required to include... a procedure for testing, using **post-decarboxylation** or other similarly reliable methods, delta-9 tetrahydrocannabinol concentration levels of hemp produced in the State or territory of the Indian tribe..."*

Because the text of this bill requires all states to report the amount of THC after decarboxylation, it de facto defines "THC" as what many would call "Total THC" (a combination of THC and THCA, corrected by a decarboxylation factor of 0.877 – more on that later!).

"Hemp" vs. "Marijuana"

Hemp and marijuana are ultimately the same species of plant – *Cannabis sativa*. The differences between hemp and marijuana is their chemical profile, and arguably also their intended use.

Hemp type varieties of Cannabis are typically defined as having low concentrations of THC and high concentrations of CBDa or CBGa, whereas "marijuana" varieties of Cannabis are typically characterized as having high concentrations of THC and low concentrations of other cannabinoids.

However, this distinction has gotten very blurred as breeders have begun focusing on cultivating Cannabis varieties that contain a wide spectrum of THC to CBD ratios, as well as CBG dominant varieties. As the value of other non-THC and non-CBD cannabinoids, like CBG, CBC, THCV, and CBDV, increases, breeders will likely focus on teasing out those other cannabinoid constituents to add to the immense variety and complexity of Cannabis chemical profiles.

Some argue that the difference between hemp and marijuana primary lies in the plant's intended use. Hemp is traditionally used for industrial purposes, whereas "marijuana" is typically used for recreational or medical purposes. But this distinction is also becoming blurred as many people have begun using hemp for medical purposes, due to the CBD and/or CBG content, and "marijuana" for industrial purposes.

Perhaps the entire dichotomy between hemp and marijuana is obsolete. After all, they are both the same plant, presenting itself in a variety of forms that can be used for a wide variety of purposes. This highlights this persistent issue surrounding Cannabis regarding the manner by which Cannabis varieties are classified. It seems inevitable that a new nomenclature will evolve as Cannabis decriminalization and legalization continues in areas throughout the world.

CASHING IN ON CBD?

> "We talk about hemp being this crop that can save the world. Well, CBD probably isn't that crop..."
>
> Samuel Moore, Hemp Farmer
> **The Curious About Cannabis Podcast**
> Behind-the-Scenes (BTS) Episode #21

There is no question that currently the hemp industry is primarily focused on one thing: Cannabidiol.

The CBD industry began growing substantially in 2017, with roots as far back as the early 2010s. In 2019, when the Farm Bill was passed in the United States, hemp became federally legal, under certain conditions and guidelines. Companies rushed to cash in on the now legal hemp commodity. Many companies interpreted the Farm Bill as having not only legalized hemp, but also CBD. However, the truth was a bit more complicated.

Technically, in the United States, CBD is a "drug" because it has undergone clinical trials and been subject to drug approval, in the form of the pharmaceutical Epidiolex, produced by GW Pharmaceuticals. While the DEA has de-scheduled Epidiolex, CBD remains a scheduled drug. To make things more confusing, The Farm Bill makes all cannabinoids and other plant compounds from hemp legal, to a limited extent. CBD is perfectly legal to possess, if derived from hemp, but once you try to feed it to people, things get tricky.

Because CBD is considered a drug, it cannot be added to foods or cosmetics unless the FDA assigns it a status called GRAS, Generally Recognized As Safe. Until the FDA undertakes the project of assigning GRAS status to CBD or other cannabinoids or Cannabinoids that may become pharmaceuticals, the only option companies have to legally add CBD to foods is by achieving "self-affirmed GRAS status." In this process, a company must assemble an independent group of scientists to oversee the required testing needed to prove that a product is safe. It can cost upwards of a million dollars or more to complete and usually takes a year or more to complete. The Food, Drugs, and Cosmetics Act provides the policy on this issue which the Food and Drug Administration (FDA) must enforce.

As of the time of this writing, there have been no indications that Congress intends on changing the FD&C Act to accommodate the CBD industry. However, this has not stopped the CBD industry from rapidly growing and establishing a foothold in the consciousnesses of consumers while regulators determine the appropriate action to take.

EVALUATING HEMP COMPANIES AND PRODUCTS

There is a plethora of hemp-derived cannabinoid products on the market as of the time of this writing. Due to an immature industry and a lack of regulatory guidance, these products exhibit a wide spectrum of quality, leaving consumers confused about how to evaluate these products to make informed decisions. In this section I will share some of the questions that go through my mind whenever I am evaluating a hemp-derived cannabinoid product (or really any Cannabis product or dietary supplement).

DOES THE COMPANY FOLLOW GOOD MANUFACTURING PRACTICES (CGMPs)?

Good manufacturing practices, or GMP, are industry standards that manufacturers are required to follow to ensure the quality of the products that they manufacture. GMP requires that companies evaluate their component ingredient suppliers, test ingredients to ensure they are of a known potency and purity, keep work areas, equipment, and utensils clean, ensure personnel wear protective equipment to combat contamination, and more.

In the US, the FDA sets basic requirements for how different types of products must be manufactured to ensure that the product is protected from contamination and that consumer health and safety is protected. The FDA has GMP rules for foods (21 CFR 110/117), dietary supplements (21 CFR 111), pharmaceuticals (21 CFR 210/211), and cosmetics (21 CFR 700).

Internationally, there are various GMP standards, such as the Pharmaceutical Inspection Co-operation Scheme (PIC/S) GMP standard, or the International Council for Harmonisation of Technical Requirements for Pharmaceuticals for Human Use (ICH). For food products, there is the international standard ISO 22000 which provides guidance on how to maintain a food safety management system to ensure the quality of food products.

HOW DOES THE COMPANY MANAGE PRODUCT QUALITY?

Companies must utilize effective quality management systems to ensure their operations produce intended results, that regulatory requirements are met, and that the company is continuously improving. An effective quality management system produces traceable records which prove to any third-parties that policies and procedures are being followed and executed as intended. The quality system also provides structure for key processes that ensure products are of a high quality. This usually includes processes like supplier evaluations, ingredient testing and inspection, environmental controls, production controls, product testing, product inspections, and production records reviews.

FIGURE 36: EXAMPLES OF QUALITY CONTROL STEPS IN PRODUCT MANUFACTURING

Under an effective quality management system, materials must be held in quarantine until they are approved for use, and finished products must not be released for distribution until they have been tested and inspected.

DOES THE COMPANY MAKE MEDICAL CLAIMS?

Always be wary of bold medical claims about products that have not undergone any clinical trials to back up the claims. Currently the FDA does not permit any medical claims about hemp-derived cannabinoids to be made by any producers about hemp based products, without written approval from the FDA. This is not to say that all medical claims about cannabinoids like CBD are deceptive or wrong. It is true that CBD, for instance, has therapeutic applications, under certain conditions, for certain medical conditions, for some people. If a company makes therapeutic claims about their product, ask for evidence. If they cannot provide evidence, the best approach is skepticism.

One thing to be wary of regarding medical claims is the use of references to research literature. Often companies may not make direct medical claims about their products but may share research articles about the medical benefits of an ingredient in their product, such as CBD. Often what happens is the reader is misled into believing that the research results of a study somehow represent the company's product – which is not necessarily the case.

WHAT IS THE SOURCE OF CBD, CBG, CBN, ETC?

CBD can come from a variety of sources. It is well-known now that CBD can be sourced from the Cannabis plant. CBD can also be produced in "bioreactors" which consist of micro-organisms like yeasts or bacteria that can produce target compounds. Additionally, CBD can be produced in a laboratory through chemical reactions. Some companies produce CBD synthetically using a compound called olivetol sourced from lichen and other natural sources.

But even within the world of hemp-derived cannabinoids, there are many different types of extracts, each with different chemical characteristics and levels of phytochemical diversity. It is first important to understand how the extract was produced. What was the quality of hemp material used for extraction? Were only female flowers extracted, or were whole plants ground down and extracted? How refined was the extract before it was used in the product? There is a big difference between the chemistry of a crude alcohol extract versus a highly refined cannabinoid distillate. If a product says that it is "broad spectrum" or "full spectrum", what does the company mean by those terms?

WHAT IS THE CANNABINOID POTENCY?

Always determine the potency of a product before consuming it. Recently I was in a store and came across a CBD product that featured in bold typeface across the label: "1000 mg". I immediately thought to myself, "1000 mg of what?". Of course, I knew that the manufacturer intended for me to assume it referred to CBD, but I found it suspicious that it did not specifically say what compound the 1000 mg statement referred to. Upon review of the ingredients, I found that the product contained "1000 mg of hemp". That left me more confused. Do they mean hemp flower? Hemp extract? If so, what kind of extract?

This experience highlights some of the critical problems with hemp product marketing, at least at the time of this writing. Always determine the potency of a product before consuming it. If you cannot determine the potency of a product through the product's label, do not purchase or consume that product. However, even if you figure out the potency of a CBD product, how do you know you can trust the potency claim?

WHAT IS THE QUALITY OF THE OTHER INGREDIENTS IN THE PRODUCT?

When evaluating hemp cannabinoid products, or any Cannabis product, it is important to understand what the other ingredients are in the product, and what the quality of those ingredients might be. For instance, many ingestible CBD products are made with MCT oil, as an alternative to ethanolic (alcohol) tinctures. But MCT oil can be sourced from a variety of sources, including palm, coconut, and dairy products. Some MCT oils are standardized and some are not, meaning that some MCT oils have other chemicals in them other than the primary medium chain triglycerides, whereas standardized MCT oils only contain defined concentrations of medium chain triglycerides and nothing else.

Some MCT oils are made from mixed sources, whereas other are sourced only from a single source. It is important to note that palm sourced MCT oil is currently under criticism for exacerbating environmental decline and wildlife species loss in areas where the palm is cultivated. It is generally recommended to source MCT oil from coconut sources only to minimize the negative environmental impacts of MCT oil production.

Additionally, ethanol can be produced from a variety of sources, such as grape, corn, sugarcane, barley and many other plants. The cultivation of these different crops has different environmental impacts.

It is also important to understand whether there may be other ingredients in a Cannabis product that may affect the way that the CBD or other Cannabis ingredient may interact with the body. A product that contains a variety of other medicinal plant ingredients may exhibit markedly different effects than a product whose primary ingredient is only Cannabis extract.

When evaluating a Cannabis product manufacturer, it is important to understand what quality control measures the company is taking to evaluate the quality of their additional ingredients, especially if ingredients are being sourced from other countries that may have different quality standards and regulations. In general, component ingredients of Cannabis products should be tested for identity, potency, and purity before being used in a product. Although component ingredients typically come with associated test results, demonstrating the identity, potency and purity of the ingredient – manufacturers must establish rationale for trusting those supplied test results. To do this, they must submit component ingredients for verification testing routinely so that they can have confidence that the test results received with a product are accurate. This is required under US FDA GMP rules, although many Cannabis manufacturers, as of the time of this writing, are not compliant with these rules.

HAS THE FINISHED PRODUCT BEEN TESTED FOR POTENCY & PURITY?

Once a CBD or hemp product has been manufactured, it needs to be tested by an accredited third-party laboratory to ensure that the product has a known potency and is free from contaminants. This allows the manufacturer to back up their safety claims about the product.

Notice that I say that products need to be tested by *an accredited third-party* laboratory. It is generally not enough for a company to test their own products using their in-house testing laboratory. This presents opportunity to cast doubt on the integrity and reliability of the data. By having a third-party laboratory that is accredited for the scope of testing being performed on the product, the company is demonstrating that their claims are trustworthy and backed by someone that has no financial interest in their company or product.

THE FUTURE OF HEMP

It is likely that hemp regulations across the world are going to continue to evolve in response to the demands of farmers, product manufacturers, and consumers. As it becomes easier for producers and researchers to work with hemp, novel uses of the plant and its chemical constituents will likely be identified.

For instance, some researchers are looking at how to use hemp as a source for the cannabinoid cannabigerol (CBG) which might have some therapeutic use as a cannabinoid intoxication reliever (de Meijer and Hammond, 2005) among other applications. In other words, it might have the potential to alleviate a particularly stressful "high" in a Cannabis consumer – perhaps more effectively than CBD.

Indeed, as of 2018, CBG dominant varieties of hemp began significantly appearing in the hemp market. Unless there is some legal impediment, it is likely that Cannabis breeding will focus on teasing out as many cannabinoids and terpenoids as possible within the limitations of the plant's genes, and perhaps even outside of those limits as genetically modified Cannabis becomes more common. Along with the popularity of hemp-derived CBG, there is also a growing demand for other hemp-derived cannabinoids like CBN, CBDV, CBC, and delta-8-THC.

One issue facing hemp's use in other industrial applications such as in construction materials or fiber, is that the value of a hemp crop per acre can be orders of magnitude greater if cultivating the crop for cannabinoid-rich resin yield. Until the market matures and it makes financial sense for farmers to cultivate hemp varieties for other uses, it is likely that hemp farming will remain focused on resin-rich varieties for the foreseeable future.

For more information about hemp including a history of the use of hemp in the United States, I recommend the book, *The Emperor Wears No Clothes* by Jack Herer.

Did You Know?

Hemp seed oil contains an excellent ratio of Omega 3 and Omega 6 fatty acids! According to Callaway (2004), *"The omega 6 to omega 3 ratio in hempseed oil is normally between 2:1 to 3:1, which is considered optimum for human health."*

Enduring Understandings

- The term "hemp" has been applied to many fiber crops throughout history.
- Today, "hemp" is thought to primarily refer to varieties of Cannabis which contain less than 0.3% THC.
- "Hemp" and "marijuana" are the same species of plant – *Cannabis sativa*.
- Hemp varieties of Cannabis can be used industrially for a wide variety of purposes including food, fiber, biofuel, building materials, animal feed, and more.

PART III

CANNABIS, CANNABINOIDS, AND THE HUMAN BODY

Essential Questions:

How does Cannabis elicit effects from the human body?

What are the components of the Endocannabinoid System?

How are phytocannabinoids, endocannabinoids, and synthetic cannabinoids similar and different?

How might Cannabis use affect human health?

Chapter 15:
MEET YOUR ENDOCANNABINOID SYSTEM

"I look at the endocannabinoid system as a lipid signaling network…it's at the bottom of a pyramid, with all other physiological systems stacked on top of it…"

Kevin Spelman, PhD, BTS #4 Curious About Cannabis Podcast

Learning Questions
- What is the endocannabinoid system?
- What are cannabinoid receptors?
- What are examples of common endogenous cannabinoids produced by the human body?
- How do exogenous cannabinoids, like THC or CBD, affect the endocannabinoid system?
- What happens when the endocannabinoid system is disturbed or out of balance?

Cannabis elicits effects from the human body through a number of different mechanisms. However, one of the primary methods that many cannabinoids in Cannabis interact with the body is through a physiological system in the body called the **endocannabinoid system**. It was only within recent decades that the endocannabinoid system was described and recognized (Rosaria *et* al., 2010).

The endocannabinoid system is a lipid signaling system in the body which shows activity beginning in very early stages of brain development (Trezza and Campoiongo, 2013). The system consists of three parts: the cannabinoid **receptors**, the **endocannabinoids**, and the various **enzymes** responsible for endocannabinoid synthesis and breakdown (Diomelli, 2003;

Di Marzo *et al.*, 2005). Cannabinoid receptors are found all throughout the body and control movement, memory, sleep cycles, body temperature regulation, appetite, and the body's ability to sense harmful stimuli (Bellocchio *et al.*, 2008; Kano *et al.*, 2009; Sagar *et al.*, 2009). There has also been some evidence that **the endocannabinoid system plays an important role in modulating the immune system** (Killestein *et al.*, 2003). Although there are many theories of how the endocannabinoid system might modulate the immune system, much more research is needed to further elucidate how this might occur and what various compounds, receptors, and enzymes might be involved.

The modulation of endogenous cannabinoids and receptors is now thought by some researchers to be a key component of several adverse medical conditions. For example, some animal models have shown that **obesity might be correlated with excess production of endocannabinoids,** leading to over excitation of the endocannabinoid system resulting in irregular hunger cravings and dysregulated insulin activity (Pagotto et al, 2005).

Fibromyalgia is a complex pain disorder that is frequently diagnosed but not understood. It is generally characterized by an increased sensitivity to pain which manifests a variety of symptoms. In one study, mice were given an injection of a compound that blocks cannabinoid production to see how it affects their sensitivity to pain (Richardson et al, 1997). The result was an increased sensitivity to pain, or **hyperalgesia**. In another study, a synthetic cannabinoid was used to block capsaicin (the spicy compound in chili peppers) induced hyperalgesia in rodents (Li et al, 1999). Although there seems to be some correlation, further research is needed before determining any causal connections between medical conditions like fibromyalgia with endocannabinoid derangements.

CANNABINOID RECEPTORS

Phytocannabinoids are effective in humans because they bind to certain receptors in the human body. **Receptors** are biochemical mechanisms that rest along cell walls and have the ability to send signals to the inside of the cell by interacting with compounds outside of the cell. It is the cell's way of perceiving what is outside of the cell, so to speak. Receptors have **receptor sites** that are shaped in such a way that only certain compounds can fit, sort of like a lock and key. Once a compound binds with the receptor site, the receptor is either **agonized** or **antagonized**. If the cell is agonized, it has been excited or activated. If the receptor is antagonized, it means that the compound is hogging up space on the receptor site, blocking other compounds from binding to the site or reducing the effects of other compounds that might come and bind to the cell's receptors. This limits or prevents **signal transduction** within the cell. Signal transduction is the series of events that follow inside the cell after a compound has attached to a receptor.

214

CB1 Receptors

CB1 receptors are located primarily throughout the brain and spine (Elphick, 2001) affecting cognition, emotion, learning, memory, movement, pain, digestion, and immune function. They are the most abundant g-coupled protein receptor in the brain, making it a critical component of the way that different components of the brain communicate with one another. To put this into perspective, other examples of g-protein coupled receptors that you might be familiar with are dopamine, serotonin, metabotropic glutamate, and GAPA receptors.

There are an abundant number of CB1 receptors located in the **hippocampus**, which is the part of the brain responsible for memory. Depending on what cannabinoids are interacting with the CB1 receptors in the hippocampus, memory might be protected or compromised. CB1 receptors are also found on various periphery tissues and organs, such as the skin.

CB2 Receptors

CB2 receptors are mostly found in immune cells (Pertwee, 2002) but are also found throughout the body and even on neurons (Onaivi et al, 2012). Many of these cells modulate **cytokine** release, which affects immune system responses like the production of **Killer T cells**. Because inflammation is largely an immune system response, cannabinoids can reduce inflammation by suppressing the immune system.

"Changes in endocannabinoid levels and/or CB2 receptor expressions have been reported in almost all diseases affecting humans, ranging from cardiovascular, gastrointestinal, liver, kidney, neurodegenerative, psychiatric, bone, skin, auto-immune, lung disorders to pain and cancer, and modulating CB2 receptor activity holds tremendous therapeutic potential in these pathologies." (Pacher and Mechoulam, 2011)

Did You Know?

CB1 receptor signaling is crucial to newborn survival according to a study conducted by Fride et al (2001). Endocannabinoids like Anandamide and 2-AG stimulate CB1 receptors which signal the newborn mouse pup to suckle for food. If CB1 receptors are blocked in a newborn pup, the pup will not suckle and will eventually die of starvation.

CB1/CB2 Receptor Complexes

The story of CB1 and CB2 receptors is a bit more complex than it may seem, as chemical receptors, in general, do not always appear separate from one another. Chemical receptors are able to form complexes, often referred to as heteromers, where their activity can be unique compared to if the receptors were separated. Heteromerization occurs in various circumstances in the endocannabinoid system, with one example being the presence of CB1/CB2 receptor complexes, where CB1 and CB2 receptors appear side by side and influence each other's activity. These CB1/CB2 receptor complexes have not been thoroughly investigated; however some limited research has been done with individual cannabinoids to understand how different cannabinoids may affect these complexes.

GPR55, GPR18, AND GPR35 RECEPTORS

There are several other miscellaneous g-protein coupled receptors in the body that cannabinoids interact with, including, but not limited to, GPR55, GPR18, and GPR35. "GPR" stands for **g-protein coupled receptor**. Both the CB1 and the CB2 receptors are also g-protein coupled receptors. THC activates **GPR55** just as potently and with greater efficacy than the CB1 receptor (Ryberg *et al.*, 2007). The over-stimulation of GPR55 receptors is now implicated in conditions like osteoporosis and cancer. The activation of the **GPR18** receptor by certain cannabinoids has been shown to affect blood pressure in rodent models (Penumarti and Abdel-Rahman, 2014). **GPR35** signaling could play a role in metabolic disease, like diabetes, hypertension, asthma, pain, and inflammatory bowel disease (Milligan, 2011).

CANNABINOID RECEPTOR AFFINITY AND EFFICACY

A compound's **affinity** for a receptor is a measure of its likelihood to bind to a receptor. If the compound exhibits no affinity for a receptor, it will steer clear and not interact with the receptor. If a compound exhibits affinity for a receptor, that affinity can then be characterized in a variety of ways according to a spectrum of **efficacy** measured in terms of agonism vs antagonism, or action vs. non-action.

Cannabinoid	CB1 Affinity	CB2 Affinity
THC	Partial agonist	Partial agonist
CBD	Antagonist/Inverse agonist/Allosteric Modulator	Inverse agonist
CBG	Protean agonist?	Partial agonist
CBC	Antagonist/Weak agonist	Antagonist/Weak agonist
CBN	Weak agonist	Potent partial agonist
THCV	Antagonist at low dose; Agonist at high dose	Partial agonist
Anandamide	Partial agonist	Partial agonist
2-AG	Potent agonist	Potent agonist
*CB1 binding affinity data for CBG is currently contradictory and inconclusive		

FIGURE 37: CANNABINOID RECEPTOR AFFINITY PER COMMON PHYTOCANNABINOIDS AND ENDOCANNABINOIDS

If a compound binds to a receptor but elicits no response, it is an **antagonist**. It does not stimulate the cell in any way, and just takes up space on the receptor site, effectively blocking other compounds from binding to that receptor location. If a compound binds to a receptor and elicits a positive response, it is classified as an **agonist**. This is usually thought of as "stimulating" or "activating" the cell. THC is a CB1 and CB2 **partial agonist**. Many synthetic cannabinoids are **full** or **super agonists** of CB1 receptors. If a compound binds to a receptor and elicits a negative response, it is classified as **an inverse agonist**. CBD acts as an inverse agonist to CB2 receptors.

Receptor Binding Efficacy

Imagine receptor binding like turning a volume knob. A super agonist would be equal to turning the volume up. An inverse agonist would be like turning the volume down. A silent antagonist would be as if the volume knob were stuck and could not be turned up or down. In much the same way, agonists stimulate receptors and increase activity in the cell. Antagonists do not affect the activity of the receptor but can block other compounds from reaching the receptor. Finally inverse agonists reduce the natural, or basal, level of activity of the cell. If the cell already exhibits zero activity, then it cannot be inversely agonized.

To make things a bit more complicated there are activities like allosteric modulation and protean agonism, which are much less straightforward. **Allosteric modulation** occurs when a compound binds to part of a receptor, but not necessarily the "bullseye" of the receptor, technically referred to as the **orthosteric site**, or "primary site" of action. An allosteric action is one that typically changes the shape of a receptor or otherwise affects a receptor in such a way that it will behave dfiferently when something attempts to bind to the orthosteric site. CBD is an allosteric modulator of CB1 receptors, for instnace, and it is thought that this allosteric modulation activity is how CBD antagonizes the activity of THC.

Protean agonism is a concept which describes a compound's ability to elicit different effects depending on the state of a receptor. Proteus was a Greek god that could manipulate his form depending on who viewed him. In this same spirit, protean agonists are able to stimulate a receptor when the receptors' sites are largely inactive, but it may perofrm the opposite action when many of the receptor's sites are already active. CBG is thought to potentially be a protean agonist of CB1 receptors, because in some cases CBG has been shown to stimulate CB1 receptors, however it is not good at competing with other compounds for access to CB1 receptors, and may even serve as an inverse agonist if CB1 receptors are already being stimulated be another compound.

FOUR CLASSES OF CANNABINOID RECEPTOR AGONISTS

Class Type	Description	Examples
Classical Cannabinoids	ABC-tricyclic benzopyrans	THC, CBD; HU210
Non-classical Cannabinoids	Characterized by opening of dihydropyran ring; many have high affinity for both CB1 and CB2 receptors	CP55,940
Aminoalkylindoles	Initially developed as anti-inflammatory drugs and analgesics, later found to be CB receptor agonists; These cannabinoids have provided assistance in developing selective CB2 agonists	WIN55,212-2
Eicosanoids	Acylethanolamides	Anandamide
	Acylesters	2-AG

FIGURE 38: CLASSES OF CANNABINOID RECEPTOR AGONISTS

Table information source: Yao and Mackie, 2009

BEYOND CANNABINOID RECEPTORS

Cannabinoids not only act on cannabinoid receptors, but a variety of other receptor types as well. For instance, CBD has been shown to interact with vanilloid, adenosine, serotonin, and GPR55 receptors. Understanding how the endocannabinoid system is tied in with other receptor types and pathways will be critical to learning how cannabinoids can best be utilized in medicine. Below are brief descriptions of other receptor types that some cannabinoids interact with.

VANILLOID RECEPTORS
(TRPV-1, TRPA-1, TRPV-2, ETC)

Vanilloid receptors are primarily involved in pain perception, temperature regulation, and taste. The chemical compound capsaicin is a vanilloid compound primarily found in chili peppers and is the culprit behind the burning sensation felt when eating spicy food. Capsaicin binds to TRPV1 receptors, causing a burning sensation, although no tissue damage is occurring. There are a variety of types of vanilloid receptors. The endocannabinoid

NADA exhibits affinity for both cannabinoid and vanilloid receptors. CBD exhibits affinity for TRPV1 receptors. TRPV1 receptors have recently been suggested to be included as part of the endocannabinoid system.

ADENOSINE RECEPTORS
(A1, A2A)

Adenosine receptors have varying functions throughout the body but are primarily implicated in regulating the heart, controlling neurotransmitters like glutamate and dopamine, and signaling anti-inflammatory action. CBD causes a variety of A2A receptor mediated actions, like neuroprotection (protection of brain cells).

SEROTONIN RECEPTORS
(5HT)

Serotonin receptors are heavily implicated in many psychological disorders such as anxiety and depression as well as pain disorders like chronic migraine. Serotonin receptor signaling affects blood vessel constriction and dilation. In heavy doses, CBD exhibits affinity for serotonin receptors. THC has been shown to stimulate 5HT production and limit uptake.

Serotonin and cannabinoid receptors often appear together throughout the brain as receptor heteromers. Chronic THC consumption increases this heteromerization of cannabinoid and serotonin receptors. It should be noted that these kinds of heteromers are commonly seen in models of anxiety, depression and other mental health disorders, indicating that chronic THC consumption may change the structure of chemical receptors in neurons in the brain to reflect these patterns, and may explain why some chronic Cannabis users sometimes develop anxiety and depressive conditions.

This kind of heteromerization also occurs with dopamine receptors in the brain, and THC administration strengthens the connections between dopamine receptors and cannabinoid receptors. It should be noted that research has indicated that CBD may reverse these heteromer effects and help restore the original phenotype of neurons in the brain that express these chemical receptors.

PPAR-GAMMA
(PEROXISOME PROLIFERATOR ACTIVATED RECEPTORS)

PPARs are unique receptors types found in the nucleus of cells that, when activated, can manipulate the transcription of genes. In other words, these receptors can manipulate DNA to influence the activation or prevention of gene expression. PPAR-gamma receptors are linked to things like insulin sensitivity, glucose storage, and other metabolic activities. As a result, the manipulation of PPAR receptors is a new target for diabetes therapies.

CBD agonizes PPAR-gamma receptors in the body, potentially indicating a therapeutic role for CBD in diabetes treatment. Along with stimulating PPAR receptors directly, CBD can lead to indirect stimulation of PPAR-gamma receptors through natural endocannabinoids. It was once thought that this activity was due to FAAH inhibition, however researchers discovered that, while it is the case in mice that CBD inhibits FAAH, which leads to a subsequent increase in endocannabinoid concentration in the body – in humans, this enzyme suppression effect has not been demonstrated (Elmes et al, 2015). Whatever the mechanism may be, CBD causes levels of Anandamide to increase in the body which then go on to interact with a myriad of chemical receptors including PPAR-gamma.

THE ENDOCANNABINOIDS

Unlike many other types of chemicals in neurons, endocannabinoids are not stored up in the body, but rather are produced on demand. They are also considered **retrograde messengers** because they are produced in post-synaptic neurons and travel *backwards* across the synapse to the pre-synaptic neuron, the opposite of how most neurotransmitters travel. Basically, endocannabinoids have a unique ability to travel upstream, so to speak.

One primary effect that cannabinoid receptors have on neurons, is that when activated they affect the opening and closing of ion channels around the cell, which changes how the cell releases neurotransmitters, ultimately affecting their sensitivity and how the cell communicates with other cells. This usually blocks the release of neurotransmitters into the synapse between neurons. **This is how pain responses are thought to be diminished after endocannabinoid receptor stimulation.** It has been demonstrated that cannabinoids also have the ability to modulate calcium, sodium, potassium, and TRPV1 ion channels through a receptor independent mechanism (Oz M, 2006).

ANANDAMIDE OR
N-ARACHIDONOYL ETHANOLAMINE (AEA)

Anandamide gets its name from the Sanskrit word *ananda* which means "bliss". It is sometimes called "the bliss compound." Anandamide is a partial CB1 and CB2 receptor agonist, similar to THC, and was the first endocannabinoid discovered (Devane et al, 1992).

Anandamide and similar compounds have been discovered in dark chocolate (Tomaso et al, 1996). Although anandamide was discovered first, it is not in as high concentrations in the body as other endocannabinoids, like 2-AG.

2-ARACHIDONOYLGLYCEROL (2-AG)

2-AG was the second endocannabinoid discovered and is a potent CB1 receptor agonist. 2-AG is the most abundant endocannabinoid present in the body. CBD administration triggers the production and release of 2-AG throughout the body. 2-AG is degraded by the enzyme monoacylglycerol lipase (MAGL).

THE BIOSYNTHESIS AND DEGRADATION OF ENDOCANNABINOIDS

All endocannabinoids are **eicosanoids**, which are oxidative products of long carbon chain molecules derived from omega-3 or omega-6 fatty acids which control many different bodily functions like inflammation, immunity, and central nervous system signaling. Other examples of eicosanoids include leukotrienes, prostaglandins, and thromboxanes. Many of these compounds are involved in biological activity like inflammation responses and bronchoconstriction and are key components of inflammatory conditions like asthma.

OMEGA 6 FATTY ACID, LINOLEIC ACID

OMEGA 3 FATTY ACID, ALPHA LINOLEIC ACID

> *Take a moment to examine the shape of Arachidonic acid as it compares to endocannabinoids like anandamide and even exogenous cannabinoids like phytocannabinoids and synthetic cannabinoids.*
>
> *How are these various compounds similar?*
>
> *How are they different?*

Eicosanoid biosynthesis typically begins with a compound called **arachidonic acid (AA)**. Arachidonic acid is not an essential fatty acid, but many different compounds rely on it and depending on certain chemical deficiencies in the body, it could become a "**conditional essential fatty acid.**" Usually mammals will metabolize linoleic acid, a polyunsaturated omega-6 fatty acid, into arachidonic acid (Simopoulus, 2016). If there is a problem with the enzymes involved in this breakdown, arachidonic acid must be obtained from other sources. When endocannabinoids break down, they generally break down into arachidonic acid along with whatever other base chemical groups may be present, like glycerol in the case of 2-AG, or dopamine in the case of NADA.

Endocannabinoids consist of compounds that belong to two primary chemical families: N-acylethanolamines and 2-monoacylglycerols (Fezza et al, 2014). Much of the endocannabinoid research going on currently is exploring what enzymes might be responsible for the synthesis and breakdown of these varying compounds in order to better understand the chemical "map" of endocannabinoid synthesis and metabolism pathways.

ANANDAMIDE BIOSYNTHESIS AND METABOLISM

Anandamide production is said to begin with a compound called **N-arachidonoyl phosphatidylethanolamine** (NAPE). A variety of enzymatic activities can follow involving α/β-hydrolase 4 (ABHD4), lyso-phospholipase (lysoPLD), protein tyrosine phosphatase non-receptor type 22 (PTPN22), and N-acyl-phosphatidylethanolamines-hydrolyzing phospholipase D (NAPE-PLD) which would transform NAPE directly or indirectly into Anandamide (AEA).

There are several known degradation enzymes that break AEA down into various other components. Fatty acid amide hydrolase (FAAH) can degrade AEA to arachidonic acid and ethanolamine. 12-lipoxygenase (12-LOX) will degrade AEA to 12-hydroxyanandamide (12-HAEA). Cyclooxygenase-2 (COX-2) degrades AEA to prostamides F2a (PMF2a). Finally, cytochrome p450 degrades AEA into 5,6-epoxyeicosatrienoyl ethanolamides (5,6-EET-EA).

There are a number of known compounds that can inhibit the activity of FAAH, affecting the breakdown of anandamide and helping it circulate in the body longer. Many pharmaceutical companies have been examining FAAH inhibitors for a long time to determine if they could be valuable as treatments for anxiety, chronic pain, and neurodegenerative disorders. However, manipulating enzymes can be tricky, and dangerous.

In 2016 a clinical trial examining the effects of an FAAH inhibitor on endocannabinoids in human subjects went horribly wrong, leaving one volunteer dead and five others hospitalized. It turned out, upon further examination, that the FAAH inhibitor used in the trial also inhibited other enzymes. It was also found that the dose is incredibly important, because some FAAH inhibitors are active and safe at low dosages but can become dangerous at higher dosages. Rodent models used to examine the safety of these compounds are not always helpful as the results don't necessarily scale to humans.

Examples of Naturally Derived FAAH Inhibitors	
Compound	Example of Natural Source
Cannabidiol (CBD)	Cannabis
Alkylamides	Echinacea
Kaempferol	Many Vegetables
Guinensine	Black Pepper

FIGURE 39: NATURALLY DERIVED FAAH INHIBITORS

N-arachidonoyl phosphatidylethanolamine (NAPE) can transform directly or indirectly into anandamide through various enzymatic processes.

COMMON ANANDAMIDE METABOLIC PRODUCTS

Enzyme	Chemical Byproduct(s)
Fatty acid amide hydrolase (FAAH)	Arachidonic acid and ethanolamine
12-lipoxygenase	12-hydroxyanandamide
Cyclooxygenase-2 (COX-2)	Prostamides F2a
Cytochrome p450 complex	5,6-epoxyeicosatrienoyl ethanolamides

FIGURE 40: COMMON ANANDAMIDE METABOLIC PRODUCTS

2-AG BIOSYNTHESIS AND METABOLISM

2-AG, on the other hand, goes through a much different synthetic mechanism. 2-AG is synthesized either through diacylglycerol lipase or phospholipase C from 1-acyl-2-arachidonoylglycerol (DAG) or 2-arachidonoylglycerol-3-phosphate (2-AG-3P), respectively. The enzymes monoacylglycerol lipase (MAGL), a/B-hydrolase domain 6 and a/B-hydrolase domain 12 break 2-AG down into arachidonic acid and glycerol. Alternatively, 12-lipoxygenase (12-LOX) can degrade 2-AG into 12-hydroxyarachidonoyl-glycerol (12-HETE-G) and cyclooxygenase-2 (COX-2) can degrade 2-AG into prostaglandinglycerol E_2-G (PGE$_2$-G). These are only the pathways that have been illuminated thus far. It is likely that other synthetic and metabolic pathways will be described after future research. (Fezza et al, 2014)

The synthetic and degradation pathways of other endocannabinoids are not well described or understood. Understanding these pathways will help identify new targets of drug therapy for a wide variety of ailments. Already, research is beginning to support the concept of a "clinical endocannabinoid deficiency" syndrome (Russo, 2004; Smith and Wagner, 2014). It is thought that clinical endocannabinoid deficiency could be an underlying factor behind many ailments such as migraine, fibromyalgia, and irritable bowel syndrome. Others have proposed the concept of a spectrum of endocannabinoid derangements including conditions involving surpluses of endocannabinoid signaling, potentially contributing to conditions such as schizophrenia, obesity, metabolic disorders and more (Leweke et al, 1999; Alvheim, 2012).

MAGL or other enzymes degrade 2-AG

2-AG can degrade to arachidonic acid and glycerol

Other Endocannabinoids

N-Arachidonoyl Dopamine (NADA)

ARACHIDONIC
ACID

DOPAMINE

The endocannabinoid N-**Arachidonoyl dopamine (NADA)** is a newer endocannabinoid of interest isolated from the brains of rats that acts as both a CB1 and Vanilloid TRPV-1 receptor agonist, similar to Anandamide (AEA) but different as NADA is a more potent Vanilloid receptor agonist and a more effective CB1 receptor agonist than AEA (Marinelli et al, 2007). NADA has been demonstrated as a potent vasorelaxant, or blood pressure reducer, by both this interaction with CB1 and TRPV-1 receptors as well as with CB1 and particular endothelial receptors, depending on where the blood vessels are located in the body (Sullivan et al, 2004).

Despite the fact that NADA has the word dopamine in its name, it does not exhibit much direct affinity for dopamine receptors (Bisogno et al, 2000). **NADA breaks down into its primary components: dopamine and arachidonic acid.**

Virodhamine (OAE)

Opposite of Anandamide, whose name is rooted in the Sanskrit word *ananda*, meaning "bliss", **this endocannabinoid gets its name from the Sanskrit word for "opposition"**, *virodha*. This is because this compound utilizes a chemical bond that is somewhat opposite than what is seen in Anandamide. Virodhamine utilizes an ester bond where Anandamide utilizes an amine bond. Virodhamine was the first endocannabinoid discovered that *antagonizes* the CB1 receptor, rather than agonizing it like Anandamide (Porter et al, 2002). This can effectively reduce the effects of Anandamide and other CB1 agonist endocannabinoids by taking up space on CB1 receptors without affecting signal transduction.

Despite this antagonist activity, **Virodhamine** acts as a full agonist at CB2 receptors, which are most densely located in immune system cells (Porter et al, 2002). **While Virodhamine has been reported to be found in brain tissues, subsequent studies have failed to demonstrate its presence** (Yao and Mackie, 2009).

Lysophosphatidylinositol (LPI)

Lysophosphatidylinositol, besides being a difficult word to pronounce, is a ligand associated with the putative cannabinoid receptor GPR55. This is interesting because most cannabinoids exhibit low affinity for the GPR55 receptor type. The shape of the GPR55 receptor is much different than other cannabinoid receptors, ultimately compromising the ability of most cannabinoids to bind to it (Oka et al, 2007).

GPR55 receptors can be found in a variety of tissues including breast adipose, or fatty, tissues, the testis, spleen, and the brain (Sawzdargo et al, 1999; Brown and Wise, 2001). Despite the locations of these receptors, the function of GPR55 receptors is mostly a mystery, though it's over stimulation has recently been associated with carcinogenesis and osteoporosis.

WHAT HAPPENS WHEN THE ENDOCANNABINOID SYSTEM IS OUT OF WHACK?

In 2004 Dr. Ethan Russo published a paper entitled *Clinical Endocannabinoid Deficiency (CECD): Can this Concept Explain Therapeutic Benefits of* Cannabis *in Migraine, Fibromyalgia, Irritable Bowel Syndrome and other Treatment-Resistant Conditions?* As indicated by the subtitle, this paper hypothesized that certain treatment resistant pain conditions might be explained by endocannabinoid deficiencies. If these conditions are in fact caused by endocannabinoid deficiencies, they might be best treated with cannabinoid compounds and certain enzyme inhibitors to maintain cannabinoid concentrations in the body for longer periods of time.

Conditions like migraine and fibromyalgia can be thought of as pain sensitivity disorders. Some cannabinoid research has shown that pain sensitivity in animals is increased when cannabinoid receptors are blocked. This would lead one to assume that if someone had a deficient endocannabinoid system, they might be more sensitive to pain. These conditions along with irritable bowel syndrome are also heavily affected by inflammation. The anti-inflammatory effects of cannabinoids have been repeatedly demonstrated. Additionally, these conditions have a relatively high comorbidity rate, meaning that these three conditions (migraine, fibromyalgia, and IBS) often appear together. If endocannabinoid deficiency is a critical component of these diseases, then one treatment target could be effective in alleviating symptoms of all three conditions at once.

Along with studying endocannabinoid deficiencies, researchers are also interested in exploring endocannabinoid surpluses which may be responsible for increased risks of obesity and diabetes. **The concept of endocannabinoid derangements as the pathology for disease is new and will require much more research before it is better understood to the point that dosage and formulation can be based on information about a patient's endocannabinoid levels.**

THE ENDOCANNABINOIDOME

As mentioned previously, the concept of the endocannabinoid system is rapidly expanding to encompass non-cannabinoid receptors and ligands. When endocannabinoids and cannabinoid receptors are broken down in the body, they can form other pharmacologically active compounds, making it even more challenging to understand how the endocannabinoid system influences physiology. It is becoming more and more clear that the components of the endocannabinoid system perform different functions in different tissues and cells. In some ways it is like the body consists of a series of interconnected, but unique endocannabinoid systems. This complex network of endocannabinoid systems and non-cannabinoid influencers has been referred to as the

endocannabinoidome (di Marzo and Wang, 2014). The concept of the endocannabinoidome is very much an emerging concept that requires refinement and further study but demonstrates how the discovery of the initial components of the endocannabinoid system is affecting the entire way that researchers conceptualize human physiology. Elucidating the endocannabinoidome will certainly be an important target for future Cannabis and cannabinoid research.

Enduring Understandings

- The endocannabinoid system (ECS) is a chemical signaling system primarily consisting of cannabinoid receptors, endogenous cannabinoids, and enzymes responsible for building or breaking down receptors and cannabinoids – although the definition of the ECS is rapidly expanding as non-cannabinoid receptors, like TRPV1, are included.
- The most common cannabinoid receptors in the body are cannabinoid type 1 and type 2 (CB1 and CB2) receptors.
- The most common endogenous cannabinoids produced by the body are Anandamide and 2-AG.
- The concept of the endocannabinoid system is rapidly expanding and evolving, now often referred to as the endocannabinoidome which encompasses the many non-cannabinoid receptors, ligands and enzymes involved in the activity of the endocannabinoid system.

Chapter 16: Synthetic and Semi-Synthetic Cannabinoids

Learning Questions

- What are synthetic cannabinoids?

- What are the health risks of ingesting synthetic cannabinoids?

- What are semi-synthetic cannabinoids?

- Why are semi-synthetic cannabinoids being pursued over synthetic cannabinoids?

To research the endocannabinoid system and the role of cannabinoid receptors in the body, synthetic cannabinoids have been developed which perform a variety of functions, typically **agonizing** (stimulating) or **antagonizing** (blocking/muting) a specific cannabinoid receptor type. By using synthetic cannabinoids for *in vitro* (cell culture) and *in vivo* (animal) research studies, researchers can better understand what functions cannabinoid receptors serve and how their activity affects other cells, organs, and physiological systems.

Over time, some of these cannabinoids escaped the laboratory and made their appearance on internet retail outlets and in a variety of "herbal incense blends", namely herbal blends produced under the brands *Spice* or *K2*. These herbal blends typically have highly potent synthetic cannabinoid compounds mixed into plant material to provide intoxicating effects like THC. These products are sometimes sought after as a Cannabis alternative because the metabolites of these synthetic cannabinoids will not cause the user to fail a standard drug test.

Consumption of synthetic cannabinoid laced materials such as *Spice* or *K2* have been associated with nausea, vomiting, increased blood pressure, and chest pain (Fattore and Fratta, 2011). Several fatal case studies have been reported including suicides and fatal heart ischemia, or dangerous narrowing of the heart arteries (Fattore and Fratta, 2011). According to the Drug Abuse Warning Network, 11,406 emergency room visits in 2010 were associated with the consumption of herbal products containing synthetic cannabinoids (Drug Abuse Warning Network, 2012).

Name	Pharmacology	Notes	Indications
Nabilone	Partial CB1 and CB2 agonist	delta-6a,10a-dimethyl heptyl tetrahydrocannabinol (DMHP) – the first synthetic cannabinoid	Primarily to treat nausea and anxiety; has been demonstrated to be effective for treating multiple sclerosis, pain, dementia-related agitation, PTSD nightmares, and headache
Dronabinol (Marinol; Cesamet)	Partial CB1 and CB2 agonist	Synthetic THC	Primarily to treat nausea and lack of appetite; has been demonstrated to be potentially effective for treatment of GI problems, spasticity, schizophrenia, OCD, trichotillomania, and more.
Liquid Dronabinol (Syndros)	See Dronabinol	Synthetic THC	See Dronabinol

FIGURE 41: EXAMPLES OF CLINICALLY APPROVED SYNTHETIC CANNABINOID PRODUCTS APPROVED FOR USE IN THE UNITED STATES

Data Source: Ware MA. 2015. Synthetic Psychoactive Cannabinoids Licensed as Medicines. Handbook of Cannabis. Oxford University Press. Chapter 21. pp. 393-414

COMMON SYNTHETIC CANNABINOIDS

CANNABICYCLOHEXANOL (CCH)

Cannabicyclohexanol is a cannabinoid receptor agonist produced by Pfizer in 1979. In 2009 it was announced that this compound was one of the primary active ingredients in *Spice* products (Auwarter et al, 2009). It is a potent CB1 receptor agonist.

JWH-018

JWH-018 is a full CB1 and CB2 receptor agonist. It causes tolerance more quickly than other related cannabinoids, like THC (Atwood et al, 2010). This is also a primary psychoactive compound found in *Spice* products. JWH stands for John W. Huffman, the organic chemist at Clemson University that synthesized this and other synthetic cannabinoid compounds.

JWH-073

JWH-073 is a partial agonist of the CB1 and CB2 receptors. It produces effects similar to that of THC. This was also a primary psychoactive compound found in *Spice* products.

HU-210

"HU" stands for Hebrew University, where this compound was synthesized. **HU-210** is a highly potent compound that exhibits an extended duration of action and greater potency than that of THC (Devane et al, 1992). Research employing HU-210 and other similar synthetic cannabinoids have revealed the endocannabinoid system's role in affecting inflammation and neuroprotection (Ramirez et al, 2005; Jiang et al, 2005; Darlington, 2003).

EXAMPLES OF SEMI-SYNTHETIC CANNABINOIDS

Semi-synthetic cannabinoids are formed by removing or adding simple functional groups to existing phytocannabinoids, effectively altering their pharmacological activity and affinity for chemical receptors like cannabinoid receptors. As researchers discovered the downsides of full or ultra-agonistic synthetic cannabinoids, a lot of focus began shifting toward the realm of semi-synthetics – most notably with the VCE-003 class of cannabigerol derivatives and the hexahydrocannabinoids.

VCE-003 and Derivatives

VCE-003 is, at its core, a CBG molecule that has had its aromatic ring changed to a quinone structure, featuring two double bonded oxygens. One consequence of this change is that VCE-003 is better at stimulating PPAR receptors (Appendino, 2015). This cannabigerol quinone derivative has been shown to demonstrate neuroprotective and anti-inflammatory effects in experimental models of multiple sclerosis (Granja et al, 2012).

Hydrogenated Cannabinoids, aka Hexahydrocannabinoids (HHCs)

Hydrogenation is the process of saturating a molecule with hydrogens, essentially replacing any double bonds in the molecule. To date there have been hydrogenated versions of THC, THCA, CBD, and CBDA produced synthetically, as well as others. The resulting molecules are hexahydrocannabinol (HTHC), hexahydrocannabinolic acid (HTHCA), hexacannabidiol (HCBD), hexacannabidiolic acid (HCBDA), respectively. Some of these hydrogenated cannabinoids have been studied as potential anti-cancer compounds and have been shown in cell culture models to inhibit the proliferation of cancer cells as well as the formation of tumors (Thapa et al, 2011; Scialdone, US Patent US9694040B2).

Enduring Understandings

- Synthetic cannabinoids are typically cannabinoids produced in laboratories to study cannabinoid receptor activity by dramatically stimulating or antagonizing receptors.

- Many synthetic cannabinoids have escaped from the research laboratory and made their way into consumer products.

- Some of the effects associated with potent synthetic cannabinoid agonists that may be found in products like Spice or K2 include nausea, vomiting, increased blood pressure, and in some cases temporary loss of consciousness (passing out).

- Semi-synthetic cannabinoids are derived from naturally occurring phytocannabinoids by manipulating the functional groups or saturation of the molecules.

- Several semi-synthetic cannabinoids have demonstrated greater neuroprotective, anti-inflammatory, and anti-cancer activity compared to naturally occurring phytocannabinoids.

- The safety of semi-synthetic and synthetic cannabinoids needs to be further elucidated.

Chapter 17:

CLINICAL CANNABIS RESEARCH

"We have now a lot of evidence, both laboratory and clinical, that better results accrue when dealing with complex mixtures from Cannabis extracts compared to pure compounds."

Ethan Russo, MD, BTS #5 Curious About Cannabis Podcast

Learning Questions
- What are the various ways that medical claims are derived?
- How toxic are cannabinoids?
- What are the health risks associated with Cannabis use?
- How does Cannabis interact with other drugs?
- What are the therapeutic potentials and limitations of Cannabis?

Medical claims are derived through a variety of methods. Usually these methods include **anecdotal reporting, case studies, surveys, *in vitro* studies, *in vivo* non-human animal models, or human preclinical and clinical trials.** When reading about the medical claims of a product, it is important to understand how a claim about a product was derived in the first place to determine if the claim is worth considering.

Anecdotal reporting consists of first-hand or eyewitness reports. Sometimes anecdotal reports lead to future clinical trials which verify those reports, while other times anecdotal reports end up being proven incorrect. Anecdotal data is considered to be very low-quality data, in terms of predictive power, as it only represents a sample of one person and is highly susceptible to mistaken interpretation, placebo/nocebo effects, uncontrolled variables, or erroneous recall. **Case studies** are professional reports of observation of a subject over a period of time. **Surveys** are used to collect data from a population to understand behavior and attitude trends.

In vitro **studies** are studies performed in a sterile controlled environment like a petri dish. These are studies typically consisting of growing certain cells in a petri dish and then exposing the cells to various compounds to record any changes that are exhibited. *In vitro* actually means "in glass". *In vivo* studies are performed in live organisms. Typically, *in vivo* **studies** are performed on rodents and dogs. Human clinical trials are studies performed on humans to determine the effects of a compound. A placebo containing an inactive compound is used to determine if any exhibited effects are more profound than the psychological effect of simply taking a "medicine."

	Type of Research	Description
Lesser Predictive Quality	Anecdotal Reporting	Eyewitness testimony, personal accounts; impossible to test or falsify
	Case Studies/Observational Studies	Professional observations; less subjective than anecdotes
	Surveys	Population behavior and attitude assessment using questionnaires; biased toward people that will answer surveys
	in vitro Studies	Cell or tissue culture studies to assess how something will affect particular tissue types, chemical receptors, etc.; results can be limited in scalability or practical significance to animals
	Pre-Clinical *in vivo* Non-Human Studies	Often rodent or monkey based to evaluate health effects and safety profile in mammals
	Single Blind, Placebo Controlled Human Clinical Trials	The participants do not know who received placebo, but administrators know; study is repeatable, but administrator may introduce bias accidentally by knowing who received placebo.
Higher Predictive Quality	Double Blind, Placebo Controlled Human Clinical Trials	Neither the participants nor the administrators know who received placebos; study is repeatable and highly controlled.

When an *in vivo* study is performed in a non-human animal, the dosages used in the study must be scaled up in a particular way to determine what the **human equivalent dose (HED)** would be. It is incorrect to assume that the dose identified as effective in an animal study will be the same dose that a human would require. Particularly, care must be taken to understand how the study animal's body surface area, which is correlated with metabolic rate, and weight are different from a human. This method of taking these two factors into account when scaling a dose is called allometric scaling. However, even this method is not without its problems. This is why researchers always apply a safety correction factor to any identified HED. For instance, if the HED of a dose used in a rodent study were 20mg/kg, researchers might divide that value by 10 to start a study at 2mg/kg when first administering a drug to humans, just to be extra safe.

Cell culture models are performed in sterilized and controlled environments with reactions occurring in isolation of exposure to other compounds that might be present in a human body system. The behavior of rodents can sometimes be difficult to interpret. Humans are often eating a variety of foods and ingesting a variety of other medicines or drugs that will interfere or confuse the effects of cannabinoids. The cannabinoids themselves exhibit unique effects on cannabinoid receptors, leading to competing effects.

There are a variety of informational charts in circulation which detail the health effects of each individual cannabinoid and terpenoid, but these are *very* limited in their practical application and should be considered largely entertainment or speculation than education. The majority of research that has looked at how cannabinoids might influence human health has been through *in vitro* cell culture models or *in vivo* rodent models, each with their own significant limitations for scaling up result interpretations to the human biological system. Very few completed Cannabis or cannabinoid studies have yet been replicated and some studies that have been replicated ended up contradicting one another.

Despite the limited number of actual human clinical trials currently completed, there is already promising data supporting the therapeutic value of Cannabis. **Human clinical trials have been successful in determining cannabinoid compounds as effective treatments for a variety of conditions including nausea, pain, inflammation, spasticity, reduced appetite, and sleep disturbance** (Whiting et al, 2015). More human clinical trials are required to establish what other medical conditions might be effectively treated with Cannabis or cannabis compounds and what dosages and preparation methods are required to obtain desired medicinal effects in a practical way.

STAGES OF HUMAN CLINICAL TRIALS		
Trial Phase	Sample Size	Purpose
Phase 0	Very Small	Proof of Concept; How does the drug work?
Phase 1	Small	Is the drug safe?
Phase II	Moderate	How effective is the drug?
Phase III	Large	Randomized, blind testing; drugs are usually approved after Phase III
Phase IV	Very Large	Determine long-term safety of a drug, usually after it has been approved

Whenever a medical claim is made about any compound or natural product, it is important for a potential consumer to do their research to see how the claim was made and if the results of the study that made that claim can be applied to the human body in a realistic way. On the flip side, it is the responsibility of every Cannabis company to use information responsibly, cite informational sources, and avoid misleading health claims for the sake of marketing.

HOW IS CANNABIS COMMONLY CONSUMED?

METHODS OF ADMINISTRATION

Cannabis and its chemical constituents can be consumed, or administered, in a variety of ways commonly including pulmonary methods (through the lungs), oral (edibles), sublingual (under the tongue), and epicutaneous/topical (on the skin) administrations, however, Cannabis can also be administered in the form of nasal sprays, vaginal or rectal suppositories as well as direct injection in muscle tissue or blood, though these methods are currently uncommon.

TYPES OF CANNABIS PRODUCTS

Some common types of Cannabis products typically available at a legal Cannabis dispensary include:

➢ Dried and cured flowers (buds)
➢ Concentrated resins and semi-solid extracts
➢ Topical oils, creams, salves, and balms
➢ Topical sprays
➢ Sublingual drops or sprays
➢ Infused edibles (cookies, candies, caramels, etc)
➢ Food oils (olive, sunflower, coconut, etc)
➢ Tinctures
➢ Suppositories

Each method of administration demonstrates markedly different levels of bioavailability.

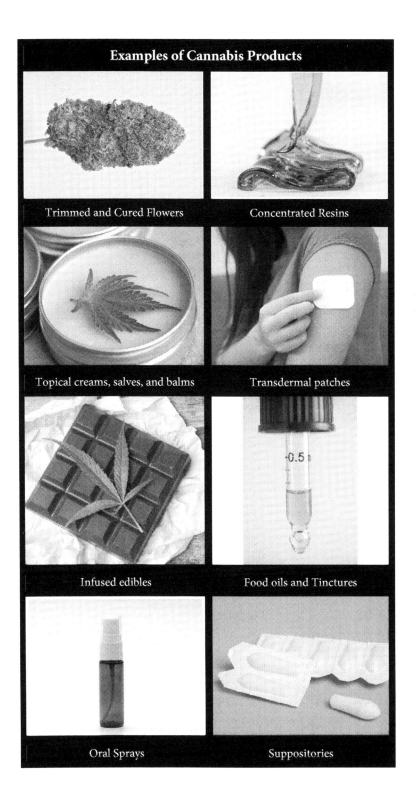

Examples of Cannabis Products

Trimmed and Cured Flowers   Concentrated Resins

Topical creams, salves, and balms   Transdermal patches

Infused edibles   Food oils and Tinctures

Oral Sprays   Suppositories

CANNABINOID DOSING

How much of any particular cannabinoid does someone need to ingest to achieve a therapeutic response? This is a tricky question to answer for many reasons. One is that cannabinoid product formulations can vary substantially, product to product. A product featuring a cannabinoid isolate, such as CBD or THC isolate, is going to behave much differently than a product featuring a wider diversity of phytochemistry from the Cannabis plant or elsewhere. Additionally, each person's biochemistry may be different, influencing how they will respond to cannabinoid treatment. To further complicate matters, the bioavailability of different cannabinoids varies.

Finally, cannabinoids tend to stick to fatty tissues in the body and release slowly overtime. This means that there is a big difference between taking a cannabinoid product once, versus taking one every day. Taking a cannabinoid product daily results in a slow buildup of cannabinoids in the body, which will continue to release into the body even when the user stops taking the product. It may be possible to find adequate effects at very low dosages, if the product is taken every day. However, if acute relief is needed, a large dose may be needed.

There is some research that has been done that shows that Cannabis extracts with a wider diversity of phytochemistry may perform better than cannabinoid isolates – but there still needs to be a lot more research done on this topic to really understand what factors influence these differences in responses (Gallily et al, 2015; Russo, 2019).

A 2019 review of cannabidiol (CBD) dosing used in clinical trials revealed that, for many conditions, dosages of less than 2.5mg/kg of body weight were largely ineffective, except in the case of treating sleep or anxiety (Millar et al, 2019). In Epidiolex trials, dosages of 5mg/kg to 20mg/kg were utilized to treat epilepsy in children, with clinicians advising not to exceed 15mg/kg to avoid adverse side effects. For the cannabinoid pharmaceutical Sativex, which features a standardized Cannabis extract consisting of equal parts THC to CBD, it is recommended to titrate up from approximately 2.5mg THC and CBD to 30mg THC and CBD per day for multiple sclerosis symptoms. The recommend dosing for the THC pharmaceutical Marinol indicates that dosing should start at 2.5mg orally twice daily for anorexia and 5mg/m^2 4-6 times per day for nausea and vomiting associated with chemotherapy.

Clearly cannabinoid dosing is complex for many reasons, so what can be done in light of this complexity? In general, it is often recommended to start off with low, sub-therapeutic, doses and slowly work up to a minimum effective dose. Usually a dose of somewhere around 1 or 2mg of THC or CBD is considered a suitable starting point, and subsequent doses can increase in 2 to 5mg increments until an optimum dose is found. It is also generally recommended to keep journals or "dose diaries" when taking Cannabis or cannabinoid-based products to determine which products and dosages are working best.

CANNABINOID BIOAVAILABILITY AND ABSORPTION

Bioavailability is a measurement of the amount of a compound that will readily make its way to a "site of action" in the body, like a chemical receptor. Often this is considered the same as the amount of an active substance that makes its way into the blood.

In general, cannabinoids are not very bioavailable, with the vast majority of cannabinoids consumed excreted from the body without reaching any sites of action. This is primarily due to the fact that cannabinoids are very lipophilic (oily) compounds which become bound very quickly in the blood to fatty acid binding proteins, which then causes them to become bound with glucose (sugar) before being eliminated from the body.

Cannabinoids also do not dissolve very readily in gastric fluids, which makes it difficult for cannabinoids to be absorbed in the digestive system. In addition, cannabinoids "stick" to a lot of tissues within the body, restricting their ability to reach sites of action.

Bioavailability and absorption can vary for many reasons including unique body chemistry, dosage, administration method, and consumption behavior. Although up to half of the THC present in a flower or extract may be bioavailable, depending on the consumption method, very little of it ever makes it to the brain. According to one study, only 1% of THC brought into the lungs reaches the brain. (Adams and Martin, 1996; Huestis, 2007)

Administration Route	Cannabinoid Bioavailability	Approximate Time to Onset
Pulmonary (Inhalation)	2 - 56% (30% average)	30 sec. – 5 minutes
Oral	10 - 20%	20 – 90 minutes or more
Sublingual (Under the Tongue)	1.5 – 10%	5 – 10 minutes
Buccal (Inside of Cheek)	See Sublingual	See Sublingual
Epicutaneous (Topical)	?	10 – 30 minutes
Vaginal or Rectal Suppository	<14%	5 – 25 minutes

SOURCE: HUESTIS MA. 2007. HUMAN CANNABINOID PHARMACOKINETICS. CHEM BIODIVERS. 4(8): 1770-1804

FIGURE 42: CANNABIS PRODUCT ADMINISTRATION ROUTES, BIOAVAILABILITY, AND TIME TO ONSET

The most common administration route used among medical Cannabis patients is **pulmonary**, or **respiratory**, delivery through smoking or vaporizing of the Cannabis flowers or extract. This allows for effects to manifest within seconds of administration, rather than thirty minutes or more when administered orally. As the cannabinoids in the smoke or vapor pass into the lungs, they are readily absorbed and delivered directly into the blood stream where they are carried to the brain and throughout the body. The sites of gas and blood exchange in the lungs are called the alveoli and are pictured on the next page.

Although pulmonary administration is the traditional method for medical Cannabis ingestion, it is typically not a method that can be accepted clinically due to negative health effects associated with smoking. An alternative to smoking is "vaporizing", or lightly heating plant material or extracts until cannabinoids are released in a thin vapor, presumably leaving behind tars and other toxic components.

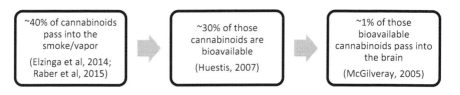

FIGURE 43: AVERAGE RECOVERY OF ADMINISTERED CANNABINOIDS IN SMOKE OR VAPOR, BLOOD, AND CEREBROSPINAL FLUID

Bioavailability Variability through Pulmonary Administration of 1g of 20% Total THC or CBD Cannabis (200mg)			
	Worst Case (2%)	**Average (30%)**	**Best Case (56%)**	**Impossibly Perfect (100%)**
In the smoke/vapor	~80mg	~80mg	~80mg	200mg
Bioavailable	~1.6mg	~24mg	~44.8mg	200mg
To the Brain	~0.016mg	~.24mg	~0.448mg	2mg

FIGURE 44: BIOAVAILABILITY VARIABILITY VIA PULMONARY ADMINISTRATION OF 200MG OF THC OR CBD

In 1996, the California branch of the National Organization for the Reform of Marijuana Laws (NORML) and the Multidisciplinary Association for Psychedelic Studies (MAPS) funded a study that examined the differences between several pulmonary delivery methods for Cannabis including three versions of water pipes, two different vaporizers, a filtered Cannabis cigarette, and an unfiltered Cannabis cigarette. The researchers examined the ratio of cannabinoids to tar to determine which administration methods presented the least risk to a user's health. They found that relative to the unfiltered cigarette, **all the devices were effective at reducing exposure to tars**. However, when the cannabinoid to tar ratio was measured, **only vaporization resulted in an enhanced cannabinoid/tar exposure ratio compared to an unfiltered cigarette**.

The first vaporizer that was examined, which was a "battery-powered metal hot plate inside a jar to trap the vapor, achieved a 26% improvement in the cannabinoid/tar ratio." The second vaporizer that the researchers tested featured water filtration. The researchers already saw that water pipes were the most inefficient at reducing the tar/cannabinoid ratio, so it was no surprise that this second vaporizer that featured water filtration had a statistically insignificant effect on the cannabinoid/tar ratio compared to an unfiltered cigarette. The author admits that using water filtration "seemed in retrospect to be a design flaw in the experiment." (Gieringer, 2001) The researchers also noticed that vaporizers produced more CBN than other methods.

To continue studying these effects, NORML and MAPS performed a second study looking at vaporization's effects of limiting carbon monoxide exposure and toxic hydrocarbon exposure. **At 185°C, or 365°F, they found that tar was reduced by over 56%, carbon monoxide was reduced by over 33%, and three toxic hydrocarbons – benzene, toluene, and naphthalene – were reduced 100%.** However, THC was also reduced by 85%. The message being that vaporization can provide less health risks, but also results in significantly less exposure to cannabinoids, potentially requiring repeated consumption and exposure to tar and carbon monoxide more frequently, but the tar and carbon monoxide exposure is likely to be less than with traditional smoking methods.

Close up of alveoli in the
lungs where gas/blood
exchange occurs.

So instead of pulmonary exposure, medical clinical trials for Cannabis and cannabinoid products typically utilize sublingual (under the tongue), nasomucosal (through the nose) or oral delivery systems. Other administration routes include topical (on the skin), intravenous (in the blood), and suppository delivery via the anal or vaginal mucosa.

PRE-1937 CANNABIS
PREPARATION

One of the most frequently studied administration routes for phytocannabinoids is through **sublingual** delivery, typically by way of a formulated spray or liquid that is dropped under the tongue. The administered compounds then readily pass through the mucous membrane of the mouth and into capillaries beneath. This method provides effects much more quickly than oral administration, usually between five and fifteen minutes, but not as quickly as pulmonary administration.

Similar so sublingual delivery, **nasal mucosal** administration is also possible. Drugs can easily be administered into the nose through a spray which lines the mucous membranes inside the nose where cannabinoids and other compounds can easily be absorbed into capillaries beneath the mucosa.

Cannabis extracts and cannabinoids can also be delivered **orally**. Cannabis products administered orally take anywhere between thirty minutes to an hour or more to produce effects. This is because orally administered drugs are subject to the first-pass effect, where the compounds must undergo hepatic metabolism in the liver before passing on into the blood and to the brain. This process results in an overall reduction in the number of target drug compounds reaching the vascular system to be distributed throughout the body. This can provide dosage and administration challenges for researchers, clinicians, dispensary workers, and patients.

CANNABIS AMERICANA
U. S. P.
Physiologically Tested

J. L. HOPKINS & CO., 160 William St. New York

Due to high demand and excess cost of importing cannabis, the united states began producing its own domestic varieties. Cannabis was a part of the US Pharmacoepia and a staple of pharmacies everywhere in the united states until it was omitted from the U.S.P. In 1942.

When delta-9-tetrahydrocannabinol (THC) passes through the **hepatic metabolism** system, it is converted to 11-hydroxy-delta-9-tetrahydrocannabinol (11-OH-THC). Even though cannabinoids are subject to the **first-pass effect** and are reduced in concentration before reaching the brain, 11-OH-THC is more potent than THC and passes the blood-brain barrier more readily. This is why users of edible products often report different effects which are often very potent as opposed to ingesting Cannabis through other administration routes like smoking, vaping, or using sublingual drops or buccal sprays.

Another way Cannabis compounds might be administered is through **epicutaneous**, or **topical**, delivery through the epidermis layer of the skin. Topical administration results in very little, if any, of the drug compounds reaching the dermis and the vascular system either due to the lack of space for compounds to pass around cells to reach capillaries in the dermis, or due to the complex lipophilic-hydrophilic layering of the transcellular pathway. Terpenes, volatile compounds that make up essential oils which are present in Cannabis, have been shown to enhance epidermal permeability, allowing for more effective absorption of target drug compounds.

FIGURE 45: ORAL VS SUBLINGUAL ADMINISTRATION DYNAMICS

Cannabis can also be delivered as a **suppository**, resulting in the absorption of target drug compounds through rectal or vaginal wall surfaces. Drug compounds administered through rectal suppository are readily absorbed in the blood vessels throughout the rectal mucosa. Drug compounds administered through vaginal suppositories pass through the vaginal epithelium, a mucosal surface, and on to capillaries which lead to systemic circulation. Drug administration through suppository delivery systems is ideal for patients with extreme nausea or vomiting tendencies that cannot tolerate other drug delivery systems. Drug administration through suppository is relatively fast acting, usually between fifteen and thirty minutes, and avoids hepatic metabolism and the production of 11-OH-THC.

Cannabinoids can be delivered **intravenously** or **intramuscularly** as well, although there is limited research about these administration routes at varying clinically significant dosages.

CANNABINOID HALF LIFE: HOW LONG DOES IT TAKE TO GET CANNABINOIDS OUT OF THE BODY?

The **half-life** of a compound is the amount of time that it takes for approximately half of the concentration of that compound to break down or be eliminated from the body. Because cannabinoids linger in the body, stuck to fatty tissues, cannabinoids have a fairly long half-life, especially for chronic users.

The half-life of THC and CBD is estimated to be anywhere from 1 to 6 days, depending on the frequency of consumption – although different studies that have attempted to ascertain the half-life of cannabinoids have been inconsistent (Huestis, 2009). This may be primarily related to the fact that different studies utilize different testing methodologies, some of which are more sensitive and can detect extremely low concentrations of cannabinoids compared to other methods. This might indicate that some studies that report lower half-lives may be mistaken because the testing methods used were simply incapable of accurately detecting extremely low concentrations of cannabinoids.

Let's put this into perspective, if we assume that for a chronic Cannabis user, the half-life of THC is 5 days, it would take approximately 100 days for the THC-COOH to reach levels below the limit for most urinary drug tests, which usually have a limit of around 50 nanograms, or 0.00005mg of THC-COOH. This seems to accurately compare to personal reports received by the author from chronic users that have had to spend up to 3 months or longer abstaining from Cannabis use in order to pass a workplace urinalysis.

Assuming an approximate 1-day (24 hour) half-life for an *infrequent* Cannabis user, approximately 90% or more THC would be eliminated within 5 days. Whereas, for a chronic user, it could take several weeks to achieve the same effect.

Half-Life Elimination Model for a Chronic Cannabis Consumer with a Starting Concentration of 100mg of THC-COOH in the Body (5 Day Half-Life)					
Mg of THC-COOH	Days	Mg of THC-COOH	Days	Mg of THC-COOH	Days
50	5	0.390625	40	0.003051758	75
25	10	0.1953125	45	0.001525879	80
12.5	15	0.09765625	50	0.000762939	85
6.25	20	0.048828125	55	0.00038147	90
3.125	25	0.024414063	60	0.000190735	95
1.5625	30	0.012207031	65	0.000095	100
0.78125	35	0.006103516	70	0.000048	105

How Does Cannabis Get People "High"?

The "high" produced from Cannabis is caused, primarily, by the stimulation of cannabinoid receptors in the brain. When the <1% of bioavailable THC makes its way to the brain, it stimulates a variety of receptors including the cannabinoid type 1 (CB1) and cannabinoid type 2 (CB2) receptors on neurons. When CB1 receptors are agonized, or stimulated, it causes a whole cascading series of effects in the body that lead to things like altered time perception, disrupted memory formation, appetite stimulation, pain reduction, and euphoria – all the typical symptoms associated with a Cannabis "high". While THC is the primary cannabinoid in Cannabis that agonizes, or stimulates, CB1 receptors, other cannabinoids may also cause intoxicating effects such as delta-8 THC, CBN, CBND, and THCv – ultimately manipulating the effects of THC and the experience of the consumer.

As CB1 receptors are repeatedly stimulated, they decrease in concentration in the brain, leading to a reduced psychoactive effect, often referred to as **tolerance**. After at least 48 hours of discontinued use, CB1 receptors may begin returning to their normal concentrations and tolerance will begin to decrease.

Some cannabinoids like CBD, CBDv, CBC, and CBG can block, or antagonize, CB1 receptors, potentially reducing or limiting the psychoactive effects of THC. It has been reported that some terpenoids may also limit or modulate the "high" associated with Cannabis such as limonene or beta-caryophyllene (Russo, 2011). Many companies and researchers and trying to understand these dynamics better so that drugs may be developed to interrupt uncomfortable or potentially psychologically dangerous Cannabis intoxication experiences.

The Entourage Effect: Cannabis as a Polypharmaceutical

Because Cannabis contains hundreds of active compounds, Cannabis is considered a **polypharmaceutical**, meaning that it is a drug made of many drugs. Previous chapters explored the various compounds in Cannabis and many of these compounds were noted for demonstrating various beneficial pharmacological actions. Many researchers are now shifting their focus toward trying to understand how these compounds interact with one another in an "entourage effect" to produce unique therapeutic or psychoactive effects.

Users often report that isolated cannabinoid products do not produce the level of therapeutic action compared to consuming whole plant botanical Cannabis or broad-spectrum Cannabis extracts. There are numerous compounds present in Cannabis that work to modulate the effects of the other present compounds. For instance, numerous terpenes like pinene and numerous cannabinoids like cannabichromene may exhibit memory enhancement effects, potentially working to limit the amnesic, or memory loss, effects of THC.

A study examining the differences in levels of an inflammatory marker called TNFa demonstrated that a plateauing of therapeutic response with CBD isolate could be overcome if using a CBD-rich Cannabis extract with a wide variety of phytochemistry (Galilly et al, 2015).

"I think the best depiction of this idea of the entourage effect, or what we have called synergy in medicinal plants, is a symphonic effect. Think about a Mozart symphony that is so incredibly beautiful - and you have a lead violin, and then you have all these other instruments. All those other instruments support the lead violin. What's happened in pharmacology is, under the illusion that we can control the dose, we've isolated the lead violin and just used that in our pharmacology. And the rationalization for this is actually not very strong scientifically..."

Kevin Spelman, PhD
The Curious About Cannabis Podcast
Behind-the-Scenes (BTS) Episode #04

ARE CANNABINOIDS TOXIC?

The **LD50**, or median lethal dose, of a compound is used to indicate the severity of toxicity of a compound. It is measured in mg/kg and is **the amount of a compound necessary to kill half of a test population**, usually of rodents. The ratio of compound concentration to body weight is then scaled up to estimate the LD50 for a human population. Many clinicians and researchers point out that this method of scaling up results from rodent LD50 models is not a suitable way to understand how toxic a compound might be to humans. Another index is sometimes used to evaluate toxicity called the **Therapeutic Index**. It is a comparison of the therapeutic effect of a compound versus any toxic effects the compound elicits.

In 1988 administrative law judge Francis Young published *Opinion and Recommended Ruling, Findings of Fact, Conclusions of Law and Decision of Administrative Law Judge* in regard to a Cannabis rescheduling petition. In this report, Young stated:

> *"...in order to induce death a marijuana smoker would have to consume 20,000 to 40,000 times as much marijuana as is contained in one marijuana cigarette...A smoker would theoretically have to consume nearly 1,500 pounds of marijuana within about fifteen minutes to induce a lethal response."*

The primary reason for the low lethality of Cannabis is due to the small number of cannabinoid receptors on the brainstem and the fact that THC and other cannabinoid receptor agonists found in Cannabis are only partial receptor agonists. Other drugs like alcohol and heroin can be dangerous in much less quantities because they have strong effects on the brainstem, which in turn affects the performance of all other organs like the heart and lungs. Overdosing on alcohol or heroin can stop the heart or lungs, but this is generally not the case for Cannabis.

The precise LD50 is difficult to ascertain. An often-quoted bit of research by Thompson et al. (1973) found that "...oral doses of delta-9-THC and delta-8-THC between 3000 – 9000 mg/kg were nonlethal."

LD50s of Major Phytocannabinoids	
D9-Tetrahydrocannabinol (THC)	3000 – 9000 mg/kg (oral, dogs)
Cannabidiol (CBD)	212 mg/kg (IV, rhesus monkeys)[1]
Cannabigerol (CBG)	5600 mg/kg (oral, rat)[2]
Cannabichromene (CBC)	270 mg/kg (IV, rhesus monkeys)[1]

FIGURE 46: LETHAL TOXICITY OF MAJOR CANNABINOIDS

[1]Rosenkrantz et al, 1981; [2]Cayman Chemical Cannabigerol MSDS, 2014

LD50s of Non-Cannabinoid Compounds	
Aflatoxin (produced by *Aspergillus sp.* Fungi)	0.003 mg/kg (oral, rat)
Cyanide	10 mg/kg (oral, rat)
Nicotine	50 mg/kg (oral rat)
Caffeine	200 mg/kg (oral, rat)
Ethanol	7000 mg/kg (oral, rat)
Sucrose	30,000 mg/kg (oral, rat)

FIGURE 47: LETHAL TOXICITY OF NON-CANNABINOID COMPOUNDS

Source: Trautmann NM and The Environmental Inquiry Team. Table 1.1 Lethal Doses of Some Common Compounds. Assessing Toxic Risk: Student Edition. National Science Teachers Association

Recall the wise words of Parascleus:

"Alle Dinge sind Gift und nichts ist ohne Gift, allein die Dosis macht es, dass ein Ding kein Gift ist."

"All things are poison and nothing is without poison; only the dose makes a thing not a poison."

Test Your Cannabis Related Medical Vocabulary!

Match these medical terms to their definitions!

_____	Acute	A	Something that provides pain relief
_____	Anesthesia	B	Refers to the heart and blood vessels
_____	Analgesia	C	Increased appetite; "munchies"
_____	Insulin	D	Severe and short-term
_____	Xerostomia	E	Refers to the stomach and intestine
_____	Polyphagia	F	Something that provides nausea relief
_____	Chronic	G	The fluid pressure inside the eye
_____	Antiemetic	H	Pain relief
_____	Conjunctival hyperemia	I	Condition of dilated blood vessels in the eyes; red eyes
_____	Analgesic	J	Hormone made by the pancreas that regulates glucose in the blood.
_____	Gastrointestinal	K	Ongoing, long-term
_____	Cardiovascular	L	Use of a substance to remove sensitivity to pain
_____	Emesis	M	Dry mouth
_____	Intraocular pressure (IOP)	N	Nausea
_____	Nociception	O	"in tissue"
_____	In vitro	P	Pain perception
_____	In vivo	Q	"in glass"

Answers: D, L, H, J, M, C, K, F, I, A, E, B, N, G, P, Q, O

HOW DOES CANNABIS INTERACT WITH OTHER DRUGS?

There is not a lot of information about how cannabinoids interact with other drugs currently available. One of the primary contraindications that is known is that THC will exacerbate any sedative effects initiated by another drug. Consuming alcohol prior to consuming Cannabis can enhance the bioavailability of cannabinoids and thus enhance the potency of psychoactive cannabinoids. Additionally, THC-rich Cannabis is known to decrease blood pressure in chronic users, which could present a risk to users taking blood-pressure lowering drugs.

CBD AND THE GRAPEFRUIT EFFECT

As mentioned previously, in certain concentrations, CBD, and to a lesser extent THC, can temporarily inhibit a set of enzymes in the liver that is responsible for transforming a wide variety of compounds into hydrophilic (water-loving) compounds so that they can be absorbed readily into the kidneys (Devitt-Lee, 2015; Bornheim et al, 1993; Yamaori et al, 2011). This set of liver enzymes is called **Cytochrome P450** and it is even responsible for metabolizing CBD itself, as well as THC and other cannabinoids. This means that **when CBD is ingested, there is a battle between CBD and Cytochrome P450 enzymes as the CBD inhibits the enzyme activity and the enzymes work to metabolize the CBD.**

Have you ever received a medication that had a label attached to the bottle stating, "Do Not Consume Grapefruit While Taking This Medication", or similar? That's because grapefruit, and various other foods, exhibit this same effect on the liver. These enzymes are responsible for metabolizing all sorts of drugs that people take, such as blood thinning or chemotherapy drugs.

If a patient is taking medications prior to beginning an intensive CBD regimen, it is possible that the levels of those medications may rise in the blood because the patient's liver will not be able to metabolize the drugs due to Cytochrome P450 inhibition – leading to recirculation of the drug back into the blood stream and throughout the body before it comes back to the liver again. This can potentially lead to dangerously elevated levels of drugs in the patient's system which could be very toxic.

On the other hand, it might be possible to titrate certain medications down in response to this inhibition so that less of a medication could then be used to achieve the same effect. In one case study, a patient was able to reduce their dose of the drug Warfarin by 30% over the course of a CBD drug trial (Grayson et al, 2017). In clinical trials that sought to identify how CBD affects the performance of the epileptic drug clobazam, researchers found that levels of clobazam increased and adverse side effects increased, which were managed once dosages of clobazam were reduced (Geffrey et al, 2015). Much more research is needed on this topic to better understand how CBD might interact with other drugs and at what dosages its effects on the liver are clinically significant.

It should be noted that much of the current research indicating that CBD inhibits these enzymes was performed using **supraphysiological** doses, meaning doses that are greater than what an average person would typically be exposed to on a regular basis. If one were to extrapolate the data from one of the most infamous studies that identified this enzyme suppression effect, it would indicate that someone would have to consume grams of CBD a day to illicit a significant inhibitory response. (Iffland and Grotenhermen, 2017)

In animal trials, the results are a bit more confounding. Rodent studies have revealed that, while CBD may suppress liver enzymes at first, CBD and some of its metabolites might actually induce, or stimulate, certain metabolic enzymes with repeated exposure. One particular enzyme that CBD and its metabolites seem to induce, CYP1A1, is responsible for breaking down many cancer-causing compounds in the body, helping prevent carcinogenic substances from reaching the blood stream. (Iffland and Grotenhermen, 2017)

However, only human trials will give us the data we need to determine whether this effect may be appreciable at typical therapeutic doses or not. Until then, it is best to exercise caution and always work with a physician when starting a new therapeutic regimen.

Examples of Common Drugs Metabolized by Cytochrome P450 Enzymes
Benzodiazepines (Valium, Xanax, Versed, Doral, Dormalin, Halcion)
Amphetamines (Adderall, Vyvance)
Caffeine
Other stimulants (Ritalin, Concerta)
Certain statins (Lipitor, Mevacor, Zocor, Simlup, Simcor, Simvacor)
Anti-arrhythmic drugs (Cordarone, Multaq, Qunidex, Cardioquin, Quinora, Norpace, Rythmol, Coreg)
Anti-migraine drugs (Cafergot, Ergomar, Elavil, Endep, Vanatrip, Nimotop)
Erectile dysfunction drugs (Viagra, Cialis, Levitra)
Acetaminophen (Tylenol)
Lamotrigine
Codeine, Methadone, Oxycodone
Antihistamines (Benadryl)
Source: https://en.wikipedia.org/wiki/Grapefruit–drug_interactions

FIGURE 48: COMMON DRUGS METABOLIZED BY CYTOCHROME P450 ENZYMES

As mentioned before, Cytochrome P450 is involved in the metabolism of THC. This has certain implications for oral dose administration. If CBD is administered and Cytochrome P450 is inhibited, less THC will be converted to 11-OH-THC, potentially limiting the sometimes-intense psychoactive effect elicited by infused edibles.

Diet is another crucial factor influencing drug metabolism. Many commonly consumed foods such as grapefruits, tomatoes, spinach and more also inhibit Cytochrome P450. **It is important to talk to your doctor about how Cytochrome P450 inhibition might affect your current medications if you are considering a chronic high dose CBD treatment**.

WHAT STRAIN IS BEST FOR MY MEDICAL CONDITION?

Dispensary technicians, physicians, nurses, and caregivers alike are often asked this question by patients wanting to treat a specific medical condition with Cannabis. The question itself is a loaded one and assumes that a Cannabis product's efficacy is correlated with the supposed lineage of the Cannabis used to produce it. As featured in Chapter 3, there are many problems associated with the taxonomy, or categorization, of Cannabis varieties. The scientific community does not agree how to categorize Cannabis, but they do agree that the indicated lineages of Cannabis varieties are not reliable.

In previous chapters we learned that a plant's chemotype, or chemical profile, is variable and influenced by both genetics *and* environment. The Cannabis plant exhibits phytochemical polymorphism, producing varying concentrations of different terpenoids throughout the plant. In addition, plants of the same strain, grown in the same area, may exhibit different chemotypes. Even after the plant is harvested, the chemistry is always changing.

In a 2016 interview, Cannabis researcher Dr. Ethan Russo commented, "Since the taxonomists cannot agree, I would strongly encourage the scientific community, the press, and the public to abandon the sativa/indica nomenclature and rather insist that accurate biochemical assays on cannabinoid and terpenoid profiles be available for Cannabis in both the medical and recreational markets. Scientific accuracy and the public health demand no less than this." (Piomelli and Russo, 2016)

Keep an experience journal that you can share with your physician to find trends that might help you identify Cannabis products that will work best for you. Some of the information you should document in an experience journal include:

Attribute	Description/Example
Product type	Flower, tincture, edible, concentrate
Strain name	"Blue Dream", "Jack Herer", "Granddaddy Purple"
CBD:THC ratio	20:1 (high CBD), 4:1, 2:1, 1:1, 1:2, 1:4, 1:20 (high THC)
Potency	15% Total THC, 6% Total CBD, 15mg THC, 20mg CBD
Dose amount	1 gram, 1 cookie, 2 mL, 1 unit
Dominant terpenes	Myrcene, limonene, linalool
Notable smells	Fruity, floral, earthy, spicy, fuely
Distinct colors	Dark purple, pink tones
Administration route/Consumption method	Vaporization, sublingual, oral, topical, smoking
Pre-consumption pain score	1 (no pain) – 10 (unbearable pain)
Pre-consumption mood description	Anxious, serene, angry, sad, bored, happy, hopeful
Time of administration	5:30pm PST
Time of onset	5:42pm PST
Post-consumption pain score	1 (no pain) – 10 (unbearable pain)
Post-consumption mood description	Anxious, serene, angry, sad, bored, happy, hopeful
Narrative	Stream of consciousness description of experience before, during, and after consumption

FIGURE 49: EXAMPLE CANNABIS EXPERIENCE JOURNAL ENTRY

CANNABINOIDS AND THE GUT MICROBIOME

Research is now showing that there is a very deep connection between gut health, the immune system and mental health. This connection is sometimes referred to as the "gut-brain axis" (Carabotti et al, 2015). Evidence suggests that the gut and the brain excert bi-directional effects on one another, meaning that the gut affects the brain and the brain affects the gut. It's not a one-way street.

One way that the gut and the brain are linked is through a direct connection between the autonomic and central nervous systems. Research has demonstrated that the ecosystem of bacteria and fungi that live in the gut affect the development of the enteric nervous system (ENS) and central nervous system (CNS). The enteric nervous system is part of the autonomic nervous system and is sometimes referred to as the body's "second brain". Although the ENS communicates with the CNS to control reflexes and other bodily functions, if it loses contact with the CNS – for instance if the vagus nerve is severed – it will continue to function on its own (Li and Owyang, 2003). The ENS also produces neurotransmitters like the ones found throughout the CNS, such as serotonin, acetylcholine, and dopamine (Goyal and Hirano, 1996).

Endocannabinoids play a critical role in regulating how the vagus nerve affects gut motility and nausea responses through CB1, CB2, and TRPV1 receptors (Storr and Sharkey, 2007). It has also been shown that endocannabinoids play a role in visceral pain responses in the gut (Storr and Sharkey, 2007).

Besides the vagus nerve and the gut-brain axis, the activity of the gut is immensely influenced by the ecosystem of bacteria that reside in the gut. There are approximately 100 trillion cells that make up the gut microbiome in each of our bodies! (Cani et al, 2015) That's 100,000,000,000,000 cells! To put that into perspective, that is ten times the number of cells that make up the entire human body!

These micro-organisms perform a number of different functions, primarily helping our bodies digest food and metabolize compounds produced during digestion. When gut microflora communities are thrown out of whack, often through improper diet, the use of antibiotics, disease, or genetic predisposition, these microorganisms can cause things like inflammation and gut permeability. Conditions like obesity and diabetes are associated with increased gut permeability. Generally, when the abundance and diversity of microorganisms in the gut are reduced, inflammation and metabolic syndromes follow (Cani et al, 2015).

Cannabinoids also affect the permeability of intestinal walls. When the gut's lining is too permeable, it results in a condition often called "leaky gut," where things leak out of the gut and into nearby tissues, resulting in inflammation and alterations to the types of bacteria in the surrounding area. In an *in vitro* study, THC and CBD were both found to reduce the damaging effects of inflammation on intestinal permeability (Alhamoruni A et al, 2004). In the same study, the common endocannabinoids Anandamide and 2-AG were found to promote permeability, indicating that endocannabinoids could damage the gut in certain scenarios (Alhamoruni A et al, 2004).

The endocannabinoid system is also involved in hunger signaling, influencing the types of foods that reach the gut, ultimately influencing the community of microflora in the gut. Research into understanding how phytocannabinoids like THC or CBD affect gut microflora is still relatively new. A recent studying examining the effects of a CBD-rich Cannabis extract on gut microflora revealed that initially CBD increased the abundance of one microbe, *Akkermansia muciniphila*, but ultimately ended up decreasing the relative abundance of all species of gut flora (Kortubash et al, 2020). Another study has shown that when THC and CBD are administered together, they may prevent the accumulation of *Akkermansia muciniphila* and possibly prevent microbial imbalances that could exacerbate symptoms of multiple sclerosis (Al-Ghezi et al, 2017). This indicates that CBD-rich

Cannabis extracts with little to no amount of THC in them may skew the gut microbiome toward imbalance in some people. However, if someone may be experiencing an abnormal deficiency of *A. muciniphila* in the gut, cannabidiol may increase *A. muciniphila* to adequate amounts without encouraging imbalance, but more research is needed.

Diet is another important factor influencing the gut microbiome. It is generally well known that THC-rich Cannabis consumption can cause a condition of urgent hunger called "the munchies". This is because the body uses certain cannabinoid receptors and endocannabinoid signaling to trigger hunger signals in the brain. For instance, researchers have found that whenever rodents taste fatty foods, endocannabinoid levels increase in certain parts of the intestines (DiPatrizio et al, 2011). This rise in endocannabinoid signaling includes CB1 receptor signaling, which triggers a hunger signal in the brain and causes the rodent to consume more of the high-fat food. Because diet influences the communities of micro-organisms in the gut, this effect of hunger signaling can indirectly lead to changes in the gut microbiome, which can then go on to affect things like inflammation or even mood.

While stimulating CB1 receptors may lead to a certain type of change in the gut microflora, antagonizing, or blocking, CB1 receptors can lead to totally different effects. Mehrpouya-Bahrami et al (2017) found that blocking CB1 receptors can have profound impacts to gut microflora:

"CB1 blockade dramatically increased relative abundance of Akkermansia muciniphila and decreased Lanchnospiraceae and Erysipelotrichaceae in the gut. Together, the current study suggests that blocking of CB1 ameliorates Diet-Induced Obesity and metabolic disorder by modulating macrophage inflammatory mediators, and that this effect is associated with alterations in gut microbiota and their metabolites."

Cannabinoid	Effects on Gut Flora	Notes
CBD	Increases abundance of *A. muciniphila*, overall decrease in abundance of other flora	Related to CB1 antagonism
THC	Decreases abundance of *A. muciniphila*	Related to CB1 agonism

CLINICAL INDICATIONS OF CANNABIS AND CANNABINOID PRODUCTS

The research surrounding Cannabis and cannabinoids and their efficacy for the treatment of various conditions and symptoms is complicated. There is a wide range of studies that have been conducted utilizing various synthetic and plant derived cannabinoid compounds to test therapeutic efficacy for various conditions. However, **there are very few studies that have been conducted using vaporized Cannabis flower or whole plant Cannabis extracts**. Much of the cannabinoid research that has been performed to date has been through either *in vitro* cell culture models or *in vivo* rodent models, both limited in their scalability to humans, although they do provide pieces to the ongoing biological puzzle researchers are trying to solve.

A review of cannabinoid clinical trials published in 2015 in the Journal of the American Medical Association listed several conditions that cannabinoids can effectively treat, using data from 79 different clinical trials. The researchers concluded **that there was evidence that cannabinoids can be used successfully to treat chronic pain, spasticity, nausea, vomiting, sleep disorders, and Tourette syndrome with clinical significance** (Whiting et al, 2015).

Most of these studies did not utilize drug delivery methods of products that are being used by current medical Cannabis patients in states or countries where Cannabis use is permitted. **Only two of the included studies used Cannabis inflorescence (flower) in a smoked or vaporized form as the drug intervention. 23 of the 79 studies utilized THC as a drug intervention.** Many of the included research articles utilized synthetic cannabinoids which specifically target either CB1 or CB2 receptors exclusively and do not necessarily represent the effects of phytocannabinoids or the matrix of cannabinoids present in a Cannabis inflorescence.

In addition, **the 2015 study did not examine efficacy for conditions other than nausea/vomiting, chronic pain, spasticity, HIV/AIDS, sleep disorders, psychosis, Tourette syndrome, anxiety disorder, glaucoma, and depression (Whiting, 2015).** For instance, many patients using Cannabis as medicine report treating conditions outside of this scope including skin cancer, arthritis and other inflammatory conditions, fibromyalgia, irritable bowel syndromes including Crohn's Disease, and autism.

A report published by the National Academy of Sciences in 2017 indicated that there was conclusive or substantial evidence that Cannabis or cannabinoids are effective for the treatment of chronic pain, nausea, vomiting, and spasticity. They reported that there was moderate evidence that Cannabis and cannabinoids are effective for treating short-term sleep problems associated with sleep apnea, fibromyalgia, chronic pain and multiple sclerosis. The committee reported that there was limited evidence that Cannabis or cannabinoids could be an effective treatment for appetite and weight loss, Tourette syndrome, anxiety, and post-traumatic stress disorder (PTSD). Finally, the committee reported that there was some limited evidence that Cannabis or cannabinoids are ineffective for dementia, glaucoma, and depression associated with chronic pain.

Interestingly enough, the National Academy of Sciences report does acknowledge that there is currently not enough information available to refute any claims that Cannabis or cannabinoids may be effective for conditions like cancers, irritable bowel syndrome, epilepsy, amyotrophic lateral sclerosis (ALS), symptoms associated with Huntington's disease, motor discoordination associated with Parkinson's disease, dystonia, reduction of use of addictive substances, or schizophrenia or schizophreniform psychosis.

There is an important caveat to mention here. Cannabis is not a single static thing. Cannabis can come in a wide variety of chemical profiles and administration methods which can affect patient outcomes differently. For instance, CBD dominant chemovars of Cannabis will likely affect conditions very differently than THC dominant chemovars. But there are also many other chemovars circulating or in development, such as CBG, CBC, THCV, and CBDV dominant chemovars. Most of the data used by both the 2015 JAMA study, and the 2017 National Academy of Sciences report are based on THC-dominant products, with a small number of CBD-dominant products represented. There is still a lot to learn, research and understand regarding how cannabinoids in different ratios and in the presence of other compounds, or co-administered with other medications, will affect patient outcomes differently.

Caution should be taken when interpreting summaries like those mentioned here that purport to have identified the clinical efficacy and inefficacy of Cannabis and care should always be taken to understand exactly how these conclusions are drawn. What Cannabis was used? Was it herbal Cannabis? Cannabis extracts? Isolated cannabinoids? What cannabinoids? In what ratios? In the presence of what other compounds? At what dosages? Through what administration method? The medical use of Cannabis is a heavily nuanced topic, and there is still a lot that we do not understand and do not have enough clinical data to draw conclusions about.

HISTORY OF MEDICAL CANNABIS USE

Oral traditions of Cannabis use for appetite stimulation and fighting the effects of old age date back to nearly 3000 years BCE (Shou-Zhong, 1997). That's 5000 years ago! In 1500 BCE, the Atharva Veda indicates that Indians were using Cannabis for anxiety relief (Grierson, 1894). Cannabis is suspected to even be a component of the holy anointing oil of the Hebrews as far back as 750 BCE (Alter, 2004; Russo, 2007). The juice of the leaves was noted to be a remedy for earaches in the first century (Dioscorides and Beck, 2011). In the second century Chinese records indicate Cannabis was used in wine as an anesthetic (Julien, 1849). In the early 10th century Persian records indicate it was even used to stimulate hair growth (Lozano, 2001). In 1542 it was noted that the Cannabis roots could be boiled and used to treat gout and burns (Fuchs, 1999). Throughout the 16th century records indicate Cannabis was used for sore muscles, stiff joints, burns, wounds, jaundice, colic and even tumors (Gerard and Johnson, 1975).

In 1839 a researcher named O'Shaughnessy studied Indian use of Cannabis and performed experiments in dogs, and then later people, to determine if Cannabis was a suitable treatment for tetanus, rabies, epilepsy and rheumatoid disease (O'Shaughnessy, 1838-1840). Shortly after O'Shaughnessy published his findings, Cannabis began showing up in the European and United States Pharmacopoeias.

As records become more easily obtainable, we can find records throughout the 18th and 19th centuries of Cannabis being used to treat migraines, pain, spasticity, anxiety, depression, and insomnia (Russo, 2014).

Cannabis was even featured in the US Pharmacopoeia as a medicine until the 12th edition released in 1942 after marijuana prohibition had begun in 1937 (US Pharmacopoeia, 1942). You can still look up old issues of the USP and look for Extractum Cannabis or Tinctura Cannabis aka Extract of Hemp or Tincture of Hemp. Upon the initial publication of Cannabis in the USP in 1851, the 9th edition of the US Dispensatory had this to say about the medical use of Cannabis:

"It has been found to cause sleep, to allay spasm, to compose nervous disquietude, and to relieve pain...The complaints in which it has been specially recommended are neuralgia, gout, rheumatism, tetanus, hydrophobia, epidemic cholera, convulsions, chorea, mental depression delirium tremens, insanity, and uterine hemorrhage." (Wood and Bache, 1851)

Jump forward to 1918, the US Dispensatory revised its description of the medical uses of Cannabis based on what physicians were seeing. This 1918 update reads:

"Cannabis is used in medicine to relieve pain, to encourage sleep, and to soothe restlessness. Its action upon the nerve centers resembles opium, although much less certain, but it does not have the deleterious effect on the secretions. As a somnifacient it is rarely sufficient by itself, but may at times aid the hypnotic effect of other drugs. For its analgesic action it is used especially in pains of neuralgic origin, such as migraine, but is occasionally of service in other types. As a general nerve sedative it is used in hysteria, mental depression, neurasthenia, and the like. It has also been used in a number of other conditions, such as tetanus and uterine hemorrhage, but with less evidence of benefit. One of the great hindrances to the wider use of this drug is its extreme variability." (US Dispensatory, 1918)

THE

PHARMACOPŒIA

OF THE

UNITED STATES OF AMERICA

(THE UNITED STATES PHARMACOPŒIA)

TWELFTH REVISION
(U. S. P. XII)

BY AUTHORITY OF THE
UNITED STATES PHARMACOPŒIAL CONVENTION
MEETING AT WASHINGTON, D. C., MAY 14 AND 15, 1940

PREPARED BY THE COMMITTEE OF REVISION AND
PUBLISHED BY THE BOARD OF TRUSTEES

OFFICIAL FROM NOVEMBER 1, 1942

ELECTROTYPED, PRINTED AND DISTRIBUTED BY
MACK PRINTING COMPANY
EASTON, PA.

FIGURE 50: COVER OF THE 12TH EDITION OF THE USP

ARTICLES OFFICIAL IN THE U. S. P. XI BUT NOT ADMITTED TO THE U. S. P. XII

Acetum Scillæ	Liquor Sodii Hypochloritis Dilutus
Acidum Aceticum Dilutum	Magma Ferri Hydroxidi
Acidum Acetyltannicum	Massa Hydrargyri
Acidum Sulfuricum Aromaticum	Merbaphenum
Aconitum	Mistura Opii et Glycyrrhizæ Composita
Acriflavina	Oleum Maydis
Acriflavinæ Hydrochloridum	Oleum Santali
Æthylhydrocupreinæ Hydrochloridum	Paraffinum
Albumini Tannas	Paraffinum Chlorinatum
Ammonii Benzoas	Pepsinum
Ammonii Bromidum	Pilulæ Aloes
Ammonii Salicylas	Podophyllum
Arseni Triiodidum	Potassii Chloras
Asafœtida	Pulvis Ipecacuanhæ et Opii
Bismuthi Subgallas	Pulvis Sennæ Compositus
Calcii Bromidum	Pyrogallol
Calcii Creosotas	Quinina
Cannabis	Resina Podophylli
Cantharis	Santoninum

FIGURE 51: USP 12TH EDITION LIST OF ITEMS EXCLUDED FROM 11TH EDITION

After Cannabis prohibition began, Cannabis became unavailable as a medicine, and research into the plant progressively slowed down into the late 1950s. Modern medical research into Cannabis really took off in the 1960s when THC was isolated and synthesized (Gaoni and Mechoulam, 1964). A little-known fact – but CBD was actually isolated and characterized approximately 24 years prior to when THC was isolated (Adams, 1940). But because CBD did not elicit an intoxicating effect, it was largely ignored at first.

As THC research progressed throughout the 1960s and 1970s, research confirmed that THC could reduce nausea and vomiting associated with cancer chemotherapy (Sallan, 1975), that THC had the same analgesic activity as codeine (Noyes et al, 1975), and that THC performed as well as the anti-asthma drug salbutamol aka albuterol or Ventolin as a bronchodilator (Williams et al, 1976).

The 1980s ushered in renewed interest in CBD as well as continued research on THC. In 1981 CBD was identified as an anticonvulsant (Carlini and Cunha, 1981). A year later it would be found that CBD could help relieve the anxiety brought on by THC (Zuardi et al, 1982). In 1985, the unique flavonoid Cannflavin A was discovered, breaking Cannabis research away from the cannabinoid chemical class to encompass other types of plant compounds (Barrett et al, 1985). It was also in 1985 that the pharmaceutical drug Marinol was approved by the FDA for chemotherapy related nausea (Russo, 2014).

In 1988 scientists finally discovered a chemical receptor in the body that seemed to be responsible for most of THC's effects – the cannabinoid type 1 receptor, or CB1 receptor (Devane et al, 1988). This marks the beginning of piecing together a fascinating puzzle about a physiological system that had since been ignored – the endocannabinoid system, which wouldn't be formally named for another 10 years (Di Marzo, 1998).

In 1993 CBD's anti-anxiety effects that had been previously noted in the 1980s was again confirmed (Zuardi et al, 1993). In 1997 it was found that THC could help reduce agitation in patients with dementia (Volicer et al, 1997).

In 2003 clinical trials of the Cannabis based pharmaceutical Sativex began, investigating whether it could be effective in treating multiple sclerosis symptoms (Wade et al, 2003). In 2005 Sativex would go on to be approved in Canada for the treatment of MS related pain Rog et al, 2005). Over the years Sativex would later be approved for other types of pain such as neuropathic pain and cancer pain (Notcutt et al, 2004; Berman et al, 2004). Eventually Sativex would be approved in the UK and Spain for spasticity in MS patients (Novotna et al, 2011). In 2010 it would be discovered that Sativex can also treat nausea related to chemotherapy treatments (Duran et al, 2010).

In 2018, the United States Food and Drug Administration approved the cannabis derived cannabidiol (CBD) pharmaceutical, Epidiolex, currently for treatment-resistant forms of epilepsy in children.

Examples of Cannabinoid Pharmaceuticals					
Name	Components	Date	Indications	Approved in US?	Note
Nabilone/Cesamet	delta-6a,10a-dimethyl heptyl tetrahydrocannabinol (DMHP)	1985	Cancer related nausea, pain	Yes	Synthetic
Marinol	Synthetic THC	1985	Cancer related nausea and pain	Yes	Synthetic
Sativex	1:1 ratio THC:CBD Cannabis extract	2003	MS symptoms, cancer related nausea, pain	No	Cannabis derived
Epidiolex	Cannabis-derived isolated CBD	2018	Treatment resistant epilepsy	Yes	Cannabis derived

CHRONIC PAIN AND CANNABIS

One of the primary reasons that people use Cannabis is to relieve chronic pain. Cannabis is effective at alleviating pain by manipulating pain signaling and controlling inflammation. Although our understanding of the relationship between cannabinoids, cannabinoid receptors, and pain response is relatively new, it turns out that our body's own endocannabinoids have been helping modulate our pain responses all our lives.

First, it seems that cannabinoids interact with chemical pathways in the brain which control pain signaling and excitatory responses. Cannabinoids tend to decrease glutamate activity, which is responsible for causing excitatory signals, while increasing GABA activity, which causes suppressive signaling. Cannabinoids achieve this effect by manipulating calcium channels on neurons, effectively blocking them, which has subsequent effects on various neurotransmitters and receptors. In this way, cannabinoids can "turn down the volume" of pain. (Rea et al, 2007)

In addition to affecting glutamate and GABA activity to achieve pain reduction, cannabinoids can also modulate inflammation responses via the cannabinoid type 2 (CB2) and vanilloid receptors, among other more obscure receptor types. Cannabinoids can induce a certain cascade of signaling which essentially tells the body's immune system to calm down. This causes a reduction of inflammation, which can end up resulting in less pain. (Cabral and Griffin-Thomas, 2009)

Unfortunately, until recently many physical and mental health care practitioners have been dismissive of anecdotal claims that Cannabis reduces pain, often interpreting such claims as an excuse to "get high" and indulge in substance abuse. This often resulted in patients feeling withdrawn and uncomfortable to share their Cannabis use with their doctor, and at times patients have even reported feeling attacked and ridiculed by health care professionals for sharing their experience. It is critically important that the future of health care recognizes the validity of many of these anecdotal claims and takes them seriously, otherwise the doctor-patient relationship may become eroded and a distrust in the provider may be cultivated within the patient.

Cancer and Cannabis

Cannabinoids have already been shown to be effective in treating many cancer-associated symptoms either caused by the cancer or by the chemotherapy treatment. **Cannabinoids have been reported to be effective at treating cancer-associated anorexia, chemo or radiotherapy induced nausea and vomiting, relief from insomnia, enhanced mood, appetite stimulation, and pain relief (Engels et al, 2007).** Along with treating the symptoms of cancer and cancer treatments, cannabinoids have also exhibited specific anticancer properties in animal models (Guzman, 2003; Sarfaraz et al, 2008; Pisanti et al, 2013; Velasco et al, 2012; Velasco et al, 2015).

When cancer is present in the human body, CB1 and CB2 receptor expression tend to increase in the diseased tissues. This lets us know that the endocannabinoid system must play an important role in the progression and regulation of cancer. CB1 receptor expression can even be correlated with disease severity and cancer aggressiveness (Malfitano et al, 2011; Velasco et al, 2015).

Both CB2 and GPR55 receptors also seem to follow this same pattern (Valesco et al, 2015). Although cannabinoids and cannabinoid receptor expression play a critical role in cancer growth, it also plays a critical role in tumor suppression. Blocking CB1 receptor expression in animals has resulted in carcinogenesis (cancer growth) in the intestines of mice, demonstrating that CB1 receptor activity actively suppresses tumor growth (Wang et al, 2008; Valesco et al, 2015).

Research has provided mixed results concerning how cannabinoids influence cancer. Some reports show cannabinoids reducing the prevalence of cancer while some other studies report cannabinoid induced cancer growth (Cudaback et al, 2010; Hart et al, 2004; McKallip et al, 2005; Zhu et al, 2000; Valesco et al, 2015). Nonetheless, **cannabinoid treatments have been shown to promote apoptosis (cell death) of cancer cells, impair cancer cell growth, and slow or block the spread of cancer (Velasco et al, 2012; Velasco et al, 2015).** The primary way that cannabinoids kill cancer cells is by preventing the growth of blood vessels in the cells and/or causing vascular endothelial cells to kill themselves (Valesco et al, 2015). Cannabinoids also affect autophagy, which is the process in the body by which cellular debris is broken down and eliminated from the body. When apoptosis occurs, and cell death is initiated, it is important that the body also engages in autophagy to handle the resulting cellular debris, so they do not build up in the body. If cellular debris builds up in the body, it can cause inflammatory responses. Think of autophagy as your body's way of producing a series of "pac men" that gobble up cellular debris when cells die.

Unfortunately, much of the research that has been conducted thus far concerning Cannabis, cannabinoids and cancer has largely been with synthetic cannabinoid compounds of varying dosage, quality, and administration routes used. Many of the studies performed to date have not utilized large randomized sample populations. More research will need to be performed before appropriate data will be available that can help shine more light on how cannabinoids can best be utilized as a treatment for not only cancer symptoms, but for the treatment of cancer itself.

Epilepsy and Cannabis

Cannabis reportedly can reduce the intensity and frequency of seizures in some individuals. Numerous examples have been featured in the media lately highlighting stories of children that have regained their lives by utilizing cannabidiol rich Cannabis treatments. One famous example is that of Charlotte Figi who inspired the famous CBD rich Cannabis strain, Charlotte's Web. However, it must be noted that the epidemiological data supporting the use of Cannabis for the treatment of seizures is not very strong. According to a review performed by Szaflarski and Bebin (2014), most interviews of epilepsy patients that have used Cannabis as an alternative treatment reveal that most of the time Cannabis does not actually provide appreciable relief from seizures. In many cases, Cannabis exacerbated seizure symptoms, rather than providing relief.

CBD has demonstrated antiepileptic effects in many animal research models, although it is unclear how CBD produces these effects (Szaflarski and Bebin, 2014). A series of experiments has shown that the CB1 receptor is critical in controlling seizures and that CBD exerts its anti-seizure effects through receptors other than those found in the endocannabinoid system.

It could be speculated that the relatively new appreciation of the diversity of THC/CBD ratios found among Cannabis varieties has not been well represented in previous studies. High resin yielding CBD dominant Cannabis plants are relatively new to the market and many people seeking alleviation of spasticity symptoms with Cannabis have perhaps been using THC dominant varieties. **As cannabinoid ratio data is gathered in future research, a clearer picture of how Cannabis can treat epilepsy symptoms will develop**. Ultimately at this point, there is little quality data available that can lead one to draw any conclusions, but better-quality research projects are currently being designed and implemented. As more states legalize Cannabis and allow its research, this data will become available.

Cannabinoid Assisted Neuroprotection

Some cannabinoids have demonstrated neuroprotective effects. For instance, cannabidiol (CBD) has demonstrated neuroprotective, anti-oxidative, and anti-apoptotic effects against β-amyloid peptide toxicity, a critical component of Alzheimer's disease (Iuvone et al, 2004). Both THC and CBD have exhibited neuroprotective effects against glutamate toxicity in rodent cortical neuron cell culture studies (Hampson et al, 1998). In rodent models, THC as well as endocannabinoids have exhibited neuroprotective effects against **ischemia**, a condition characterized by insufficient blood flow to the brain (Louw et al, 2000; Sinor et al, 2000). Cannabinoids have also been indicated as effective in protecting the brain during a concussion, which has gathered the attention of sports communities.

Pediatric Medical Cannabis Use

There is a limited amount of information currently available about the use of Cannabis medically in children. Most of the information that is available is in the form of case studies produced by doctors and nurses that have worked with pediatric patients to treat a medical condition with cannabinoids or herbal Cannabis. Much of this data that *is* available is difficult to interpret, because dosages, administration methods, and product formulations are not standardized. In addition, many of these reports feature very small sample sizes, sometimes as low as just one individual. The results of small sample sizes cannot be confidently extrapolated to a larger patient population. (Alcorn et al, 2019)

Because children are growing and changing so rapidly, dosing for children is highly dynamic, depending on the age range of the child. Traditionally, the primary age ranges considered for pediatric dosing are:

- Pre-term newborn infants born at less than 36 weeks of gestation
- Term newborn infants that are age 0 to approximately 28 days
- Infants and toddlers that are age 28 days to approximately 2 years
- Children that are age 2 to 11 years
- Adolescents that are age 12 to 18 years

Before really solid Cannabis or cannabinoid dosing guidelines can be developed for pediatric patients, the safety and the efficacy of Cannabis for different medical conditions must be studied in each of these age groups. Some health care professionals and caregivers that administer medical Cannabis or cannabinoids to children rely on scaling down dosing information available for adults down to children based on body surface area and body weight.

However, this is not always appropriate, because there can be a number of changes happening within a child that will affect the way that Cannabis constituents are processed in the body, which do not correlate directly with body surface area and body weight. For instance, one example is in metabolic rates in children. A child's metabolic rate can dramatically change at different stages of life, without being directly correlated to the child's size. One study found that scaling dosing for hydrophobic drugs, like cannabinoids, tends to work well enough based on body weight for patients between 1 month and 1 year of age, however for older children, this model was less effective, and instead dosage scaling based on body surface area was more effective (Johnson, 2008).

To deal with this problem of a lack of dosage recommendations, parents, caregivers, and healthcare professionals are left with the classic trial and error approach, where low dosages are initially used, and then slowly scaled up until a therapeutic or adverse response is obtained.

Research is mixed regarding whether health care professionals support pediatric use of Cannabis to treat medical conditions. In one study, physicians that were surveyed cited that the primary barriers to their support for pediatric Cannabis use are a lack of formulation, potency, or dosing standards (Ananth et al, 2018). The primary conditions currently being treated with Cannabis in children are cancer-related nausea, epilepsy, motor disorders, and autism.

One case study reports cardiac arrest and death in an 11-month old male child following THC exposure (Nappe and Hoyte, 2017). No other risk factor could be identified other than THC metabolites in the child's body, leading the physicians to present the possibility that THC may have caused inflammation of the heart (myocarditis) which eventually led to a heart attack. While it is impossible to say whether THC was the primary factor responsible for the child's death, it at least highlights a risk factor that all parents and pediatricians should be aware of regarding pediatric Cannabis use or accidental pediatric Cannabis exposure.

BACK INTO THE FOLD: STANDARDIZING CANNABIS MEDICINE

In 2020 researchers representing an expert panel on Cannabis for the United States Pharmacopeia (USP) published a paper entitled "Cannabis Inflorescence for Medical Purposes: USP Considerations for Quality Attributes" in which they provide a framework for bringing Cannabis back into the United States Pharmacopoeia as a standardized medicinal herb (Sarma et al, 2020). At the time of publication, this was incredibly significant news and signals a path toward reintegrating Cannabis into the medicinal plant toolbox that it had been excommunicated from nearly a hundred years prior.

The identification of standardized quality attributes for herbal Cannabis is important for integrating Cannabis into the national and global natural products industry, whether as THC-rich medical or adult use Cannabis (aka "marijuana") or as CBD or CBG-rich Cannabis ("hemp"). This allows companies to use these quality attributes to assess the acceptability of Cannabis ingredients, for example. Prior to these recommendations, Cannabis infused product manufacturers had to establish their own quality guidelines or rely on the quality guidelines provided by their respective state, which may or may not be adequate. These recommendations also provide a reference point for states that have not yet legalized medical or adult-use Cannabis, or that have not adopted testing regulations yet for Cannabis products. It may also be a path toward standardizing all Cannabis testing requirements among all states in the United States, as well as across countries around the world.

It should be noted that these USP recommendations are for quality attributes associated with herbal Cannabis (Cannabis inflorescence). At the time of this writing there is still a lot of work to be done to define quality attributes for other Cannabis products, like extracts.

Summary of Recommended USP Quality Attributes for Herbal Cannabis

Quality	Example(s)	Description/Notes
Naming	"Cannabis Inflorescence"	Dried pistillate (female) inflorescence of the plant Cannabis sativa L., family Cannabaceae, including its subspecies, varieties and chemotypes.
Identification	Macroscopic/Microscopic HPTLC HPLC and GC	
Chemical Profile	Type I – THC Dominant Type II – THC/CBD Type III – CBD Dominant	Dominant and co-dominant terpenes should also be identified.
Contaminants	Pesticides, Elemental Contaminants, Microbial Contaminants, and Mycotoxins (See below)	
Pesticides	See USP Chapter <561>	
Elemental Contaminants	Arsenic: 0.2 ug/g Cadmium: 0.2 ug/g Lead: 0.5 ug/g Mercury: 0.1 ug/g	
Microbial Contaminants	Total Aerobic Bacteria: 100,000 CFU/g Yeast/Mold: 10,000 CFU/g Bile-Tolerant Gram-Negative Bacteria: 1,000 CFU/g Salmonella: ND E. Coli: ND	More stringent requirements recommended for sensitive or at-risk populations
Mycotoxins	Total Aflatoxins (B1, B2, G1, G2): ≤ 20 ppb B1 Aflatoxin: ≤ 5 ppb	
Water Activity	0.6 ± 0.05 aw	
Foreign Organic Matter	≤ 5% of stems ≤ 2% other	Stems must be 3mm or less in diameter, otherwise they are considered "other"
Total Ash and Acid-Insoluble Ash	≤ 20% Total Ash ≤ 4% Insoluble Ash	
Packaging and Storage	8 – 15°C ≤ 40% relative humidity	
Labeling	Cannabis Inflorescence Type I Cannabis sativa L. 250mg/g Total THC Dominant Terpenes: Myrcene, Limonene, Terpinolene	Any other cannabinoids over 10mg/g should also be labeled.
Adulteration	Presence of synthetic cannabinoids	

FIGURE 52: SUMMARY OF USP RECOMMENDATIONS FOR CANNABIS QUALITY

Chapter 18: SIDE EFFECTS OF CANNABIS CONSUMPTION

Learning Questions

- What are the most common side effects of THC-rich Cannabis use?
- What are the most common side effects of CBD-rich Cannabis use?
- How does THC-rich Cannabis impact mental health?
- How does Cannabis affect men and women differently?
- How does Cannabis impact other areas of health such as the immune system, cardiovascular health, gastrointestinal health, sex and reproduction, or motor function?

This chapter focuses on highlighting some of the various side effects of Cannabis use – with the focus being on THC-rich Cannabis, though references are made to CBD-rich Cannabis where appropriate. Although from a physiological perspective Cannabis is a relatively safe plant to consume – meaning that it is not likely to kill you – it *does* present some risks for users and it is important to understand the effects associated with Cannabis consumption.

WHAT HEALTH RISKS ARE ASSOCIATED WITH CANNABIS CONSUMPTION?

Although there have been no reported overdose fatalities directly attributed to Cannabis, Cannabis and Cannabis derivative products can hold a variety of potential health risks, depending on the dose, method of ingestion, frequency of exposure, and internal biochemistry of the user. Although the health effects of acute administration of cannabinoids to humans has been studied to some extent, there is not much reliable information about the health risks of long term, or chronic, use of Cannabis in various forms and administration routes. Data that does exist often does not account for confounding factors like socioeconomic variables, diet, exercise, alternative drug delivery systems than smoking, other health conditions present, or other drug (licit or illicit) use present. A user's history of use can also influence adverse effects. **Many of the adverse psychological effects associated with acute high-THC Cannabis exposure such as anxiety and paranoia, are more common in naïve or anxious users and can often be controlled by dose modulation** (Ashton, 2001).

THC is the most commonly studied cannabinoid, so many of the reported health effects of Cannabis are associated with the effects of THC consumption, but do not take other cannabinoids, Cannabis constituents or their synergies into account. Many Cannabis health reports also examine smoking without considering other administration routes. As research continues, a more mature picture of the toxicity and health effects of Cannabis compounds and Cannabis products will develop. Some primarily reported adverse health effects of high-THC Cannabis consumption include (Volkow et al, 2014; Ashton, 2001; Hall and Degenhardt, 2009):

Adverse Health Effects of Short Term High-THC Cannabis Use	Adverse Health Effects of Long Term High-THC Cannabis Use
Short term memory loss; difficulty learning or retaining information	Tolerance and Dependence
Motor coordination dysfunction	Chronic bronchitis and emphysema (if smoking)
Anxiety, paranoia	Memory impairments
Increased heart rate (made worse by smoking)	Increased risk of heart attack and palpitations (made worse by smoking)
	Cannabinoid dependent hyperemesis (chronic nausea and vomiting)

FIGURE 53: PRIMARY REPORTED ADVERSE HEALTH EFFECTS OF HIGH-THC CANNABIS CONSUMPTION

Along with these commonly reported adverse side effects, high-CBD Cannabis and CBD extracts have their own set of adverse side effects including hepatic drug metabolism inhibition, blood pressure changes, gastrointestinal irritation, drowsiness, and even increased tremor activity in some individuals with Parkinson's disease (Bergamaschi et al, 2011). Although CBD has been demonstrated as safe in various clinical trials, it is still important to work with a physician when considering a CBD treatment, especially if you are taking other drugs, to ensure that CBD's effects on drug metabolism and bioavailability do not cause accidental overdose or toxicity of other medications.

Potential Adverse Side Effects of CBD
Inhibition of drug metabolism
Manipulation of drug bioavailability
Immune system suppression
Tremor in Parkinson's disease patients
Decrease in blood pressure, resulting in lightheadedness or drowsiness
Minor gastrointestinal irritation

FIGURE 54: REPORTED ADVERSE SIDE EFFECTS OF CBD

Many of the adverse health effects of Cannabis consumption can be directly linked to smoking, but less correlated with exposure to cannabinoids or other Cannabis compounds. Inhaling smoke into the lungs causes a variety of health effects including paralyzing of cilia throughout the lungs, increasing heart rate, and initiating pro-inflammatory responses. Smoking typically results in **carbon monoxide exposure** which increases carbon monoxide levels in the blood, reducing the ability of the blood to efficiently carry oxygen throughout the body. Chronic exposure to carbon monoxide can lead to heart disease and neurological damage.

Many of the negative health effects of smoking Cannabis can be alleviated by utilizing other delivery methods like sublingual sprays, Cannabis infused edibles or vaporizing the plant material at lower temperatures. Vaporizing, or "vaping", still produces particulates that are irritating to the lungs but avoids combustion and pyrolization, thus preventing exposure of the lungs to various aromatized hydrocarbons that can be dangerous and potentially carcinogenic. Vaporizing typically results in the same level of cannabinoid bioavailability as smoking while drastically reducing carbon monoxide exposure (Abrams et al, 2007).

Care should be taken when using portable vaporizers as they can very easily heat up to the point of combusting the material. Vaporizers produced with glues, plastics, and other heat sensitive materials may present health risks. Some vaporizable products designed for portable vaporizers may contain additives to improve the smolder or draw of the vapor or smoke such as propylene glycol or vegetable glycerin. These additives can potentially present health risks such as respiratory irritation and damage upon chronic exposure. **Digital temperature programmable desktop vaporizers are generally preferred for minimizing health risks associated with smoking or vaporizing.**

Cannabis can also serve as a vector for contaminants entering the body such as biological contaminants like yeasts, molds, and bacteria, as well as chemical contaminants such as pesticides, industrial contaminants, residual solvents, or metals. Consumers with compromised immune systems are especially at risk for suffering adverse reactions to Cannabis if it contains contaminants. In some cases, Cannabis contaminations can be fatal to immunocompromised individuals.

The same 2017 National Academy of Sciences study which was referenced in the previous chapter concerning the clinical indications of Cannabis and cannabinoids also identified the statistical evidence for various reported adverse effects of Cannabis. The health risks that they identified as being supported with substantial, moderate or limited statistical evidence are: testicular tumors, heart attack and stroke risk, increased risk of prediabetes, chronic bronchitis, chronic obstructive pulmonary disease (COPD), increased risk of motor vehicle crashes, increased risk of injuries, lower birth weight of offspring, pregnancy complications, admission of infants to neonatal intensive care units (NICU), acute impairment of learning, memory and attention, development of schizophrenia or psychoses, increased risk of mania or hypomania, increased risk of suicidal ideation and suicide completion in heavier users. It should be noted that these risks are associated with statistical significance, not necessarily clinical significance, and are primarily associated with THC-dominant Cannabis products. To learn more about the difference between statistical significance and clinical significance, see Chapter 23.

COMMON SIDE-EFFECTS OF THC-RICH CANNABIS CONSUMPTION

THE MUNCHIES – APPETITE STIMULATION

One of the most well-known side effects of Cannabis consumption is colloquially referred to as "the munchies" and is characterized by abnormally stimulated appetite and cravings. This is caused by CB1 receptor stimulation in the brain. Research has shown that mice that do not have CB1 receptors will not feel the need to eat and will die of malnourishment. That's how important our CB1 receptors are to our day-to-day regulation of food intake.

RED EYES – CONJUNCTIVAL HYPEREMIA

Conjunctival hyperemia, or increased blood flow to the blood vessels in the eyes, causes the "red eye" phenomenon

Conjunctival hyperemia, or red eye, is a common acute side effect of Cannabis consumption. This is caused by altered blood flow in the body leading to **dilation of the blood vessels in the eye**, making them bigger and more visible, thus leading to a red appearance throughout the eye. Blood vessels exist throughout the eye in the vitreum, or jelly, of the eye ball. Most of the eye usually appears white because these blood vessels are very small. When the blood vessels enlarge, due to lack of sleep, allergies, or chemical initiated vasodilation, the eye ball appears red.

DRY MOUTH - XEROSTOMIA

Xerostomia is the medical term for "dry mouth" or "cotton mouth," an effect common to many Cannabis users. **Xerostomia is caused by effects elicited from cannabinoids or other compounds present in Cannabis and is not an artifact of smoking** (Veitz-Keenan and Ferraiolo, 2011). Persistent xerostomia can lead to an increased risk of other oral conditions such as tooth loss and decay (Veitz-Keenan and Ferraiolo, 2011). **To combat xerostomia, sugar-free gums, hard candies, and mints can be used to stimulate salivation** (Gupta et al, 2006; Friedman and Isfeld, 2011). Products with alcohol compounds such as xylitol and sorbitol can be used to help fight the development of tooth decay (Burt, 2006).

Memory Loss

Short term memory loss is a well-documented side-effect of the consumption of high THC/low CBD Cannabis products. The science behind this effect has to do with a region of the brain called the **hippocampus, which is involved with memory and learning and is saturated with CB1 receptors.** The hippocampus is very important for the formation of new memories about experiences (Eichenbaum and Cohen, 1993; Squire and Schacter, 2002). When THC or other cannabinoids stimulate CB1 receptors in the hippocampus, it often causes a disruption of normal functioning leading to altered and potentially impaired memory formation and retention. This can lead to one common effect where an individual may not remember the topic of a conversation by the time the conversation has ended. There are also rare reports of total temporary amnesia caused by acute Cannabis use (Stracciari et al, 2003).

It should be noted that Cannabis does not disrupt all types of memory and learning, but rather only short-term memory and a specific subcategory of long-term memory, called **episodic memory**. In addition, researchers have found evidence that long term uses develop compensatory behaviors to compensate for these memory impairments (Schoeler and Bhattacharyya, 2013). Episodic memory is often called the "memory of events" and relates to memories of experiences in a particular time and place, as opposed to the memory of facts, called **semantic memory**, or **implicit memory**, which includes things like motor and cognitive skills, perceptual skills, conditioned responses, and habits. This is, for example, why many college students can get away with consuming copious amounts of Cannabis while still achieving good grades and actively learning. The downside is they may not remember many of the actual experiences that they had in college.

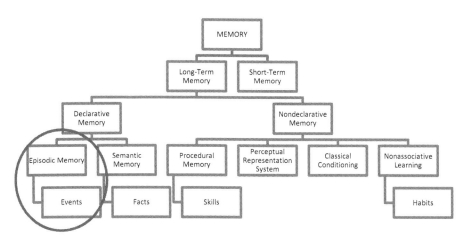

Although THC may impair memory, some cannabinoids and terpenes exhibit memory *enhancement* effects, at least in rodent research models. The following cannabinoids and terpenes are reported to exhibit memory enhancement effects:

Alpha-Pinene   Beta-Caryophyllene
Cannabichromene (CBC)   Cannabigerol (CBG)   Cannabidiol (CBD)

CANNABIS SMOKING AND MOUTH HEALTH

There are several studies that have attempted to determine what effects pulmonary use of Cannabis through smoking has on the environment within the mouth. The concern is not just because of the general effects that smoking, regardless of the material, has on the mouth. Part of the concern rests in the immunosuppressive properties of THC and other cannabinoids. This suppression of immune cell activity could mean that the body is more susceptible to bacterial and viral infections, but more research is needed to better understand these types of relationships.

One condition that seems to occur more frequently in Cannabis (smoking) users than non-smokers is **Leukoedema** (Darling and Arendorf, 1992). Leukoedema is a condition which causes the oral mucosa to alter in appearance, becoming wrinkled. This condition can also be caused by habitual oral activities such as cheek sucking or nut chewing (Van Wyk et al, 1979; Pindborg et al, 1968).

Chronic Cannabis smoking has also been associated with **gingival enlargement**, or the enlargement of the gums (Swati et al, 2012). Heavy acute and chronic Cannabis smoking can also cause **uvulitis**, which is the swelling of the mucosal tissue around the uvula, causing the uvula to get very large (Swati et al, 2012). This can cause problems swallowing and breathing deeply. There is some evidence to suggest that Cannabis smokers have higher incidences of gingivitis, but it is hard to determine if this is because of Cannabis smoking, or from a lack of oral hygiene or other confounding factors (Silverstein et al, 1978).

Chronic Cannabis smoking is also associated with increased populations of the fungus *Candida albicans* in the mouth, although it is not associated with an increased incidence of **candidiasis**, the term used for *C. albicans* infections (Versteeg et al, 2008). *C. albicans* is responsible for conditions like thrush and the common yeast infection. It is a polymorphic species that can change between a yeast and a pseudomold depending on its environment. The increased presence of *C. albicans* is particularly of concern for immunocompromised patients because **candidemia**, the term used for a systemic *C. albicans* infection, can be fatal if the fungus reaches the bloodstream. Strains of *C. albicans* can be resistant to anti-fungal medications, increasing the severity of the infection (Chong et al, 2012). The immunosuppressive properties of some cannabinoids might potentiate this effect.

There are mixed research results when it comes to Cannabis smoking and the likelihood of developing **oral cancers**. Theoretically it would seem like the hydrocarbons, benzopyrene, and other compounds in the smoke would promote premalignant tumors that could become cancerous. Indeed, one study does link Cannabis smoking with oral premalignant lesions, including **leukoplakia** and **crythroplakia** (Hashibe et al, 2002; Versteeg et al, 2008). **Another series of studies, however found that there was not an association between oral cancer prevalence and Cannabis smoking, whether acute or chronic** (Rosenblatt et al, 2004).

CANNABINOID HYPEREMESIS SYNDROME (CHS)

Cannabinoid hyperemesis syndrome, or CHS, is a condition usually characterized by severe nausea and vomiting precipitated by Cannabis use or cannabinoid exposure (Galli et al, 2011). CHS generally affects chronic Cannabis users that have used Cannabis for more than a year, though reports are highly variable and inconsistent. Some users report having used Cannabis for nearly a decade or longer before CHS symptoms begin, while others experience symptoms much sooner.

It is unknown how prevalent CHS may be among chronic Cannabis users, for several reasons. Cannabis is still illegal in many places in the world, which dissuades users from reporting their Cannabis use to their physician. This can lead to underdiagnoses or misdiagnoses with conditions such as cyclical vomiting syndrome (CVS). On the other hand, in areas where Cannabis is legal and its use is prevalent, physicians may be more likely to assume that chronic nausea and vomiting symptoms are correlated with Cannabis use without performing in-depth investigations, leading to overdiagnosis and misdiagnosis. Additionally, the symptoms of CHS can overlap with a variety of other conditions, making it challenging to diagnose.

One of the tell-tale signs of CHS is frequent showering and hot baths, which can relieve the sensation of nausea. The primary treatment for CHS is to discontinue Cannabis use. It has been reported that other cannabinoids besides THC will trigger CHS symptoms, including CBD, and it is not advised that patients diagnosed with CHS engage the use of any cannabinoids for that reason (Alice Moon, *viva voce*). A reported remedy that may ease nausea symptoms is the application of capsaicin on the stomach (Stumpf and Williams, 2020). Both the application of capsaicin, as well as the use of hot showers or baths, likely elicit their therapeutic actions through the stimulation of TRPV1 receptors, though other mechanisms are likely also at play.

The exact mechanisms of CHS are not well known. DeVuono and Parker (2020) speculated that chronic doses of THC lead to dysregulation of the endocannabinoid system through CB1 receptor downregulation, which in turn increases endocannabinoid system enzymes that go on to decrease the levels of endocannabinoids present at any time in the body. This in turn would cause changes to TRPV1 receptor distribution. The upregulation of TRPV1 receptors could theoretically lead to symptoms like sweating, thirst, increased heart rate, decreased body temperature, and digestion disruption. These symptoms can go on to elicit anxiety and depression in patients, which can cause a feedback loop that intensifies all of the other symptoms, ultimately leading to the primary outwardly visible symptoms of CHS – nausea and vomiting.

The year 2020 has been a breakthrough year for published CHS research, and it is likely that as more places throughout the United States and the world legalize Cannabis, CHS will be diagnosed more frequently and thus recognized as a priority for clinical research. Outspoken CHS survivor and Cannabis advocate, Alice Moon, maintains a website, http://www.cannabinoid-hyperemesis.com, that compiles information about cannabinoid hyperemesis syndrome to assist those that may be suffering from this condition, as well as researchers hoping to learn more about the condition.

HOW DOES CANNABIS AFFECT MEN AND WOMEN DIFFERENTLY?

There is a problem plaguing biomedical research, currently. It's a problem that could have profound implications for how we interpret most of the biomedical research data that currently exists. The problem is that women and people of color are drastically under-represented in our medical research. It is very common for medical research data derived primarily from Caucasian male patient populations to be assumed to be directly applicable to women and people of color. When it comes to differences between cis gendered and trans gendered individuals, the data is even more absent.

When it comes to Cannabis, one of the first things that is important to understand, is that the endocannabinoid system is connected to the reproductive system and hormone signaling. Gonadal hormones influence the endocannabinoid system. Endocannabinoid levels vary when a woman is on her period, versus when she is not, for instance. This all complicates the puzzle of understanding how Cannabis affects the body.

There is some evidence that **anandamide levels peak in women during ovulation** and are at their lowest during the luteal phase of the menstrual cycle (Cui et al, 2017). These changes in anandamide levels are correlated with changes in sex hormones in the body, indicating an interplay between the endocannabinoid system and the menstrual cycle. On a practical level, what these differences may mean, therapeutically, is that lower dosages of cannabinoid treatments may be necessary during ovulation versus other phases of the menstrual cycle. This also may mean that a transgender person undergoing transition therapy may experience the effects of Cannabis differently as their hormone profile changes in their body.

Anecdotally clinicians have reported that Cannabis affects people of different ethnicities uniquely as well (Curious About Cannabis Podcast, BTS #19). There are likely other ways in which Cannabis affects people differently that will continue to be understood as Cannabis is further studied in the future. It is critical that future research focuses on teasing out these differences in effects to maximize the efficacy of Cannabis or cannabinoid therapies while minimizing any potential risks in vulnerable populations.

MENTAL HEALTH RISKS OF THC-RICH CANNABIS USE

There is some evidence that Cannabis use can exacerbate underlying mental health conditions in particularly susceptible individuals. Cannabis use has demonstrated the **potential to facilitate mania symptoms** in bipolar patients. Cannabis use also has the potential to exacerbate anxiety or panic conditions, although this is usually the case with naïve or acute users, rather than chronic users. There is still no causal evidence to show that Cannabis use alone leads to any particular mental health disorder, although it can produce a variety of temporary acute psychological symptoms (paranoia, anxiety, etc) while also exacerbating existing mental health conditions.

CANNABIS AND DISORDERS OF THE BIPOLAR SPECTRUM

Individuals with bipolar disorder (BD) are more likely to engage in substance use than any other "Axis 1" disorder such as major depressive disorder, schizophrenia, or panic attack disorder (Leweke and Koethe, 2008). Many studies looking at Cannabis use in the bipolar population are limited due to low sample size and limited data on **comorbidity**, or co-occurrence, between BD and Cannabis use (Agrawal et al, 2011). A meta-analysis performed by Agrawal et al revealed that BD patients are nearly seven times more likely to report a lifetime history of using Cannabis. One particularly interesting finding is that individuals diagnosed with BD tend to continue using Cannabis despite continuing or discontinuing the use of other drugs like alcohol, nicotine, or cocaine (Agrawal et al, 2011).

Zuardia et al (2010) looked at whether cannabidiol (CBD) was an effective treatment for manic episodes of bipolar affective disorder and found that doses of 600 to 1200 mg of CBD per day were ineffective, however the study was limited by a small sample size. Another confounding caveat is that it has been demonstrated in other studies that

CBD might provide better symptom relief in the presence of THC or other cannabinoids rather than being administered alone (Lemberger et al, 1976; Karniol et al, 1974).

Much of the reported Cannabis use among individuals with BD occurs immediately after a mood episode such as depression, mania, or hypomania (Agrawal et al, 2011). Changes in frequency of psychosis, rapid cycling, and depressive episodes do not seem to be associated with Cannabis use, even Cannabis use at an early age, according to one review (Agrawal et al, 2011). However, per this same meta-analysis performed by Agrawal et al (2011), individuals with BD using Cannabis report general disability associated with life functioning more frequently compared to those with BD that do not use Cannabis frequently. Mania in people with BD is highly comorbid with Cannabis use, but so far there is no clear understanding of whether Cannabis use exacerbates mania episodes or, conversely, if mania symptoms encourage or exacerbate Cannabis use.

One challenge to interpreting some of the data relates to a discrepancy in how researchers describe the frequency of Cannabis use in users. Some studies define "lifetime Cannabis use" as simply having consumed Cannabis several times throughout life while other studies define chronic or lifetime Cannabis use as having consumed Cannabis once or multiple times a year for multiple years. Some researchers define chronic use as consuming at least one Cannabis cigarette a day for multiple years. It is important to note how these terms are defined before interpreting a research paper looking at the effects of lifetime or chronic Cannabis use.

CANNABIS USE AND DEPRESSION

Euphoria or elevated mood is a commonly reported side-effect of the consumption of high THC containing Cannabis products. It makes sense then that Cannabis might be an effective antidepressant. The endocannabinoid system has been investigated over recent years to determine its possible connection to depression. Some researchers have found that **patients with major depression tend to have reduced endocannabinoid levels which correlate with the length of the depressive episode** (Hill et al, 2008). Studies have been performed with rodents that demonstrate **antidepressant effects elicited by the stimulation of CB1 receptors** by THC and Cannabis extracts (Hill and Gorzalka, 2005). Other studies contradict these findings. **Some research reveals that if CB1 receptors are blocked, anti-depressant effects can manifest.** Rodents were given drugs which specifically block the CB1 receptor. The rodents subsequently displayed antidepressant-related behaviors in tail suspension and forced swim tests (Shearman et al, 1003; Witkin et al, 2005).

The phytocannabinoids cannabigerol (CBG), cannabidiol (CBD) and cannabichromene (CBC) have exhibited significant antidepressant effects in rodent models (Musty and Deyo, 2006; Cascio et al, 2010; Russo, 2011). CBC exhibits antidepressant behavior that is up to ten times more potent than CBD in tail suspension and forced swim tests (Musty and Deyo, 2006). Along with phytocannabinoids, there are a variety of terpenes present in Cannabis that exhibit anti-anxiety or antidepressant effects including limonene, linalool, and myrcene (Russo, 2011).

On the other hand, **Cannabis use might also have the potential to exacerbate depression symptoms in some patients**. Graaf et al (2010) performed an in-depth review to determine if there might be an association between early Cannabis use and future depression spells. Their results indicate a moderate risk association, with women more likely to experience a depressive episode than men after consuming Cannabis early in life. This study did not identify distinct levels of Cannabis use (chronic vs acute use), thus somewhat limiting the quality of the data. A 2003 study conducted by Degenhardt et al discovered a "modest" association between depression and chronic Cannabis use but did not discover an association between depression and acute or infrequent use. Another 2008 study found a significant association between Cannabis use in early adulthood with later suicidal ideation, however, they did not discover any associations between *adolescent* Cannabis use and suicidal ideation or attempts (Pedersen, 2008).

DID YOU KNOW?

Serotonin is one compound heavily implicated in depression and other mental health conditions.

Serotonin receptors and CB1 receptors are often found together in some brain tissues in animals (Hermann et al, 2002). CB1 receptors have been shown to help control serotonin release in mouse brain tissues (Nakazi et al, 2000). Research has also shown that serotonin receptors are a key component in the memory impairment effects of THC.

More research will help elucidate the endocannabinoid-serotonin relationship to better treat depression and related conditions!

Problems with Rodent Models of Mental Health

The **tail suspension test** and the **forced swim test**, also known as the **behavioral despair test**, are two commonly used techniques to study depression in non-human animal studies. Many of the research studies examining the effectiveness of cannabinoids as anti-depressants utilize these two models.

The tail suspension test involves suspending mice by their tails, usually by taping their tails to a beam, so that they cannot get away and they have no way of grabbing anything. The mouse's "escape oriented behaviors" are monitored and quantified. The more the mouse moves and acts like it is trying to free itself, the less depressed the mouse is said to be. Researchers expose different mice to different drug candidates and measure how long it takes the mouse to give up its fight to escape.

The forced swim, or behavioral despair test, involves introducing a mouse to a pool of water from which the mouse cannot escape. Similar to the tail suspension test, to evaluate the mouse's behavior, its time spent doing things other than just keeping its head above water to avoid drowning. The less the mouse fights to escape and avoid drowning, the less depressed it is said to be.

There is a lot of debate over the validity of these types of study models for depression. These study models are cheap and reliable, but it is hard to determine if the models *actually* measure what they aim to measure. Does the mobility behavior of the rodent *actually* represent depression in some useful way that applies to humans?

CANNABIS USE AND POST TRAUMATIC STRESS DISORDER (PTSD)

Posttraumatic stress disorder (PTSD) is a condition characterized by heightened fear responses, inability to sleep, depression, anxiety, anger, avoidance behavior, recurrent memories, amnesia, and suicidal ideation after a high stress and traumatic event. PTSD is often comorbid with other psychological disorders and can be hard to diagnose or treat (Albucher and Liberzon, 2002). Commonly prescribed drugs for PTSD are often ineffective (Ipser et al, 2006). Recently, the endocannabinoid system has been investigated as a potential site of treatment for PTSD (Newmeister, 2013).

Many individuals with PTSD also use Cannabis. A study by the National Comorbidity Study showed that a patient with PTSD is three times more likely to use Cannabis regularly compared to someone without PTSD (Kessler et al, 1995). **Some researchers have suggested that individuals with PTSD often use Cannabis as a self-medication, taking advantage of Cannabis' amnesic, or memory impairing, properties** (Trezza and Campolongo, 2013). Cannabinoids can make it harder for the brain to recall memories while also making it easier for memories to be forgotten (Niyuhire et al, 2007; Atsak et al, 2012; Marsicano et al, 2002; Lutz, 2007). This effect can be of potential benefit to someone with PTSD that may be haunted by intrusive traumatic memories.

Researchers searching for evidence of this potential medicinal value of Cannabis have produced varying and contradictory results. Some studies show that stimulating cannabinoid receptors after a stressful event can actually promote harmful memory production and PTSD behavior (Campolongo et al, 2009; Hauer et al, 2011) while other studies have shown that cannabinoid agonists given to rodents after a stressful event actually promoted a healthier response to the event (Ganon-Elazar and Akirav, 2009, 2012,

2013). A survey performed in California of 170 patients at a medical Cannabis dispensary revealed that the primary reason that patients with PTSD use Cannabis is for help sleeping through the night (Bonn-Miller et al, 2014). It is speculated that this is because Cannabis use is often associated with reduced instances or conscious recall of dreams while sleeping. This could then mean that nightmares could be reduced or extinguished by cannabinoid receptor manipulation.

CANNABIS USE AND SCHIZOPHRENIA

Patients with schizophrenia often consume Cannabis (Koskinen et al, 2010). Some researchers have proposed that risks for both schizophrenia and Cannabis use are linked to common genetic causes, leading to high rates of comorbidity (Power et al, 2014). The effects of long term Cannabis use in conjunction with schizophrenia are not well understood. A study performed in 2014 attempted to review published studies investigating the effects of Cannabis on schizophrenia symptoms. The researchers concluded that there is still not enough information to draw any practical conclusions about whether Cannabis improves or worsens the mental health of individuals with schizophrenia (Rathbone et al, 2014). Many of the published studies so far report very small sample sizes, limiting the quality of the results. Different patterns in data may emerge when larger sample sizes are utilized.

A 2010 meta-analysis of Cannabis use in patients with schizophrenia published in the *Schizophrenia Bulletin* revealed that, of the data that was then available, schizophrenia patients that had also used Cannabis performed better on tests of visual memory, working memory, and executive functioning than patients that had not used Cannabis. This trend is generally associated specifically with chronic use of Cannabis. In contrast, the same 2010 study also found that schizophrenic patients that use Cannabis also tended to have displayed earlier ages of onset and more positive symptoms. If other substances, like cocaine or alcohol, are used in conjunction with Cannabis, mental performance usually decreases compared to the use of Cannabis alone. (Yucel et al, 2010)

CANNABIS USE AND HALLUCINATIONS

There is some evidence that Cannabis use may elicit auditory hallucinations, most remarkably in the form of "speech-illusions" while listening to white noise. Researchers in the Clinical Psychopharmacology Unit at University College in London presented participants with white noise and vaporized Cannabis or placebo and found:

"On placebo, 35% of adolescents and 15% of adults heard speech illusion during the 'random noise only' stimuli, compared to 55% of adolescents and 45% of adults on active cannabis. As predicted, relative to placebo, active cannabis led to a greater likelihood of experiencing speech illusion..." (Mokrysz et al., 2017)

Visual hallucinations are rarely reported from Cannabis use but may occur upon ingestion of very large doses. A study in 2006 looked to replicate another study examining whether Cannabis use in schizophrenic patients is associated with changes in hallucination symptoms. The authors conclude, "The strong association between cannabis abuse and fewer negative symptoms in schizophrenia was thus replicated in this sample, but once co-morbid addictive disorders had been controlled no influence of cannabis abuse on hallucinations was detected." (Dubertret et al, 2006)

It is more common for paranoid or delusional behavior or thinking to be reported after Cannabis use, though these symptoms are not really hallucinations, per se, but would be considered psychomimetic, or "imitating psychosis".

CANNABIS, ANXIETY, AND PANIC ATTACK DISORDER

Cannabis' anxiety and paranoia inducing effects are generally well known and documented. Acute doses of Cannabis can induce fear, anxiety, and phobia (Crippa et al, 2009). One research group found that 21% of their study's subjects that used Cannabis had high levels of anxiety (Reilly et al, 1998). Cannabis use in teenagers and young adults is often associated with heightened levels of anxiety (Dorard et al, 2008). Cannabis use and panic attack disorder are also often comorbid.

There is debate about whether Cannabis can help treat anxiety and panic attack disorder or if it purely exacerbates anxiety and panic conditions. Although there is evidence supporting the idea that Cannabis can contribute to anxiety and panic attack disorder, there is also a growing body of evidence that *long-term* users of Cannabis achieve relief from anxiety and panic attack (Crippa et al, 2009).

Anxiety caused by Cannabis use is most likely to occur if the user is less familiar with the drug's effects, if the individual consumes Cannabis in a new or stressful environment, or if the individual consumes high concentrations of cannabinoids or Cannabis products. Crippa et al (2009) proposed this list of risk factors for anxiety produced by the consumption of Cannabis:

Individual and genetic vulnerability	*History of previous anxiety episode*
Personality Traits	*Presence of anxiety disorders/symptoms*
Gender	*Basal anxiety levels*
Frequency of Use	*Abstinence states*
Dose and quantity consumed	*Environment and context of use*
Proportions and concentration of	*(set and setting)*
cannabinoids	

To minimize anxiety symptoms and risk of panic when consuming Cannabis,

➤ Familiarize yourself with Cannabis and its associated effects.

- ➤ Be careful consuming Cannabis in new settings.
- ➤ Avoid consuming Cannabis in uncomfortable or stressful settings.
- ➤ Be aware of the potency of the Cannabis product and monitor your dose.
- ➤ Schedule consumption appropriately. The psychoactive effects of inhaled Cannabis typically last approximately two to three hours. The effects of ingested Cannabis could last much longer.

IS CANNABIS ADDICTIVE?

Cannabinoids elicit effects from the brain's reward centers in much the same way as other drugs or pleasurable behaviors, potentially leading to dependence and tolerance symptoms. **After sudden cessation of chronic Cannabis use, non-life-threatening withdrawal symptoms can emerge such as sleeplessness, loss of appetite, depression and irritation**. Although these withdrawal symptoms are often reported to be much milder than withdrawal symptoms from other substances of abuse including alcohol, nicotine, and caffeine, some users attempting cessation report relatively profound withdrawal symptoms for up to two weeks or longer after cessation.

When addressing the question of whether Cannabis is addictive, it is important to first define the term "addiction". Addiction is often characterized by compulsive behavior, despite negative consequences. The concept of "addiction" is often broken up into two primary categories: substance addiction (previously often referred to as chemical dependence) and process (or behavioral) addiction. A substance dependence is usually defined as a state of being in which the body reduces its own production of endogenous chemical compounds, creating a dependence for exogenous (outside the body) chemical compounds to avoid withdrawal effects. Process addictions are characterized as behavioral addictions that do not feature the administration of exogenous chemical compounds but still feature characteristics like tolerance, withdrawal, repetitive reward seeking behavior, and continued behavior despite negative consequences. Examples of process addictions include gambling addictions, shopping addictions, exercise addictions, etc.

Today it is more common to encounter the concept of substance use disorder spectra when studying addiction. The DSM-V, a diagnostic manual that mental health professionals use to diagnose behavioral and psychological disorders, identifies Cannabis Use Disorder as one of these substance use disorders, but is careful to point out that Cannabis Use Disorder should not be diagnosed if the *only* symptom(s) a patient exhibits is the typical tolerance and/or withdrawal symptoms associated with the medical use of Cannabis (or any other drug). A key component of diagnosing substance use disorder is drug seeking or use behavior that *compromises relationships and obligations*. It should be noted, though, that a diagnosis of substance use disorder does not necessarily imply the presence of a chemical dependency on the substance. It simply reflects the fact that the substance is taken frequently despite consequences.

Some research has explored whether the potency of Cannabis has any effect on the likelihood of developing dependence symptoms. One report found that the symptoms of Cannabis dependence increase when tobacco is consumed in conjunction with Cannabis (Ream et al, 2008). Some evidence supporting the concept of Cannabis dependence lies in the fact that the brain experiences a deficit in dopamine release in certain areas of the brain during chronic Cannabis use (Giessen et al, 2016). Dopamine is a neurotransmitter commonly associated with pleasure and reward perceptions and behaviors. Primarily substance dependence is defined neurologically as decreased or blunted dopamine levels in the brain. If cannabis produces decreased functioning of dopamine receptors after use, an argument could be made that cannabis can produce dependence in users. The user would develop a need to stimulate dopamine receptors through the introduction of chemicals outside of the body because the body would not produce dopamine as easily on its own.

Cannabinoids do not cause the same sort of stark chemical dependencies that many other common drugs of abuse such as opiates or stimulants might cause. This may be because cannabinoids and their metabolites become stored in adipose, or fatty, tissue and steadily release over time after cessation of use. It may also be because phytocannabinoids do not cause drastic changes to the way the body produces its own cannabinoids.

To understand why the symptoms of Cannabis withdrawal are often mild, it is critical to understand the common cause of physical withdrawal symptoms. One of the causes for withdrawal is the body's sudden lack of a necessary neurotransmitter, which causes a myriad of physical problems. This generally happens because the targets of many drugs of abuse, like serotonin and dopamine, are slowly built up by the body, stored in little sacks called vesicles, and released on demand. When someone takes a drug like cocaine, it triggers a distinct release of chemicals from these vesicles in the brain, which the brain had spent considerable time building up. Once those chemicals are dumped and depleted, there is a considerable deficit and the body must take time to recover. This physiological deficit is what produces most physical withdrawal effects. If this happens repeatedly, the body may stop producing endogenous compounds and depend on exogenous compounds, resulting in chemical dependence.

However, the body does not store endocannabinoids in vesicles like it does with serotonin and dopamine. Instead, endocannabinoids are synthesized on demand, as needed, escaping this effect of chemical dumping and deficit. However, repeated Cannabis use *can* cause a reduction in concentration of cannabinoid receptors in the body, leading to a tolerance effect, because there are fewer receptors to stimulate, resulting in less of an effect experienced by the user. Some cannabinoids, like CBD, can actually stimulate the body's own production of endogenous compounds.

To review, neurologically there may be evidence that Cannabis causes mild dependency, based on how Cannabis affects dopamine in the brain. Mental health professionals recognize a condition called Cannabis Use Disorder, which may or may not feature chemical dependency. Cannabis use does lead to tolerance and withdrawal symptoms. Typically, these withdrawal symptoms are relatively mild because the body rarely experiences a very sudden deficit of cannabinoids like it might with other targets of drugs of abuse, although some users report difficulty quitting or maintaining abstinence from Cannabis use. At the end of the day, if someone's Cannabis use is persisting despite negative consequences to the user and the user's relationships, it is highly probable that a substance addiction is present.

ADOLESCENT CANNABIS USE

There is much debate over whether children are at a greater risk of developing long-term adverse health effects from THC-rich Cannabis consumption. There is some research that suggests that adolescent THC-rich Cannabis use can cause impaired adult memory function, particularly regarding emotional memory (Ballinger et al, 2015).

A study published recently that investigated data from a longitudinal study found that adolescent Cannabis use did not seem to correlate with any significant mental or physical health risks later in life (Bechtold et al, 2015). Other studies typically rely on broad drug-use survey data collected from school surveys which may or may not be reliable. Most studies looking at childhood Cannabis use are not longitudinal studies that follow subjects into adulthood. Many of these studies do not exclude confounding factors like cigarette smoking, non-Cannabis related health complications, diet, exercise, etc. More long-term research will have to be conducted before the long-term health effects of Cannabis use started during adolescence can be properly evaluated.

A negative effect that Cannabis use can have on adolescents is that it may affect the developing child's social behavior negatively, potentially delaying or stunting the child's emotional maturation and development of sophisticated social skills. If a child consumes Cannabis and consequently reduces social interaction or begins to associate Cannabis use with common activities like eating, entertainment, sports, etc, it may become difficult for the individual to later find as much pleasure in those activities without consuming Cannabis.

Cannabis' deleterious effects on memory can have profound consequences for a child's ability to learn. Cannabis can affect a person's ability to concentrate on a topic or comprehend complex information as is required in a school setting. Over time, if an individual repeatedly consumes Cannabis and has persistent difficulties keeping up with school, there may be a variety of other cultural and social consequences such as lower grades and less available educational and professional opportunities later in life.

OTHER EFFECTS OF THC-RICH CANNABIS USE

EFFECTS OF CANNABIS USE ON INSULIN SENSITIVITY AND BLOOD GLUCOSE STORAGE

There has been a long running debate over whether Cannabis helps a person lose weight. Many Cannabis consumers consume excess calories, but do not appear to be more overweight on average than non-Cannabis consumers. It turns out that there is some interesting science behind this idea.

Penner et al. examined data of Cannabis use, insulin levels, and blood glucose for over 4000 adult men and women and determined that individuals that were current users had on average **16% lower fasting insulin levels and smaller waist circumference** (Penner et al, 2013). Fasting insulin is the insulin present in your blood before eating a meal. High insulin levels are typically associated with obesity.

Insulin helps glucose, or sugar, enter cells of tissues for storage or processing. When insulin binds to an insulin receptor on a cell, it triggers a cascade of effects. Channels on the cell wall are opened which allow glucose to enter. The glucose is then typically converted to a compound called pyruvate, which is then broken down into basic carbon chains, or fatty acids. Alternatively, glucose may end up getting linked together to form glycogen. This process is how the body stores energy away for later use. Glycogen is typically stored in muscles and the liver, while fatty acids are stored in adipose, or fatty, tissue throughout the body. When fatty acids and glycogen are metabolized, energy is released which fuels the work of the rest of the body.

Higher levels of insulin in a healthy person without insulin tolerance usually indicate that sugar will be readily processed and stored in tissues throughout the body. Lower fasting insulin levels would mean that sugar will have a harder time getting converted to fat, theoretically leading to smaller waist circumference on average, although this same effect could also result in significant increases in blood glucose (blood sugar).

Another study found that active Cannabis smoking seemed associated with **reduced incidences of diabetes mellitus** (Alshaarawy and Anthony, 2015). The authors of the study point out that the relationship is contrary to results obtained from previous preclinical animal studies and more research is needed to understand this effect.

Another study has found that Cannabis use is associated with a **lower risk of insulin resistance in HIV patients**. Insulin resistance is a serious condition preceding type

2 diabetes and heart disease in which the body's cells become resistant to insulin, so insulin ends up building up in the blood without serving a function. This can lead to increased blood pressure, obesity, and dyslipidemia. **Dyslipidemia** is a condition in which there are elevated amounts of fats and other lipids in the blood because they are not being stored in other cells, either due to saturation or insulin resistance.

EFFECTS OF CANNABIS ON THE IMMUNE SYSTEM

CB2 receptors are expressed in a variety of immune system cells including B and T lymphocytes, Th1 cells, Th2 cells, Treg cells, Macrophages, microglia, and natural killer cells (Galiegue S et al, 1995). Generally, **cannabinoids act as immunosuppressants**, meaning they inhibit the immune system response in one or more ways. Although most *in vitro* and *in vivo* research indicates a potent immunosuppressive effect of THC and CBD, research examining viral load in HIV positive patients indicates that neither smoked Cannabis nor synthetic THC seems to cause any negative effects on viral load over a 21-day period (Abrams et al, 2003; Ware, 2015).

Cannabinoids primarily modulate the immune system by affecting cytokines. Cytokines are a group of small proteins that affect cellular communication to help guide immune system cells toward areas of inflammation, infection, etc. Some cytokines are pro-inflammatory, while others are anti-inflammatory. **THC and CBD dampen the response of pro-inflammatory cytokines** and enhance the response of anti-inflammatory cytokines (Cabral et al, 2015).

Understanding how cannabinoids affect the immune system could lead to better treatment options for patients with inflammatory neurodegenerative diseases like Alzheimer's disease, Parkinson's disease, and Amyotrophic lateral sclerosis, as well as autoimmune disorders in which the patients are slaves to their own over active immune systems, such as Behcet's disease, psoriasis, multiple sclerosis, rheumatoid arthritis, and more.

EFFECTS OF CANNABIS ON HEART HEALTH

Cannabis can elicit numerous cardiovascular effects depending on the dominant cannabinoids present. Different cannabinoids have a variety of effects on the heart. The research on this topic is a bit difficult to wade through because cannabinoid effects on the heart, and other systems of the body, are dose dependent and can bring out varying effects and varying dosages.

Researchers found that when anesthetized animals are given THC, often blood pressure reduces, or alternatively blood pressure rises at first and then comes down followed by a condition called **bradycardia**, or an abnormal slowing of heart rate

(O'Sullivan, 2015). CBN has not typically affected heart rate or blood pressure when administered by itself.

In conscious humans, these effects are bit less predictable. Based on research done for the commercial cannabinoid product Sativex®, a product containing a 1:1 ratio of THC to CBD, researchers found that both Sativex® and smoked Cannabis cause **trachycardia**, or rapid heartbeat, with this effect decreasing among chronic users (O'Sullivan, 2015; Bedi et al, 2013; Crawford and Merritt 1979; Karschner et al, 2011; Mathew et al, 1992a, 1992b; Schwope et al, 2012; Benowitz et al, 1975; Ponto et al, 2004; O'Leary et al, 2002). In other studies, both THC and THCv have been demonstrated as **vasoconstrictors**.

CBD alone seems to cause a reduction in heart rate and blood pressure in animal models, and this effect may be mediated by serotonin receptors, as administering a serotonin receptor antagonist blocks this action (O'Sullivan, 2015). Several research reports indicate that long term administration of CBD does not result in a change to blood pressure or heart rate in subjects, but more research is needed to better understand how CBD affects the human cardiovascular system (O'Sullivan, 2015; Benowitz and Jones, 1981; Bergamaschi et al, 2011).

EFFECTS OF CANNABIS ON THE STOMACH AND GASTROINTESTINAL SYSTEM

Endocannabinoid receptors are distributed throughout the gastrointestinal system including the stomach, gut, and colon. Endocannabinoids like 2-AG have been implicated as serving a protective role in the stomach (Kinsey et al, 2011). CB1 receptor activation has been shown to reduce gastrointestinal motility in rodent models (Pinto et al, 2002). CB1 and CB2 receptor agonism is associated with reduced visceral sensitivity and pain in rodents (Duncan and Izzo, 2015). CB1 and CB2 receptor agonism has also been demonstrated to effectively alleviate inflammation in models of Irritable Bowel Disease/Syndrome (IBD/IBS) (Alhouayek et al, 2011, 2012; Bento et al, 2011; D'Argenio et al, 2006; Duncan and Izzo, 2015; Engel et al, 2008, 2010; Kimball et al, 2006; Massa et al, 2004; Singh et al, 2012; Storr et al, 2008, 2009). These effects could be critical to treating painful GI inflammatory conditions like Crohn's Disease.

Referring to a retrospective observational study of Irritable Bowel Disease/Syndrome by Naftali et al (2011), Duncan and Izzo report:

"Of the 30 patients, 21 improved significantly after treatment with cannabis. The need for other medication was significantly reduced and the number of patients requiring surgery decreased during cannabis use." (Duncan and Izzo, 2015)

Cannabinoids have also been shown to have effects limiting colon cancer. Some cannabinoids have been shown effective at promoting apoptosis of colon cancer cells as well as limiting the cancer's proliferation. The oxidation of CBD leads to a compound called HU-331 which has demonstrated antiangiogenic and proapoptotic properties (Duncan and Izzo, 2015; Peters and Kogan, 2007).

Beyond cannabinoid receptors, vanilloid receptors also play important roles in the gastrointestinal system. Many cannabinoids interact with both TRPV1 and TRPV2 receptors including CBD, CBG, CBGV, and THCV (De Petrocellis et al, 2011). One study has shown that CBC interacts with TRPV1, TRPV3, and TRPV4 receptors in the GI tract (De Petrocellis et al, 2012). Vanilloid and cannabinoid receptors occur together in primary afferent nerves in the gut (Izzo and Sharkey, 2010).

Although Cannabis is sometimes used to treat nausea, it seems that chronic consumption of Cannabis in some users can actually precipitate nausea symptoms and even chronic vomiting in a condition referred to as Cannabinoid Hyperemesis Syndrome. Individuals suffering with this condition often learn various coping behaviors like frequent hot showers or baths, which help reduce the nausea. This condition was recognized relatively recently, and it is still unclear how prevalent Cannabinoid Hyperemesis Syndrome is, but symptoms typically are relieved through cessation of Cannabis use.

EFFECTS OF CANNABIS ON SEX AND REPRODUCTION

As mentioned previously, the endocannabinoid system is intricately linked to the reproduction system in humans. Besides the ECS' involvement with various sexual hormones, the ECS is also associated with sperm availability in men and ova availability in women, implantation, basic physiology of the reproductive tract, and mating behavior (Stuart et al, 2015; Bradshaw and Allard 2011; Bradshaw et al, 2006; Maccarrone et al, 2000, 2004; Sun and Dey, 2012; Wang et al, 2004).

Cannabinoids are involved in the regulation of certain sex steroids like gonadal hormones through the regulation of the release of a compound called gonadotropin-releasing hormone (GNRH) (Stuart et al, 2015). THC seems to have varying effects between males and females. A research study that examined how ovariectomized female rats (rats with ovaries removed) respond to THC with and without the addition of a sex hormone and found that the ovariectomized rats experienced less pain relief than those with the added hormone (Stuart et al, 2015; Craft and Leitl, 2008).

It should be noted that at least one case study has suggested that the swings in blood pressure caused by cannabinoids, combined with the swings in blood pressure caused by the act of sex and orgasm, reportedly caused a stroke in a male subject (Alvaro et al, 2002).

In men, the cannabinoid system may be linked to the regulation of erectile functioning. CB1 receptors are present on the neurons responsible for signaling the production of neurotransmitters and other compounds that cause erections (Stuart et al, 2015). In one study, researchers administered a CB1 antagonist to the paraventricular nucleus of the hypothalamus in the brains of male rats which induced erections (Shamloul and Bella, 2011). It is possible that Cannabis use could impair reproductive ability for males as Cannabis smoke causes an increase in compounds that can cause oxidative damage in the body, which is associated with poor sperm quality, low fertilization rates, increased abortion rates, and increased incidence of disease in offspring (Stuart et al, 2015).

In women, low doses of Cannabis may excite the libido, while increased doses are likely to depress the libido, though this effect is not consistent among women (Stuart et al, 2015; Gorzalka et al, 2010). This enhancement effect does not seem to extend to other characteristics like level of vaginal lubrication, orgasm frequency, or orgasm strength (Stuart et al, 2015; Gorzalka et al, 2010). It is speculated that Cannabis was at one time or another used for several sex or reproductive treatments including menstrual irregularity, dysmenorrheal, childbirth, decreased libido, gonorrhea, urinary retention, menopausal symptoms, and more (Russo, 2002).

Some epidemiological studies have found that Cannabis use during pregnancy is associated with low birth weight, cognitive defects, and other negative birth outcomes, but these studies are still limited in their ability to determine causality as they are often plagued by confounding variables like diet, cigarette and alcohol use, exercise, etc. At the same time, other longitudinal studies have determined that prenatal Cannabis exposure was not associated with these effects but rather does seem to be associated with hyperactivity and impulsivity in offspring, however the significance of the correlation weakens when other extraneous variables are considered (Goldschmidt et al, 2000; Fried and Smith, 2001).

In one particular study of mothers in Jamaica, researchers determined that babies that had been exposed to Cannabis during breastfeeding as newborns exhibited no differences from babies that had not been exposed to Cannabis (Dreher et al, 1994). During a five year follow up for a similar study that instead focused on Cannabis exposure during pregnancy, these results were confirmed. In fact, those children that had been exposed to Cannabis during pregnancy tested better for autonomic stability and reflex behavior. Researchers concluded that aspects related to school attendance and home environment were more predictive of child outcomes than Cannabis exposure during pregnancy (Hayes et al, 1991).

In *Reproduction and Cannabinoids: Ups and Downs, Ins and Outs*, the writers offer this sentiment:

"Although it is not certain that smoking cannabis when pregnant harms the fetus, it is probably unwise to subject a developing nervous system to exogenous cannabinoids because it could potentially disrupt the endogenous cannabinoid system, a system that ensures proper neural development." (Stuart et al, 2015)

EFFECTS OF CANNABIS ON DRIVING ABILITY

There is also great debate over the relationship between Cannabis use and motor coordination impairment related to driving and piloting vehicles. Does Cannabis impair driving skills similarly to alcohol to warrant legal consequence? While Cannabis use does alter psychomotor coordination, there also seems to be evidence that **these effects are dose related and Cannabis users are often able to compensate for their driving impairment due to a sustained or enhanced awareness of their own impairment** (Sewell et al, 2009). In other words, a "high" driver might actually drive more carefully because they are conscious that they are impaired. **If Cannabis use is combined with alcohol use, however, impairment effects tend to become substantially worse than they would be with either Cannabis or alcohol used alone** (Sewell et al, 2009). There is also some evidence that acute Cannabis users exhibit greater impairment symptoms than chronic users, further complicating the issue.

Determining Cannabis intoxication at the time of a traffic stop is very difficult due to the persistence of cannabinoids in the body for prolonged periods of time after initial administration. For chronic users that consume Cannabis daily for years, they could stop consuming Cannabis and be likely to fail any variety of drug tests well over a month later. Some states in the US have instituted THC blood level limits for driving, similar in theory to the Blood Alcohol Content (BAC) used for determining legal suitability to drive after alcohol consumption. Other states rely on field sobriety tests and obvious signs of recent Cannabis use to discern Cannabis impaired drivers. Some companies are pursuing the development of roadside saliva tests that could potentially discern Cannabis use within a three or four-hour time frame (Jehanli et al, 2001). Even so, **the debate remains as to whether roadside drug testing for Cannabis, due to the persistence of exogenous cannabinoids and metabolites in the body after administration as well as the difficulty correlating concentrations of cannabinoids in the body with significant levels of impairment, can be used to properly identify impairment or endangerment to society at all.**

Never drive or pilot a vehicle or operate heavy machinery after consuming THC-rich Cannabis or cannabinoid products. DUI and DWI laws in the United States are applicable to driving under the influence of Cannabis, the same as driving under the influence of alcohol.

Enduring Understandings

- There are variety of ways of studying medical effects and deriving medical claims, each with different levels of predictive power associated with them.

- The type of medical research of the lowest quality, meaning the least predictive power for a generalized population, is anecdotal reporting. The type of medical research of the highest quality, meaning the greatest predictive power, are placebo-controlled double-blind clinical trials.

- There is little clinical research that has been performed with herbal Cannabis or Cannabis extracts. Most Cannabis research is performed with isolated cannabinoids and mixtures of isolated cannabinoids.

- Cannabinoids exhibit exceptionally low toxicity with very high LD50s. It is considered physically impossible to lethally overdose on traditional herbal Cannabis.

- Cannabis is a polypharmaceutical – meaning that it contains many active compounds that work together to elicit effects greater than the sum of their parts. These effects are often referred to as "entourage effects".

- Sexual hormones affect how cannabinoids interact with the body, leading to differences in effects between people with testosterone dominant sex hormones versus estrogen dominant sex hormones.

- Some of the primary health risks of THC-rich Cannabis use are memory and attention disruptions, anxiety, paranoia, motor discoordination, increased heart rate, and increased risk of stroke and heart attack. Additional risks may incur if smoking such as chronic bronchitis or COPD. If pregnant, Cannabis use can potentially cause low birth weight and may exacerbate other pregnancy complications. Adverse neonatal, perinatal, and postnatal effects may be more primarily associated with smoking than cannabinoids themselves and more research is needed.

- Tolerance and dependence can develop with repeated Cannabis use.

- A wide variety of therapeutic uses of Cannabis and cannabinoids have been identified, and many medical experts agree that Cannabis or cannabinoids can be effective at treating chronic pain, spasticity, nausea, and other conditions.

- Most medical research on Cannabis and cannabinoids has focused on either THC or CBD dominant chemovars, which represents a very narrow window of chemical varieties of Cannabis available. Future research is likely to focus on elucidating how cannabinoids in various ratios to one another as well as how CBG, CBC, THCV, and CBDV dominant chemovars affect medical conditions uniquely compared to THC or CBD dominant chemovars.

PART IV

INSIDE THE CANNABIS LABORATORY: EXTRACTION AND TESTING

Essential Questions

What services do commercial Cannabis testing laboratories typically offer?

How do labs prove their accuracy?

What are some ways Cannabis testing can go wrong?

What questions could you ask a laboratory to evaluate their competency?

Chapter 19:

CANNABIS EXTRACTION TECHNOLOGIES

Learning Questions
- What are the various ways that Cannabis extracts are commonly produced?
- What is supercritical fluid?
- Why is ethanol a generic solvent for extracting a broad spectrum of phytochemicals?
- Why are hydrocarbons a powerful solvent for selectively extracting cannabinoids and terpenoids?
- How are Cannabis extracts refined?

There are several ways to extract cannabinoids and other terpenoids from the Cannabis plant. Some simple methods include just shaking the plant material over varying sized mesh filters that dry sift the trichomes from the plant. More commonly, though, Cannabis extractions are being conducted using a variety of solvent systems. A solvent is a liquid that can dissolve things. The most popular solvents used for Cannabis extractions are alcohol, organic solvents like butane and propane, lipids (fats), and supercritical fluid CO_2.

LIPID EXTRACTIONS

Lipids are oily things like waxes and fats. Lipids are nonpolar, so they can act as efficient solvents for extracting cannabinoids and other nonpolar compounds from Cannabis. Traditionally butter and various plant oils (olive, avocado, coconut, sunflower) are used for lipid extractions. Cannabis infused butters and food oils have the advantage of being safe and ready to consume. Not only can lipids serve as efficient carriers for cannabinoids, they may also enhance the bioavailability of cannabinoids and other compounds in the body (Nanjwade et al, 2011).

Caprylic acid, an MCT oil component featuring an 8-carbon chain tail.

Some Cannabis products including tinctures and salves are produced with "MCT" oil. MCT stands for medium chain triglyceride. Medium chain triglycerides are fatty acids that have tails of 6 – 12 carbon atoms long. Because medium chain triglycerides have these long tails of hydrogen and carbon, they are oily and nonpolar – perfect for extracting or mixing with other oils like cannabinoids or terpenoids.

# of Carbons in Tail	Common Name	Categorical Name	Molecular Structure of MCT Oil Component
6	Caproic acid	Hexanoic acid	
8	Caprylic acid	Octanoic acid	
10	Capric acid	Decanoic acid	
12	Lauric Acid	Dodecanoic acid	

FIGURE 55: COMMON MCT OILS

Some lipids can help serve as dietary supports for the endocannabinoid system. For instance, extra virgin olive oil contains phenolic compounds which may boost the production of cannabinoid receptors in the body (Notarnicola et al, 2016). In addition, olive oil has been demonstrated as a mildly effective skin penetration enhancer and can boost bioavailability. Omega fatty acids have been demonstrated to exhibit anti-inflammatory effects via cannabinoid receptors and can also be used as carriers for cannabinoids and terpenoids (McDougle et al, 2017)

HYDROCARBON SOLVENT EXTRACTIONS

Hydrocarbon solvents are, as the name implies, solvents that are composed of hydrogen and carbon. Cannabinoids and terpenes are nonpolar, so they mix easily with organic nonpolar hydrocarbon solvents like propane or butane. During the extraction process, the solvent passes across the plant material and the nonpolar compounds in the plant attach to the solvent, producing a liquid mixture of solvent and Cannabis extract. The solvent is then evaporated off, or **purged**, resulting in the final Cannabis concentrate product, typically referred to as a "hash oil", such as **butane hash oil**, or **BHO**.

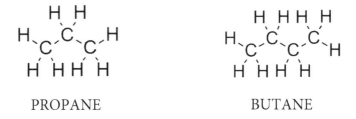

PROPANE   BUTANE

An **alkane** is another term used to describe a carbon compound surrounded by hydrogen. Alkanes are the bases for other organic compounds. For instance, if you add an oxygen-hydrogen group to any alkane, like ethane, it becomes an alcohol, like ethanol.

Alkanes Table (Simple to Complex; Most Volatile to Least Volatile)	
Alkane	**Molecular Formula**
Methane	CH4
Ethane	C2H6
Propane	C3H8
Butane	C4H10
Pentane	C5H12
Hexane	C6H14
Heptane	C7H16
Octane	C8H18
Nonane	C9H20
Decane	C10H22

FIGURE 56: ALKANES TABLE

The fewer carbons present in the compound, the higher the volatility. Methanol is the most volatile alcohol while Ethanol is slightly less volatile. Solvent that is left behind in a concentrated extract is called a **"residual solvent."**

ETHANOLIC EXTRACTIONS

Ethanolic extractions are those involving alcohol, specifically ethanol, or ethyl alcohol. Alcohol acts as a good solvent for extracting cannabinoids and other terpenoids because it can bind to both polar and nonpolar compounds. Alcohol is easy to obtain, and the extraction process is relatively simple, making the extraction method more feasible for home preparations. Usually ethanolic extractions result in a tincture that can be consumed alone or diluted in a drink. Sometimes extractions are conducted with a sugar alcohol called **glycerol**, or **glycerin**. Final products utilizing glycerol as a solvent are called **glycerites**, whereas extracts suspended in alcohol or more commonly referred to as **tinctures**.

Basic ethanolic extractions result in a tincture product that is seemingly low in cannabinoid content by weight, usually between 1-10%. However, because the product is weighed down by the alcohol, and possibly sugar, it is very easy to consume heavy quantities of the material. For instance, a 3% THC tincture would contain 30 mg/g of THC. A gram of tincture could easily be consumed in a single spoonful.

Ethanolic extraction products can be made more potent by evaporating, or "purging", the alcohol out of the extract, resulting in a thick resin sometimes called "RSO".

REMOVING GREEN COLOR IN ETHANOLIC CANNABIS EXTRACTS

Ethanolic concentrates or extracts might exhibit a green color, due to chlorophyll that has been extracted. This usually happens when material has soaked in alcohol for a long period of time. Chlorophyll is very soluble in alcohol. Peak chlorophyll extraction will be obtained if the plant material soaks in alcohol in the dark for 24 hours or more (Sartory and Grobbelaar, 1984). Chlorophyll has a melting point of around 152°C, or 306°F. To avoid chlorophyll in extracts, reduce temperature and time spent in solvent. UV radiation will break down chlorophyll, among other compounds in the extract, leading to a reduction of green color in the extract over time if exposed to sun light or other UV sources, changing the color from green to an amber or brown color. Washing the extract quickly with alcohol repeatedly can recapture some of the cannabinoids from the extract while leaving the chlorophyll behind.

SUPERCRITICAL/SUBCRITICAL FLUID EXTRACTION (SFE)

> "CO2 is a flexible solvent. CO2 is capable of being an excellent solvent for terpene extraction. It's also capable of extracting a lot of water, wax and nonsense..."
>
> Murphy Murri, BTS #17 Curious About Cannabis Podcast

As an alternative to more toxic solvents like hexane, methanol, or butane, carbon dioxide (CO2) can be used to extract cannabinoids and terpenoids from Cannabis. CO_2 extractions result in amber or yellow-orange oils that are commonly used in portable electronic vaporizer pens. The extraction process involves heating and pressurizing carbon dioxide to the point that it becomes a super or subcritical fluid. A **supercritical fluid** is a phase state at which the solvent is neither a gas nor a liquid but has the properties of both. It can creep into tiny spaces and pores like a gas while dissolving substances like a liquid. This makes it very efficient for extracting compounds from plants and other materials. The heat and pressure parameters can be customized to efficiently extract particular compounds, like cannabinoids or terpenes.

$$O=C=O$$

HOME ETHANOL EXTRACTION EXPERIMENT: MACERATION VERSUS PERCOLATION

Disclaimer: Check your local laws before performing an extraction on Cannabis. Cannabis extraction might be illegal where you live. The author and publisher of Curious About Cannabis™ do not accept responsibility for any illegal activity that may be conducted using the information shared here.

There are a variety of ways that someone can make an ethanolic tincture at home. In fact, herbalists have been making botanical tinctures for thousands of years! There are two primary ways to make ethanolic tinctures: maceration and percolation. Maceration is the most common method and involves letting the plant material soak in ethanol for an extended period of time before filtering the solids out of the liquid. Percolation, on the other hand, is like brewing coffee. A tool called a percolation cone is used to hold the plant material in place. The plant material is lightly soaked in ethanol to soften up the plant tissues before ethanol is poured over the plant material and allowed to drip through the percolation cone, drip by drip. But which method is better? I have my thoughts, but why don't you try an experiment for yourself!

Materials:

Glass Jars w/ Lids	Conical Metal Strainer	Coffee Filters
High Proof Ethanol (Everclear) – NO RUBBING ALCOHOL	Cheesecloth or Metal Strainer	Permanent Marker
Optional: Balance/Scale		

Procedures:

1. Before beginning, if you would like to measure the amount of alcohol that is recovered in each process, it is important to measure the weights of the jars with lids prior to starting. These weights are called tare weights, and will be used later on.
2. To perform a maceration extraction:
    a. Measure ground Cannabis into a jar.
    b. There should be approximately 4x as much ethanol as Cannabis. Take the amount of Cannabis used and multiply by 4. Then measure that much ethanol into the jar.
    c. Seal the jar.

     d.   Shake well for at least 1 minute.

     e.   Store in a cool, dark area (light and heat will alter the chemistry of the tincture).

3.   To perform a percolation extraction:

     a.   Measure ground Cannabis into coffee filter. For sake of example, let's assume you start with 10 grams of ground Cannabis.

     b.   Measure an amount of ethanol equal to four times that of the amount of Cannabis into a small jar. For example, if starting with 10 grams of Cannabis, measure out 40 grams of ethanol.

     c.   Lightly moisten the ground Cannabis with a small amount of ethanol. I recommend moistening with an amount of ethanol equal to the amount of Cannabis used. For instance, if 10 grams of Cannabis is being used, moisten with 10 grams of ethanol.

     d.   Begin pouring the remainder of the ethanol slowly over the Cannabis material and allow to drip into the jar. Be careful not to overfill. Continuing the previous example, after moistening the plant material with the 10 grams of ethanol, 30 grams of ethanol would then be poured on top.

     e.   When finished pouring ethanol, remove the conical strainer and filter and seal the jar.

     f.   Store in a cool, dark area

4.   To measure the amount of alcohol recovered from each trial, simply weigh the sealed jar and subtract the tare weight for that jar from the total weight measured.

5.   Optional: Submit each sample to a third-party Cannabis testing lab to identify the cannabinoid content in each tincture.

     a.   Which one was more potent?

Although some extractors use true supercritical fluid extraction, most Cannabis extractors actually heat and pressurize carbon dioxide just below the supercritical state, to a point called a subcritical state. The process is relatively quick and can be standardized easily with good manufacturing practices.

SFE is an often-preferred extraction method since it does not typically leave residual solvent in the produced oil and the process can be more environmentally friendly than organic solvent extraction. Commercial supercritical fluid extraction is already used commercially to decaffeinate coffee beans, extract the oils of hops for beer production, and produce essential oils from plants.

Cosolvent Extractions

While each of these extraction methods has been presented in isolation, processors actually often utilize mixtures of solvents and extraction techniques to achieve their preferred product. There are several solvents that are often used together to produce Cannabis extracts including, but not limited to: ethanol/water, ethanol/carbon dioxide (carbon dioxide expanded ethanol), carbon dioxide/butane, butane/propane, and carbon dioxide/butane/propane.

Assistive Techniques for Extraction

Microwave Assisted Extraction (MAE)

Microwave assisted extraction, or MAE, is a relatively newer extraction technique that combines traditional solvent extraction techniques with microwave heating. This heating of the solvent increases the energy present in the extraction. This typically results in shorter extractions times, less solvent used, higher yields, and lower costs. Microwave heating can be applied to supercritical fluid extraction techniques to enhance the efficiency of the technique and potentially increase yield (Staudt, et al, 2003).

Ultrasound Assisted Extraction (UAE)

The extraction process can often be enhanced by utilizing a process called focused ultrasound extraction. Focused ultrasound utilizes sound waves to generate bubbles in the solvent which gather energy and eventually pop, resulting in a forceful implosion that hits the sample matrix, effectively disintegrating the cells of the sample, allowing target compounds to better interact with the solvent and extract more effectively. This method can be especially effective for the extraction of highly volatile compounds like terpenes. Ultrasound assisted extraction, also called sonication, can be combined with supercritical fluid extraction processes, like carbon dioxide (CO_2) extraction, to **speed up production times and obtain better yields at lower temperatures and pressures all while using less solvent (Yang and Wei, 2016).**

Extract Refinement Techniques

Understanding the Extract Refinement Process

When a Cannabis inflorescence undergoes extraction, the crude oil produced, which contains essential oil and resinous components of the plant, is called an "oleoresin." Most product manufacturers do not use crude Cannabis oleoresin as an ingredient. Instead, they prefer to use extracts that have been minimally refined to remove heavy fats, waxes, and pigments. The resulting "cleaned up" extract is called an "absolute."

Many Cannabis extracts, including CO_2 extracts and ethanol extracts, are absolutes. These absolute extracts may then be even further refined to distillates, which contain only a handful of target compounds, such as cannabinoids or terpenes. A distillate can then be further refined to a single isolated compound, like CBD or THC. The following sections describe the processes associated with these various steps of Cannabis extract refinement.

Winterization

During the extraction process, many other compounds other than cannabinoids and terpenes are pulled from the product, like various waxes and fats. To remove these products from the extract or concentrate, a technique called **winterization** is often employed. Winterization involves bathing the extract in a solvent, typically alcohol, and then exposing the solution to cold temperatures for an extended period of time so that the waxes and fats precipitate out and clump together. The fats and waxes are then filtered out resulting in a final product that contains a higher concentration of cannabinoids by weight.

Filtering

Extracts can also be cleaned up by passing them through various types of filters, the most common being simple mesh filters and activated charcoal filters. Mesh filters can help remove particulates and heavy fats and waxes, especially when done after winterization. Charcoal filters can help reduce dark pigments in extracts while also helping to remove some contaminants and solvents, though it can also remove some target compounds like cannabinoids and other terpenoids.

Solvent Washing

Extracts can also be cleaned up by adding a different solvent which cannabinoids or other target compounds will exhibit a greater affinity for, but other non-target compounds will not and vice versa – adding solvents which non-target compounds will exhibit greater affinity for, leaving target compounds behind. For instance, an extract can be mixed with water and another solvent, such as ethanol or hexane, and then mixed and separated, removing some non-target compounds in the water and pulling target compounds into the other solvent. When the mixture is allowed to settle, stratified layers appear and the layer containing the target compounds can be removed and purged, resulting in an overall cleaner extract in the end.

Distillation

Fractionated distillation is a method of separating a mixture of compounds into its various components, or fractions, by taking advantage of the unique boiling points of the compounds found in the mixture. A solution can be slowly heated to various temperatures to boil off and then condense certain compounds from the mixture. By starting at the lowest boiling point and working the temperature up slowly, a variety of target compounds can be separated out and collected. Special columns called **fractionating columns** are also used to help separate compounds that have very similar boiling points. This basic concept can be applied on a variety of industrial scales to produce high quality, pure compounds of interest, like cannabinoids or terpenes.

Wiped film and short path distillation are commonly used in Cannabis extractions to produce clear distillates containing 70% or more THC or CBD. Wiped film distillation involves the use of a spinning series of paddles which spread the extract into a very thin film, allowing it to easily evaporate at lower temperatures, preventing degradation of target compounds like terpenoids and cannabinoids. Short path distillation utilizes techniques which cause the distillate to travel a very short distance to a reception flask. This is a technique commonly used for compounds that are unstable at high temperatures. Typically, terpenes will be distilled first and captured in a flask, followed by cannabinoids, leaving behind a dark non-volatile fraction that is often discarded or put through a secondary distillation. The captured terpenoids may be mixed back into the cannabinoid fraction to produce unique extract products.

Crystallization and Cannabinoid Isolation

If the concentration of a particular cannabinoid reaches an adequate purity, the molecules of that cannabinoid will begin to order themselves together into solid structures called crystals. This process is called crystallization. Different cannabinoids begin the crystallization process at different concentrations and conditions. It is most common to see CBD and THCA crystallize in concentrated Cannabis extract products.

There are various methods that are used to obtain cannabinoid crystallization, but they often begin with a distilled Cannabis extract product. One simple method is to simply obtain a concentrated extract that is of adequate purity that it will slowly crystallize on its own over time. Then the extract is simply allowed to rest until the cannabinoid of interest has crystallized and all other components of the extract have separated away from the crystals. This is the effect responsible for some Cannabis extract products labeled as "diamonds."

Another crystallization method involves dissolving the cannabinoids in a powerful solvent and then exposing the compounds to a solvent for which the cannabinoids have little affinity. This causes the cannabinoids to move closer to each other as they try to escape the unsuitable solvent, facilitating a crystallization reaction. Often a variety of cold and hot temperature treatments are also used to facilitate the crystallization process. After a successful crystallization process and harvest, the purity of the resulting crystals may be anywhere from 90 – 99%+ pure. If a purity of 95% or greater is reached, the product is often considered an "isolate".

CANNABINOID ISOLATION VIA CHROMATOGRAPHY

In additional to crystallization techniques, cannabinoids like THC and CBD can be isolated from an extract using various forms of chromatography, like flash chromatography, centrifugal partition chromatography, or basic column chromatography. In chromatographic methods, a crude oil or distillate is usually dissolved in a solvent and then passed through a stationary phase consisting of silica and various adsorbents to neutralize non-target compounds while separating the components of the sample into purified fractions.

Flash chromatography involves sending the sample through the column at a high rate of speed and pressure. Rotary Centrifugal Partition Chromatography involves sending a sample through a series of columns while they are spinning, which helps the sample separate into separate phases, which then makes it easier for each phase to separate into its unique chemical constituents.

Once the sample has separated into its various components, a producer simply needs to purge the solvent out of the sample to be left with purified forms of each component. Chromatography efficiency can vary greatly depending on the technology used and the consistency of operation.

FULL SPECTRUM VS. BROAD SPECTRUM EXTRACTS

The terms "full spectrum" and "broad spectrum" are often used to describe Cannabis extracts – but what do these terms mean? The terms "full spectrum" and "broad spectrum" are not scientific and are not well-defined. Every Cannabis company has their own definition of what a "full spectrum" or "broad spectrum" extract is, making it very confusing for customers to compare products. While reviewing various types of Cannabis products, the only conclusion I could come to was that these terms are used consistently to differentiate Cannabis extracts from cannabinoid isolates, like CBD or THC isolate.

The term "**full spectrum**" tends to imply that the full chemical profile of the plant, or some part of the plant, such as the resins, is maintained in the extract. But this is a bit of a misnomer for several reasons. First of all, as mentioned before, most hemp extracts are at least minimally refined to remove heavy fats and waxes. This right away manipulates the chemical profile. In addition, extraction techniques are not perfect, and always target some limited range of chemical compounds. While it is possible to do various types of extractions on Cannabis and then mix them together, very few companies are doing that. Finally, as of now most Cannabis testing labs cannot accurately identify all of the compounds in a Cannabis sample in such a way as to enable a producer to verify whether they did indeed capture the "full spectrum" of a Cannabis plant or flower. This is because the Cannabis plant contains hundreds of compounds, and some of those have still not been very well characterized.

While preparing to write this section I encountered a listing on a hemp wholesale website for a "full spectrum" hemp distillate extract. I thought to myself, "How can a distillate be 'full spectrum'?" Perhaps at best the producer is using the term "full spectrum" to refer to the cannabinoid fraction of the compounds found in Cannabis.

I have also seen supercritical CO_2 extracts labeled as "full spectrum" and I've seen ethanol extracts that are also labeled as "full spectrum". The chemical profiles of these three extract types – distillate, CO_2, and ethanol – are *very* different, so the term "full spectrum" cannot be reasonably applied to all three types equally.

The term "broad spectrum" seems to be a bit more honest when describing most hemp extracts. However, the term "broad spectrum" is ambiguous and, dare I say...broad. Currently the term "broad spectrum" is often applied to extracts that have had the original chemistry of the plant altered in some way, usually by decarboxylating the cannabinoids or removing THC. But this is not always how the term "broad spectrum" is used.

How phytochemically diverse must an extract be to qualify as "broad spectrum"? Does a distillate that only contains cannabinoids count as "broad spectrum", since it contains multiple cannabinoids?

The best way for consumers to handle this issue is to always ask to see the Certificate of Analysis for any Cannabis product they are considering purchasing. The Certificate of Analysis should provide details about what cannabinoids, and possibly terpenes, are in the extract. Certificates of Analysis for extracts also sometimes indicate the production method, which can help consumers infer other information about the extract. For instance, if a Certificate of Analysis of an extract indicates that the extract is a concentrated ethanol extract, you can infer that the extract contains more phytochemical diversity.

The different cannabinoids, terpenes, flavonoids, and other plant compounds found in Cannabis other than the major cannabinoids like CBD and THC can change the behavior of cannabinoids in the body, sometimes enhancing CBD and/or THC's effects, and other times perhaps reducing their effects.

Some research indicates that phytochemically diverse Cannabis extracts that have not been heavily refined, may provide better therapeutic value, at lower dosages, with fewer side effects, compared to isolated CBD. However, more research is needed to understand this effect in such a way as to be able to take advantage of it in a targeted manner.

CONTAMINANTS IN CANNABIS EXTRACTS AND CONCENTRATES

Contaminants in Cannabis extracts can come from a variety of sources at different points of the supply chain. When Cannabis resins are concentrated, chemical contaminants like pesticides and mycotoxins often will become concentrated as well. The feedstock (the raw plant material) for an extraction could be tested for pesticides prior to extraction and appear clean, but during the extraction and concentration process, trace amounts of pesticides present in the flower could get tripled, quadrupled, or more, resulting in pesticide concentrations which are then detectable at potentially dangerous levels.

Most extraction methods kill molds and bacteria. Supercritical fluid extraction exerts so much pressure that the process destroys most fungal spores. However, if mycotoxins were produced by any fungal contaminants in the plant material, those mycotoxins will remain intact and could become concentrated in the extract.

Solvents, pesticides and mycotoxins can build up in extraction equipment if it is not well maintained and cleaned, resulting in the contamination of otherwise clean material that might run through the equipment. It is important to always clean extraction equipment in between runs to ensure that there are no carry-over contaminants that are unnecessarily contaminating multiple batches of extract, rather than just one.

Some refined Cannabis extracts may be at risk of becoming contaminated with foreign matter like clay particles or silica (glass). In general, this kind of contamination can be easily prevented through the use of proper screens and filters, however Cannabis extracts contaminated with these kinds of materials, which are often used in color remediation and other forms of extract refinement, have been identified in legal Cannabis markets.

Contaminants in Cannabis can also come about because of improper packaging or storage conditions. Typically, Cannabis extracts should only be stored in containers made of materials that will not react with terpenoids or cannabinoids. Many types of common plastics and cheap metals can break down over time and leach into the extract. Alternatively, the terpene content in an extract can sometimes dissolve some cheap plastics. To stay safe, the best materials for housing Cannabis extracts are those made of glass, stainless steel, and polytetrafluoroethylene (PTFE).

Common Sources of Cannabis Extract or Cannabis Product Contamination

Life Cycle Stage	Contaminants	Source
Cultivation	Pesticides	Applied during growth
	Growth Hormones	Applied during growth
	Metals	Soil uptake
	Molds	Wet conditions during flowering
Post-Harvest Handling	Bacteria	Unhygienic handling
	Mold	Humidity in storage
	Mycotoxins	Mold
Extraction	Pesticides	Feedstock
	Solvents	Inadequate desolvation
	Mycotoxins	Feedstock
Refinement	Pesticides	Feedstock
	Solvents	Inadequate desolvation
	Mycotoxins	Feedstock
	Clays	Color remediation
	Silica	Color remediation, chromatography
Formulation/Product Assembly	Pesticides	Feedstock
	Solvents	Inadequate desolvation of extract, or other ingredient contamination
	Metals	Feedstock or ingredient contamination
	Mycotoxins	Feedstock
	Bacteria	Unhygienic handling, lack of PPE
	Unapproved additives	Ingredient in product formula not GRAS for intended use
Storage	Plastics	Incompatible Packaging
	Rubbers	Incompatible Packaging

FIGURE 57: COMMON SOURCES OF PRODUCT CONTAMINATION

When trying to determine whether a material will possibly react with Cannabis extracts, you can use **Chemical Resistance Charts**, or **Chemical Compatibility Charts**, to understand whether the material is chemically compatible. These charts are readily available for free online from a wide variety of sources. These charts list a host of common chemicals or materials followed by a series of codes that indicate whether the material is compatible with the product or not.

ADDITIVES IN CANNABIS EXTRACTS

Additives may be added to Cannabis extracts for a number of reasons – some benign, and others less so. Cannabis extracts are most commonly amended with terpenes and ethanol to obtain a desirable taste, smell, and fluid consistency. For Cannabis extract oils used for vaporizer pens, propylene glycol or vegetable glycerin may be found as additives used to thin the oil and help it smolder. In their article "How Safe Is Your Vape Pen?", the non-profit Cannabis education organization Project CBD points out that propylene glycol can actually convert to a variety of harmful compounds at high temperatures including carbonyls, like formaldehyde, which can be highly toxic and carcinogenic (Project CBD, "How Safe Is Your Vape Pen?"). In addition to propylene glycol, extracted oils intended for use in vaporizer pens may also include some flavoring agents which are safe to eat but may not be safe to inhale, such as diacetyl or acetyl propionyl (Project CBD, "How Safe Is Your Vape Pen?").

Recently, in 2019, the Centers for Disease Control (CDC) in the United States announced that there was a health crisis affecting users of vape pens. Vape pen users were turning up in hospitals exhibiting symptoms of respiratory failure and respiratory disease. Ultimately this resulted in over 2500 people suffering lung disease and over 50 deaths. Upon investigation, it was found that this issue was primarily limited to Cannabis oil vape pens found on the black market. After evaluating fluids and tissues taken from affected patients, it was concluded that at least one of the culprits was an additive called tocopherol acetate, or vitamin E acetate. Tocopherol acetate was used as a thickening agent, as well as a cheap alternative to tocopherol. Tocopherol acetate is generally regarded as safe to apply topically or consume orally, but is *not* regarded as safe to inhale. As of the time of this writing, the CDC and various research bodies are still trying to determine whether there are other culprits at play other than tocopherol acetate.

To make matters more complicated, further research revealed that THC can actually react with vitamin E acetate to form complex a THC/Vitamin E Acetate complex, which may end up resulting in a more toxic compound than vitamin E acetate itself (Lanzarotta A et al, 2020).

There is currently very little information available about the potential health effects of inhaling whatever additives may be present in Cannabis extracts. As researchers begin to focus their research efforts on investigating the compositions of commercial and black-market Cannabis extracts, more information will become available to help consumers make informed decisions that can support their health. In the meantime, if you are a Cannabis extract consumer, try to learn about how your products are made and only consume products from companies that you trust.

QUALITY CONTROL OF EXTRACTION OPERATIONS

To ensure that Cannabis extract and manufactured products are of the assumed potency and purity, Cannabis cultivators, extractors, and product manufacturers must instate a variety of common quality control measures.

Cultivator Quality Agreement

Cannabis Intake Inspection, Microextraction, and Testing

Equipment and Facilities Sanitation

Production Monitoring

Potency and Purity Testing of Final Products

Packaging and Labeling Verification

Release for Distribution

CULTIVATOR QUALITY AGREEMENTS

One of the first quality control points in extraction operations is supplier evaluation and qualification. The extractor establishes a quality standard for incoming Cannabis materials which approved suppliers must adhere to as part of their quality agreement with each other. Extractors should seek to form relationships with farms that follow Good Agricultural Practices and Good Handling Practices. It is common for quality agreements to include provisions to allow the laboratory to visit the farm for the purposes of assessing quality.

FEEDSTOCK INTAKE INSPECTION

When the cultivator is ready to deliver Cannabis to the extractor, the extractor typically quarantine's the material, keeping it separated from other "cleared for work" materials, while it undergoes a visual and chemical inspection. The extraction facility will ensure that there are no obvious signs of foreign matter in the Cannabis lot such as sticks, grass clippings, bugs, or mold. After the visual inspection, the material is often submitted to a laboratory, either in-house or third party, which tests the material for contaminants and potency.

EQUIPMENT VALIDATION

Before any equipment is used in production, it should first be validated. Equipment validation is a process which gives a producer confidence that their equipment is meeting required specifications and can perform reliably with repeated use.

PROCESS VALIDATION

Once equipment has been validated, production processes have to be validated to ensure that product manufacturing procedures produce consistent results when followed. This typically involves performing a procedure multiple times and evaluating quality control data associated with the production events to determine whether the process is functioning properly.

MICROEXTRACTION

It is possible for there to be less than detectable residues of pesticides on Cannabis which can become concentrated to detectable levels in the final extract. Because of this, it is important for extractors to perform **microextractions** on incoming Cannabis lots. Microextractions are simply small-scale extractions on a very small sample from the lot for the purposes of testing for contaminants like pesticides or metals.

EQUIPMENT AND FACILITIES UPKEEP

Laboratories featuring sound quality systems keep consistent records of equipment and facility maintenance and cleaning. Every extraction and product manufacturing event should be traceable to sanitation and maintenance records which prove that work surfaces, utensils, and equipment were clean and in good working order during production.

ENVIRONMENTAL MONITORING AND CONTROL

It is critical that Cannabis accepted by a laboratory is maintained in its receiving condition by monitoring storage conditions and moisture content of the plant material to prevent conditions that might support the growth of micro-organisms. You might ask, "But won't the extraction process kill any mold or bacteria?" The answer is, yes, the extraction process will likely kill micro-organisms, but the problem is not limited to the micro-organisms themselves, but rather extends to the toxic chemicals that they can leave behind. Some molds produce toxic byproducts called mycotoxins which can be highly carcinogenic. These mycotoxins persist after the mold dies, are highly heat tolerant, and can pass into Cannabis smoke or vapor when consuming contaminated Cannabis or a contaminated Cannabis extract. This is why careful monitoring of environmental conditions and product storage conditions is critical for quality control.

PRODUCTION MONITORING

During the extraction and product manufacturing process, the extraction laboratory may track any number of variables and data points to ensure the production of reliable, consistent products. Typically, labs measure their extraction yields, product cannabinoid content, and equipment operating parameters like temperatures and pressures, at a minimum. This allows a laboratory to understand how every batch of extract or product was produced and its resulting characteristics. These details are often captured through records called batch manufacturing records.

TESTING OF INTERMEDIATE AND FINISHED PRODUCTS

Random samples from batches of finished extracts or manufactured products are typically submitted for routine potency and contaminant testing prior to distribution. The most common tests that producers order for finished products are cannabinoid and terpene assays, pesticide screening, metals testing, and microbiological testing.

Enduring Understandings

- The most common methods of extracting chemical compounds from Cannabis include lipid, hydrocarbon, ethanol, and supercritical fluid extraction.
- Lipid extractions involve the use of fats or oils like butter, vegetable oils, MCT oils, etc.
- Hydrocarbon extractions usually involve the use of simple alkanes like butane and/or propane to extract the nonpolar fractions of Cannabis resins.
- Ethanol is a broad non-target solvent that extracts a wide spectrum of chemical compounds from Cannabis. Ethanol's selectivity can be tightened by changing the temperature of ethanol.
- Carbon dioxide can be pressurized and heated to a point that it becomes a supercritical fluid which can dissolve and pass through tissues acting as both a liquid and a gas.
- Winterization is a process by which heavier fats and waxes in a solution are precipitated out under cold temperatures.
- Crystallization is a purification process where conditions are provided under which a target chemical will group together, precipitate out of solution, and form a crystalline structure.

Chapter 20:

INTRODUCTION TO CANNABIS TESTING

"When you walk into a lab there should be evidence of quality all around..."

Anthony Smith, PhD, BTS #6 Curious About Cannabis Podcast

Learning Questions

- What are the most common services offered by Cannabis testing labs?
- What technologies and methods do Cannabis testing labs use to test Cannabis for potency and purity?
- How do Cannabis testing labs measure their own accuracy?
- How should a Cannabis Certificate of Analysis (COA) be interpreted?
- What are the ways in which Cannabis testing can go wrong?

In some places where Cannabis is legal for medical and/or recreational purposes, there are requirements that all Cannabis products are tested for potency and purity – or, in other words, how "strong" the product is and how "clean" the product is. Cannabis testing laboratories provide the technical services required to properly comply with product quality rules and regulations. Beyond the realm of the Cannabis industry, these kinds of laboratories would be considered natural products laboratories. Typically, Cannabis labs test Cannabis and Cannabis derived products for things like cannabinoids, terpenes, molds, bacteria, pesticides, residual solvents, and metals.

Although the Cannabis testing industry is relatively new with the unfolding of Cannabis legalization across the world, the natural products testing industry has been around for ages. Humans have been striving to investigate and understand the properties of nature all throughout history. The elements of nature have been sought after by philosophers, alchemists, physicists, mystics and chemists alike. Today the analysis of natural products is a customary practice, using a variety of techniques to determine both common and trace elements of a target natural product, like Cannabis flowers. Natural products analysis and research is traditionally performed for a variety of reasons like certifying the safety of a product or isolating new compounds for therapeutic research.

WHAT SERVICES DO CANNABIS TESTING LABS COMMONLY OFFER?

Laboratories providing Cannabis testing services typically offer a variety of analytical services including potency, pesticide residue, microbiology, terpene, and residual solvent analysis. Pesticide panels may vary lab to lab, especially without any regulatory oversight. Microbiology analyses may consist of testing for such things as yeasts and molds, E. coli, Salmonella, coliforms, and other bacteria.

FOREIGN MATTER SCREENING

One of the most basic forms of "testing" that labs do is called foreign matter screening. In this test, one or more samples of a Cannabis product are examined under a microscope to search for anything that does not belong, such as hair, insect parts, glass or mineral shards, and other contaminants.

CANNABINOID TESTING

Potency testing is the most common type of analysis that a Cannabis laboratory performs. Potency analysis includes the identification and quantification of phytocannabinoids. If the laboratory utilizes gas chromatography (GC) for cannabinoid testing, the laboratory will typically report Total, or Max, THC and CBD values, at a minimum. If the laboratory utilizes liquid chromatography, the laboratory will report THCA, CBDA, THC, and CBD, at a minimum. Along with these major phytocannabinoids, Cannabis laboratories often report minor cannabinoids such as CBG, CBC, CBN, THCV, and/or CBDV.

TERPENOID TESTING

Terpene analysis is a service that is in increasing demand from the Cannabis industry as cultivators want to better understand the chemotypes of their plants and patients want to better understand the therapeutic potential of Cannabis products. Terpenes have been shown to exhibit unique "entourage effects" with cannabinoids and some terpenes directly bind to cannabinoid receptors. Terpene tests offered by Cannabis labs typically report anywhere between five to thirty or more terpenes commonly found in Cannabis.

Because terpenoids are such volatile and sensitive compounds, the manner in which a laboratory handles the sample can greatly affect the terpenoids measured. Labs must go to great lengths to ensure the integrity of a sample is maintained properly and the terpenoid profile has not been altered. This is often done by keeping the sample cold and using a headspace sampler to heat the sample and extract the resulting vapor for analysis.

PESTICIDE SCREENING

Pesticide testing is one of the primary contaminant screens that Cannabis laboratories offer. Depending on the regulatory requirements in an area, a Cannabis lab may test for any variety of pesticides. It is important to understand exactly what pesticides a laboratory includes on their pesticide panels before ordering a test. In Oregon, state regulations require testing for approximately 60 different pesticides commonly utilized in Cannabis production including several commonly used organic OMRI listed pesticides.

RESIDUAL SOLVENT SCREENING

Sometimes there may be solvents left behind during the production of Cannabis extracts and/or concentrates. Cannabis testing laboratories often offer residual solvent screening services to help ensure that producers are recovering their solvents out of the product prior to packaging and sales. Usually a method called headspace gas chromatography with flame ionization detection (HS-GC-FID) is used to test Cannabis products for residual solvents.

Whenever a laboratory must sample a product for residual solvent testing, they must prepare a number of sampling tools in advance in order to avoid using cleaning solvents on tools while sampling which could contaminate the samples with trace amounts of solvent.

MICROBIOLOGICAL TESTING

There are many different fungi and bacteria that may be present in Cannabis. Some of these microorganisms can be quite toxic to consumers with compromised immune systems. Dangerous bacteria can cause food poisoning and allergic reactions. Many Cannabis testing laboratories offer a variety of microbiological testing services to identify the presence of molds, spores, and bacteria to help provide producers and consumers with peace of mind.

TISSUE CULTURE SERVICES

Some Cannabis laboratories may offer tissue culturing services. Tissue culture plants can obtain a much higher rooting efficiency than cuttings, up to 95% (Lata et al., 2010b), resulting in greater resource use efficiency. Tissue culture is also used to introduce genes to the **germplasm**. Germplasm is the term used to refer to the undifferentiated bundle of cells that can lead to the growth of a full plant. A bacterium is used to carry a new gene to the tissue. Then the tissue is exposed to an antibiotic that kills the bacteria but leaves the gene in the tissue. The plant can then adopt the gene and grow using the new genetic information. This is one form of genetic modification.

Tissue culture can also be used to create and maintain libraries of reliable plant genetics. It can also be used to produce **synthetic seeds** which are bundles of meristematic cells surrounded by a nutritive gel. These seeds can be stored for extended periods of time and then sown in soil to grow into a full clone.

CHEMOTAXONOMY AND GENETICS

Some Cannabis labs primarily focus on performing chemotaxonomy and genetic work – attempting to better understand the varieties of Cannabis and the history of the plant's evolution. In chemotaxonomy, cannabinoid and terpenoid data are analyzed, and patterns are grouped together to find chemical "fingerprints" of Cannabis varieties.

Genetic sequencing can be performed to document the genetic code of a particular variety of Cannabis. By examining genetic information, researchers can identify how genes are flowing through plant populations and which genes are unique to certain plant varieties. Researchers can also use genetic sequencing to better understand what genes control the production of various chemical compounds of interest in the plant, so that they may be manipulated through targeted breeding practices or genetic modification.

PLANT SEX DETERMINATION

Determining the sex of immature Cannabis plants is possible using PCR technology. **PCR** stands for **Polymerase Chain Reaction** and is a commonly used technology in molecular and cellular biology for analyzing DNA. It is a method of taking a small piece of DNA and replicating it many times to examine its contents. Both the germplasm of the plant seed and the cotyledons of a seedling (which were pre-formed in the embryo of the seed) can be analyzed to determine if the DNA indicates whether the plant is male, female, or likely to be a hermaphrodite.

METALS ANALYSIS

Testing for metals like Arsenic, Lead, Cadmium, and Mercury is often very expensive and requires instrumentation that is usually not used for other types of analyses. For these reasons, most laboratories do not offer metals analysis unless metals testing is required for local or state regulatory compliance. Alternatively, environmental laboratories that already perform metals testing on other plants and soils may be more likely to offer metals testing.

THE LIFE OF A LAB SAMPLE

Once a Cannabis sample is either dropped off at a laboratory or collected in the field by a laboratory technician, it is assigned a unique identifier. When the sample is at the lab, waiting to be prepared, it typically is housed in refrigerators or freezers that feature temperature monitors and alarms to ensure that the sample is always properly preserved. Cannabis samples are typically stored in temperatures anywhere between -40°C to 20°C, depending on what analyses are required. Analyses of volatile compounds, like solvents, pesticides, and terpenoids, require colder preservation than analyses of less volatile compounds like metals.

FIGURE 58: BASIC LAB TESTING WORKFLOW

At some point, either upon lab intake or prior to preparation, the sample is homogenized, meaning that it is ground and well mixed to ensure that the material is uniform throughout and any subsamples taken will be representative of the entire sample. Then, a laboratory technician will collect a subsample from the homogenized material to perform each requested analysis. Each type of lab test features unique sample size requirements that can range anywhere from 0.1g to 1g or more per analysis. The lab may prepare samples in duplicate or triplicate, requiring extra sample. Once any required samples are taken, the remainder of the original sample material is returned to controlled chilled storage.

Once a sample is collected per the requirements of the analytical method, sample preparation begins. This process can vary depending on what analyses are required, but it often involves exposing the sample to one or more solvents, cleaning the solution to filter out particulates, and then diluting the solution to a desired level. For microbiological testing, the solution is often plated onto growth media and incubated to promote the growth of target organisms like yeasts, molds, aerobic bacteria, or E. coli species.

Once the required tests are performed on the sample and the results are reported, the sample material is then marked for disposal. Some laboratories dispose of samples very quickly after reporting results while others retain samples for several weeks, months, or even years, just in case it is needed again for investigative reasons.

ANALYTICAL METHODS

There are a wide range of tried and true analytical chemistry techniques available to explore the constituents of natural products. Throughout this next section, we will explore the most common analytical techniques utilized by laboratories that focus on testing Cannabis.

WHAT IS CHROMATOGRAPHY?

Chromatography, translated as "color writing", is a method of separating mixtures into constituent compounds. Solutions are forced through either a column or plate of particles. Different molecules pass through the column or across the plate at different speeds, resulting in similar molecules grouping together and separating from the mixture. A very basic example of chromatography can be demonstrated with water, a cup, a paper towel, and a water-soluble marker. If you tear off a strip of paper towel, place a dot on one end with the marker, and then dip the strip into a cup that has a shallow reservoir of water, the water will crawl up the paper through capillary action and smear the ink across the paper, separating the colors.

Chromatography involves a **stationary phase** and a **mobile phase**. The stationary phase, as the name implies, remains in place, while the mobile phase moves across the stationary phase. Usually the sample is present in the mobile phase and the compounds separate as they move across and interact with the stationary phase. These relatively simple dynamics are the basic principles of all chromatography.

Chromatography results are visualized on graphs called **chromatograms**. The x axis is represented by the amount of time passed during the run, called **retention time**. The y axis represents the **signal** coming from the detector. The bumps on the graph are called "**peaks**" and represent the presence of different compounds: the greater the area of the peak, the greater the concentration of that compound in the sample.

There are several aspects of these peaks that are measured to determine the concentration of a compound: the **peak height, peak width, peak area, and peak symmetry**. **Peak width** and **symmetry** are usually indicators of the resolution of the data. If the peaks are tight, sharp and symmetrical, the data is thought to have high resolution. **Peak height** and **peak area** correspond to the abundance of the measured compound.

CHEMICAL ANALYSES

THIN LAYER CHROMATOGRAPHY

Thin layer chromatography is a relatively simple method of chromatography that uses a plate as the stationary phase and a solvent as the mobile phase. A sample is placed on to a specially designed TLC plate and allowed to dry. Then the plate is placed in a chamber that is saturated with a solvent and contains a bit of solvent at the base. The plate acts as a wick and sucks up the solvent. Capillary action carries the solvent all the way to the top of the plate. The plate is then removed and allowed to completely dry. Then the plate is sprayed with a special dye to give color to the compounds that have been separated on the plate. An assortment of colors, dots and smeared lines appear on the plate. These dots and lines can then be measured to get an estimation of the concentration of a chemical compound in the sample.

To make thin layer chromatography quantitative, sophisticated equipment or software that can perform pixel densitometry are used to quantify the total area of each analyte's dot. One limitation of thin layer chromatography is that it tends to over-estimate cannabinoids in low concentrations.

GAS CHROMATOGRAPHY

Gas chromatography is one of the most commonly used instruments used for compound separation and analysis. Samples are injected into the gas chromatograph and instantly vaporized. The vapor is then carried into the **column**, which is a long and very small tube which is lined with the stationary phase. A hot gas helps sweep the sample into the tube. The column is contained in an oven, as seen here. As the sample passes through the column, the oven heats up.

TRY THIS! MARKER CHROMATOGRAPHY

The concept of chromatography can be easily demonstrated at home through a very simple experiment involving a marker, a piece of paper, and a little bit of water or rubbing alcohol. Have you ever wondered what colors are hidden within a marker's ink? Try this activity out and see for yourself!

Materials

Pencil	Markers	Piece of white filter paper or card stock
Shallow glass or cup (glass recommended)	Water (for water soluble markers)	Rubbing Alcohol (for permanent markers)

Procedures

1. Fill the glass or cup with 1cm of water
2. Cut the filter paper or card stock into a long strip
3. Measure 1cm from the bottom of a strip of paper and draw a line with pencil.
4. Using the markers, place a single bold dot with each marker along the line, leaving approximately 0.5cm space between each dot.
5. Place the strip of paper into the cup.
6. Allow the water or alcohol to slowly wick up the paper. This can take several minutes.
7. Once the water or alcohol has completely saturated the piece of paper, remove the paper and examine the results. You should see that the ink from each marker has spread out revealing all of the component dyes that make up each color.

Congratulations! You have successfully performed a chromatography experiment!

Although this activity may seem very simple, it actually demonstrates all the major components of chromatography. The marker dot is your **sample**. The paper is your **stationary phase**, and the water or alcohol is your **mobile phase**. As the mobile phase moves the sample across the stationary phase, the sample separates into its component parts – or **constituents**. All forms of chromatography, however seemingly complex, all follow these basic principles illustrated in this simple experiment!

As the temperature rises, different compounds separate, stick to the column, and break away from the column. Eventually the compounds pass through a detector which sends a signal to a computer where a graph is created to visualize the compounds in the sample. This graph is called a **Chromatogram**.

Decarboxylated cannabinoid, terpenoid, and residual solvent analyses can all be performed on a gas chromatograph with reliability and accuracy. To perform residual solvent analyses on a gas chromatograph, a **head-space sampler** is needed. Residual solvents are highly volatile, meaning they evaporate easily under a little heat. For this reason, rather than sampling the liquid, the headspace sampler samples the gas that forms above the sample as the vial and the sample are gently heated to a programmed temperature.

Gas Chromatograph (above) and Liquid Chromatograph (below) Images Courtesy of Kenevir Research, also known as EVIO Labs Medford – www.EVIOLabs.com

LIQUID CHROMATOGRAPHY

Liquid chromatography is another very common method of chemical analysis and involves a cooler method of separating and detecting compounds, as opposed to gas chromatography which is a very hot method. Specifically, **High Pressure Liquid Chromatography** (HPLC), also called High Performance Liquid Chromatography, is used in natural products analysis. Liquid chromatography is particularly useful for measuring the carboxylic acid cannabinoids like THCA, CBDA, CBCA, and CBGA. Since the method is cold, the acids are never heated enough to **decarboxylate** them.

To calculate the total potential decarboxylated THC content, the THCA and THC values must be combined. **These values cannot just simply be added**. When a 100mg/g of THCA is decarboxylated, CO_2 is lost and the weight of the molecule is reduced, ending up with approximately 88mg/g of THC after decarboxylation. So if

THCA and THC values are added together without accounting for this change, an exaggerated result is produced.

FLASH CHROMATOGRAPHY

The final type of chromatography that a Cannabis laboratory is likely to utilize is flash chromatography. The "flash" in the name "flash chromatography" is in reference to the method's speed. When the technology was developed, it was thought that the process would be "over in a flash". As opposed to traditional gravity-fed column chromatography techniques, flash chromatography utilized pressurized gas to force a sample through a packed column and across an appropriate stationary phase. Flash chromatography is typically used as a sample preparation technique, to quickly separate a sample into its constituents before being analyzed by an instrument like a mass spectrometer, or even a detector on a different type of chromatograph. Some Cannabis laboratories are turning to flash chromatography to better prepare complex samples, like Cannabis infused edibles.

WHAT IS SPECTROMETRY?

Spectrometry is another method for analyzing the chemical components of materials. The word "spectrometry" gets its meaning from the fact that spectrometers measure ("-metry") spectra ("spectro-"), whether they be electromagnetic light spectra - as in infrared, ultraviolet, or x-ray spectrometry – or mass spectra, in mass spectrometry. For the purposes of Cannabis testing, mass spectrometry is the primary spectrometry method used, often in combination with gas or liquid chromatography.

In the case of mass spectrometry, the analytical instrument measures a sample's **mass spectrum**, which represents each of the mass-to-charge ratios for each ion in the sample as well as the velocity at which the ions passed through the instrument. The **mass-to-charge ratio** describes the mass of the ion in relation to the number of charges it is carrying. On a mass spectrum graph, the x axis represents the mass-to-charge ratio and the y axis represents intensity.

Spectrometry is commonly used in Cannabis testing to detect and measure trace contaminants like pesticides, growth regulators, and residual solvents. When greater sensitivity is needed for detecting very trace amounts of compounds, tandem mass spectrometers may be used.

MASS SPECTROMETRY

Mass spectrometry is a detection method that can be used in conjunction with gas or liquid chromatography to try to achieve a higher sensitivity of detection and greater confidence of compound identification. Once compounds are ionized through the gas or liquid chromatography, the ions are shot through the mass spectrometer where the ions pass between a series of magnets. The trajectory of the ions as they pass by the magnets is correlated with the mass of the compound, which can then be used to try and identify the compound. In Cannabis testing, mass spectrometry is primarily utilized in pesticide and residual solvent testing.

For particularly difficult to detect compounds, like trace pesticides, a triple quadrupole, or "triple quad", mass spectrometer is often used. A "triple quad" mass spectrometer provides greater sensitivity and the ability to detect very minute traces of compounds, sometimes in the parts per trillion range. In addition to ionizing compounds, a triple quad subsequently fragments the compounds and then ionizes the resulting fragments. Ultimately these fragments end up providing a unique "fingerprint" that can be used to identify the parent molecule. This can help differentiate compounds that are very similar and may otherwise interfere with each other on a standard mass spectrometer detector.

The mass spectra of a substantial number of compounds are stored in various libraries which can be accessed for a fee. Scientists can use these libraries to flag and tentatively identify compounds for which they do not have reference standards. These compounds are reported as Tentatively Identified Compounds, or TICs. TICs are supposed to be properly marked on test results and are not considered true quantitative results until confirmed against a reference standard. Mass spectra libraries are useful tools but are not fool-proof and can lead to misidentification of chromatographic peaks, especially for compounds in low concentrations. Mass spectrometry alone can be an inappropriate method for some analyses, as acknowledged in this excerpt from the blog of chromatography supplier, Restek:

> "When an interfering terpene, or other compound, coelutes with a terpene of interest, quantification will be compromised and, since many terpenes have the same molecular weight and share fragment ions, mass spectrometry cannot be relied upon to distinguish a terpene of interest from a coeluting interference terpene. The only way to accurately identify and quantify terpenes is to ensure that the terpenes of interest are chromatographically separated from all interfering compounds."

Source: A Preliminary FET Headspace GC-FID Method for Comprehensive Terpene Profiling in Cannabis. http://www.restek.com/Technical-Resources/Technical-Library/Foods-Flavors-Fragrances/fff_FFAN2045-UNV

INDUCTIVELY COUPLED PLASMA MASS SPECTROMETRY (ICP-MS)

When it comes to testing natural products for metals, ICP mass spectrometry is the go-to method. ICP stands for "inductively coupled plasma" which refers to the torch used to dehydrate, separate, and ionize the materials being analyzed. Once ionized, the mass spectrometer detector scans the masses of the resulting fragments to identify them. ICP-MS systems usually use Argon as their primary gas for creating ICP. The ICP torch is approximately 6000°K, equal to the approximate temperature of the surface of the sun! Because the torch is so incredibly hot, it is very efficient at separating chemical constituents and elements that are very solid and hard at temperatures greater than 200 or 300°C, like metals!

Commonly Tested Metals in Cannabis	
Lead (Pb)	Arsenic (As)
Cadmium (Cd)	Mercury (Hg)
Nickel (Ni)	Copper (Cu)

FIGURE 59: COMMON METALS TESTED BY CANNABIS LABS

Cannabis testing labs will usually not offer metals testing unless it is required by state testing regulations simply because the equipment can be very expensive, and the process is technical in a manner that is dissimilar to other forms of mass spectrometry, requiring unique expertise.

ABSORBANCE SPECTROMETRY (SPECTROPHOTOMETRY)

Absorbance spectrometry is the use of electromagnetic radiation to measure the abundance of atoms or molecules in a substance. The two most common methods of absorbance spectrometry used for cannabinoid analysis include UV and IR absorbance spectrometry. Some analytical systems may use only UV or IR, while other systems sometimes mix the two. As the light hits the sample, the different compounds absorb the light differently, generating measurable levels of absorbance, which form graphs that look similar to chromatograms.

Spectrophotometers are often small and sometimes portable, compared to more traditional analytical equipment. Some commercially available portable Cannabis testing devices utilize an economical blend of liquid chromatography and absorbance spectrometry – using packed columns and liquid solvent to separate samples into their components. The sample is then fed into a spectrophotometer which measures the absorbance of each compound, allowing for the quantitation of major cannabinoids.

ELISA (ENZYME-LINKED IMMUNOSORBENT ASSAY)

ELISA is a method traditionally used to detect pathogens in foods or bodily fluids as well as pesticide residues in water. It is a quick and inexpensive way of detecting the presence of a pesticide or a group of pesticides or toxins. Test kits are readily available that can quickly inform the analyst if a group of compounds are present in a sample by a simple change in the color of the liquid.

ELISA is limited by the fact that it can sometimes be hard or impossible to get quantitative data about one specific contaminant from an ELISA test if the kit is designed to test for multiple contaminants, like pesticides, at once. In other industries, ELISA tests are used as quality control to quickly and cheaply test samples to ensure they do not contain a particular group of contaminants, like a particular class of pesticides. If the test were to come up positive, the sample would then be sent to be analyzed on a GC or HPLC system to determine what pesticide is present and in what concentration.

MICROBIOLOGICAL ANALYSES

PLATING

One of the most common methods of quantifying microbiological components is through using inoculated petri dishes containing nutritive media, or through using commercially available 3M Petrifilm™. **Petrifilm**™ consists of a soft plate containing a nutritive surface used to culture fungi and bacteria. A plastic film covers the plate and is sealed after inoculation. To perform a mold/mildew test, a sample would be mixed with a special solvent used to collect the spores and cells without destroying them. Some of the liquid is then placed onto the Petrifilm™ where it is sealed in place. The plate is left to incubate for 2 to 5 days depending on the type of Petrifilm™ plate. Then the fungal or bacterial **colonies** on the plate are counted.

A limitation to plating methods is that sometimes non-target organisms will grow in the growth media. For instance, bacteria might grow on a culture designed for growing yeast and mold. Plating methods also generally do not inform the analyst whether any of the detected colonies on the plate are harmful to human health or not. Most plating methods do not target any particular species of micro-organism, sometimes leading samples to fail testing even if they do not present a risk to human health.

POLYMERASE CHAIN REACTION (PCR)

To overcome some of the limitations of microbiological plating, laboratories also perform DNA testing using a quick and relatively easy method of amplifying DNA and comparing it to a reference standard through a method called polymerase chain reaction, or PCR. In PCR, a small sample of DNA is replicated many times so that it may be easily measured. PCR is typically used for microbiological testing in Cannabis. Through DNA testing, it is possible to overcome one of the primary limitations of other forms of microbiological testing – poor selectivity.

There are various ways of performing PCR tests. A simple method of using PCR is through a chemical reaction that changes the solution containing the DNA a unique color if the DNA matches the target organism. This allows for cheap, simple visual determination of whether a sample "passes" or "fails" without expensive equipment. Alternatively, there is a method called real-time or quantitative PCR, or qPCR. qPCR involves expensive equipment that amplifies DNA, makes it fluoresce, and then monitors the fluorescence to measure how much DNA is present and whether it matches a reference sample. qPCR monitors the changes to DNA, while the amplification process takes place, which is why it is referred to as "real time" PCR.

COSTS OF TESTING

The costs of Cannabis testing services can vary quite a bit depending on the location of the laboratory, the methods used, and the quality of service. In essence, just like with most things in life – you get what you pay for. The following table demonstrates estimated costs of different testing services as of the time of this writing in 2020.

Service	Typical Method(s) Used	Typical Price Range
Cannabinoids	GC – decarboxylated cannabinoids LC or LC/MS – cannabinoid acids	$40 - $150
Terpenoids	GC or GC/MS Headspace GC/MS	$50 - $200
Pesticides	GC/MS-MS LC/MS-MS ELISA (qualitative)	$75 - $400
Residual Solvents	GC/MS	$50 - $150
Metals	ICP/MS	$100 - $300
Moisture Content	Loss on Drying Moisture Analyzer	$25 - $50
Water Activity	Relative Humidity Probe	$25 - $50
Yeast and Mold	Petrifilm™ ELISA (presence/absence)	$30 - $60
E. coli or Salmonella	Petrifilm™ ELISA (presence/absence) PCR	$30 - $75
Aspergillus sp.	PCR	$50 - 100
Mycotoxins	ELISA Lateral Flow (presence/absence) LC/MS	$30 - 100
Sex Testing	PCR	$5 - $10 per plant

GC – Gas Chromatograph with Flame Ionization Detector
GC/MS – Gas Chromatograph with Mass Spectrometer Detector
LC – Liquid Chromatograph, usually High Pressure LC (HPLC)
LC/MS – Liquid Chromatograph with Mass Spectrometer Detector
GC/MS-MS – Gas Chromatograph with tandem Mass Spectrometer Detectors
LC/MS-MS – Liquid Chromatograph with tandem Mass Spectrometer Detectors
ICP/MS – Inductively Coupled Plasma Mass Spectrometer
PCR – Polymerase Chain Reaction

FIGURE 60: CANNABIS TESTING SERVICES, EQUIPMENT USED, AND TYPICAL PRICE RANGES

EVALUATING A CANNABIS TESTING LABORATORY

At the time of the writing of this book in 2020, the legal Cannabis industry in the United States is still young but is quickly maturing. As Cannabis is legalized and regulated, a myriad of ancillary businesses crops up to serve the industry in some way or another. One of these ancillary businesses in the Cannabis industry are Cannabis testing laboratories.

Unfortunately, in areas that have legalized Cannabis but not yet applied strict quality standards or regulations in place, it is common to see Cannabis testing laboratories appear seemingly overnight, run by individuals with no science background or sense of scientific integrity, willing to dish out the most favorable result money can buy. Because of this, **it is important that all participants in the Cannabis industry, including consumers, learn how to critically evaluate Cannabis testing laboratories** to identify those that are competent and will provide reliable data.

LABORATORY CREDENTIALS/COMPETENCY

When assessing the scientific competence of an analytical laboratory, it is important to investigate the credentials of laboratory staff closely. Many laboratory technicians and assistants hold bachelor or master's degrees in chemistry, biology or some related science field. The executive scientist, or chief science officer, usually holds either an MS or a PhD, often with publications in peer-reviewed journals.

The laboratory manager or director should have prior experience employing a variety of analytical techniques for quantifying compounds in natural products of a variety of types of samples. The laboratory should have at least one employee that serves as quality manager who thoroughly understands how to build and manage quality assurance systems. Quality managers work with the laboratory manager or laboratory director to implement quality objectives, establish methods of measuring laboratory performance, and instituting programs for continuous improvement.

Laboratories that are accredited will maintain records called "demonstrations of capability." These records indicate exactly how each technician performed in a series of sample preparations. Typically, the technician will prepare a sample several consecutive times. The results from each of the samples is compared to one another as well as to the known concentration of the sample to determine the technician's precision and accuracy with the method being evaluated.

The consumer should feel comfortable calling a laboratory and asking for qualifications and credentials of laboratory staff to ensure that proper reliable results will be produced, especially as the Cannabis industry continues to mature. Depending on a state's rules on Cannabis testing and Cannabis testing laboratory oversight, the quality of available laboratories working with Cannabis can be extremely variable.

What if a Laboratory Outsources Their Work?

While evaluating your local Cannabis laboratories, you might find that some of them do not perform all the services that they advertise, rather opting to outsource those services to another laboratory. Discovering this might make you a bit uneasy and skeptical. Don't worry. This behavior is called **subcontracting**, and alone is not a cause for concern. In fact, in the analytical chemistry world, it is very common for laboratories to subcontract work to one another so that each lab may specialize their expertise in a core set of services while still maintaining the ability to offer clients a full range of services.

If a laboratory subcontracts any of their services, it should be evident on their test reports, or certificates of analysis. Usually accrediting bodies will require accredited laboratories to let clients know in writing of any subcontracting relationships. Once you have found out who your laboratory subcontracts services to, you can apply all the information in this chapter to that laboratory. If the subcontracting laboratory is reputable, you can breathe easy. In fact, subcontracting can sometimes provide clients with access to very reputable high-quality laboratories indirectly, which they would not be able to access otherwise, perhaps even adding value to the service.

However, if you find that a laboratory is dishonest about how they produce their data or do not indicate subcontracting laboratories on their test reports, this could indicate an intention to deceive. Alternatively, it could simply be an oversight on the lab's part with no intention to deceive. Proper due diligence can easily decipher these kinds of dilemmas.

Qualitative vs Quantitative Testing

One of the first things that is important to understand regarding lab testing is the difference between **qualitative** and **quantitative** analysis. A qualitative analysis tells you broad information about what is there, whereas a quantitative analysis tells you how much of that thing is present. For example, a test that only measures whether a pesticide is present or not in a Cannabis sample would be considered qualitative. A test that tells you the actual concentrations of pesticides present or not present in a Cannabis sample would be considered quantitative. When evaluating a laboratory's services, be sure to note whether their methods are going to give you the qualitative or quantitative information that you need. If you only need to know whether something is present or absent in a Cannabis sample, you would only need qualitative testing. If you need to know how much of any particular thing (including cannabinoids) is in a sample, you need quantitative testing.

The leap from qualitative testing to quantitative testing requires more detailed measurements and calculations, often requiring highly sensitive equipment calibrated to detect and measure the compounds in question. Because quantitative work is more technical, it often also requires more highly skilled and trained personnel to perform the work.

To summarize plainly, qualitative refers to "what", and quantitative refers to both "what" and "how much".

HOW LOW CAN THEY GO? LODS AND LOQS

"The Limit of Detection is the lowest analyte concentration likely to be reliably distinguished from the Limit of Blank and at which detection is feasible…The Limit of Quantification is the lowest concentration at which the analyte can not only be reliably detected but at which some predefined goals for bias and imprecision are met. The LOQ may be equivalent to the LOD or it could be at a much higher concentration.*"*

(Armbruster and Pry, 2008; emphasis added)

Analytical instruments all have certain detection and quantification limits for different compounds. The **limit of detection and limit of quantification** refer to points at which a compound can confidently be measured. The limit of detection is the smallest concentration of an analyte that an analytical instrument can detect. It is technically defined as the lowest concentration at which an analyte can be distinguished from a **blank** with over 50% confidence. The blank is a sample that only contains a solvent and is used to clean and detect residues out of the analytical instrument. The limit of quantification is usually slightly higher than the LOD because the LOQ value must be reliably repeatable for quality assurance purposes.

For cannabinoids, the limit of detection is often somewhere around 0.005% or 0.001% when using gas or liquid chromatography. What this would mean is that if THC or CBD were present in a sample at 0.004%, the analyst would not be able to distinguish the result from the overall "noise" that is present in the data. Because there is always a small gap of uncertainty between the LOD or LOQ and 0, **a value of zero is almost never reported in analytical chemistry**. Instead, "not detected", "ND", "<LOQ", or some similar notation is used.

The LOD/LOQ of an analytical method is particularly important in relation to pesticide testing. **It is possible for Cannabis flower to "pass" a pesticide analysis with no detectable levels of pesticides, but a resulting concentrated extract made from that material may still end up containing pesticide levels that *are* detectable**. So, what's going on? Imagine that some Cannabis flower that would be used to make a batch of concentrated extract is contaminated with approximately 0.02 ppm of some pesticide. If the LOD/LOQ for the lab's pesticide method was 0.05 ppm, then this flower material would "pass" the lab's pesticide tests with results of "none detected" or "<LOQ". When this flower is run through the extraction and concentration process, those pesticide residues would become concentrated up to 2 – 10x their original concentration as the cannabinoids are concentrated (keep in mind that many pesticides are chemically similar in structure to

cannabinoids). This would mean that when the final concentrate is tested for pesticides, a result of 0.1 ppm or more could be detected, which could be very significant depending on the pesticide detected.

SOURCES OF UNCERTAINTY

Uncertainty is inherent in science. Science does not usually produce hard facts. Instead science produces assumptions and conclusions that have varying degrees of confidence. Barwick (1999) states "the evaluation of the uncertainty associated with a result is an essential part of quantitative analysis. Without knowledge of the measurement of uncertainty, the statement of an analytical result cannot be considered complete." The International Standardization Organization lays out rules for how this uncertainty can be measured.

There are many sources of uncertainty, error, and bias throughout the testing process such as the client, the analyst, the instrument, and the computer – for instance. A client might sample their own batch using contaminated tools or an uncalibrated balance. The analyst might make slight measurement mistakes throughout sample preparation. The instrument might not inject samples correctly or the detector could malfunction. The software that integrates with the instrument might glitch. Each setting on an analytical instrument affects many other variables, which is why calibration and control standards are important. Sources of uncertainty, when identified, can be measured to determine how strong an effect the errors might have on the final result. Standard Operating Procedures are used to standardize procedures to control sources of error, minimize errors and limit biases, where possible.

RANGES OF "CORRECTNESS"

As mentioned above, rather than there being one "correct" value, in science there are often ranges of acceptable results that are considered accurate with varying levels of confidence. A result begins to become suspect when it falls outside of some acceptable range. **There is generally an accepted variance in Cannabis testing of between 10 and 20%, or approximately ±2-4 percentage points on average, for Cannabis flower**.

It is important for labs to work together to promote accuracy and reliability of results. **"Ring tests"**, or **proficiency tests**, are events where a third party provides a test sample with a known concentration of an analyte or analytes to a variety of labs to analyze. The results of the analyses are then reported, and the information is shared with the labs and potentially other parties. The information can help labs improve their methods and identify sources of variance. Ring testing helps keep labs sharp and on their toes, as they are aware that eventually they will have to compare their methods with the methods of other laboratories.

Repeated testing is always going to report slightly different results, but if quality control measures are in place, the repeated results will fall within a narrow range of variance. The lab's objective is to make that range as narrow as possible for any given sample.

Understanding Positive and Negative Predictive Power

Confidence in an analytical method stems from establishing the method's predictive power. Different types of analyses require different types of predictive power – positive and negative predictive power.

Positive predictive power: If the result is positive, how likely is it that it is *actually* positive? How does the lab determine whether a result is *really* positive?

For example, if a Cannabis flower is tested for potency and is shown to contain 22% total THC, how does the analyst know that the sample did not contain more or less? How does the analyst know that a trace cannabinoid is *actually* THCV and not just noise from the analytical instrument? The laboratory uses reference standards containing known concentrations of target analytes, builds calibration curves that determine how little or great a concentration of a compound can be accurately quantified, performs duplicate sample preparations, and utilize validated methods to prove their positive predictive power.

Negative predictive power: If the result is negative, how likely is it that it is *actually* negative? How does the lab determine whether a result is *really* negative?

For example, if a sample is analyzed for pesticides and comes back clean, how does the analyst actually know that the sample does not have pesticides in it, as opposed to a potential problem with sample preparation or recovery efficiency? Maybe there *were* pesticides there, but the laboratory mishandled the sample, making it appear as if none are there. Or perhaps the instrument's detector is not working correctly, leading to constant negative results. How does an analyst get past these doubts? Laboratories must perform efficiency tests on their methods to prove their negative predictive power.

When evaluating laboratories, ask the laboratory what steps they go through to prove their positive and negative predictive power. The answers should lie in their quality management system.

Quality Management Systems in Laboratories

Quality control in analytical laboratories is primarily about good record keeping, adhering to defined procedures, and engaging in regular quality assurance practices to achieve constant improvement. There are a variety of activities and documentation that make up a laboratory's quality management system. Anything that affects the quality of the data being collected must be documented and tracked. Analysts date and initial all notes in notebooks belonging to the lab that must remain at the lab. Laboratory Information Management Systems (LIMS) are used to digitally manage the laboratories methods, sampling workflow, employees, clients, orders, etc. Other aspects of a laboratory's quality management system include:

STANDARD OPERATING PROCEDURES

Standard operating procedures are documents which describe in detail the procedures to be used in the laboratory for each task performed. These are very important because these unchanged procedures help to differentiate sources of error. SOPs are used to train new laboratory workers while theoretically ensuring that performance will not change significantly.

REFERENCE STANDARDS

Reference standards are samples that contain a known amount of an analyte. These samples are run alongside legitimate test samples to calibrate results and ensure that suspected compounds are correctly identified.

INTERNAL VS. EXTERNAL STANDARDS

Internal reference standards are samples of known concentrations that are developed in-house and used for the purposes of instrument and result calibration and correction. External reference standards are obtained from a third-party source to check the accuracy and validity of the internal standard as well as to use as a tool for instrument and result calibration and correction.

IDENTIFYING AND CALCULATING UNCERTAINTY AND ERROR

Error can arise from a wide variety of sources. It is important for labs to recognize and calculate some of these errors to make corrections to results to make them more accurate.

PROFICIENCY TESTING/RING TESTING

It is important for laboratories to participate in proficiency testing to ensure the accuracy of their methods and results as well as helping to better the overall natural products testing industry. If a laboratory is ISO 17025 or NELAP accredited, proficiency testing is mandatory.

CONTROLLED DOCUMENTATION

All documents produced by the laboratory must be tightly monitored and controlled. Changes to paperwork must be dated and initialed. Laboratory notebooks are property of the lab and should remain at the lab. Usually a piece of software called a LIMS

(Laboratory Information Management System) is used to manage data concerning clients, analysis requests, and results. Accredited labs are subject to audits, so tight document control is crucial.

RECORDS

Records of all happenings in the lab must be kept in a safe location for the purposes of auditability and accountability.

CUSTOMER COMMUNICATIONS AND COMPLAINTS

A laboratory's quality assurance system needs to have a protocol for handling customer/client communications and complaints. A laboratory will make a mistake at some point. A system must be in place to handle complaints and customer issues in a way that does not sacrifice the laboratory's integrity or deviate from the laboratory's mission.

DATA DRIVEN QUALITY OBJECTIVES

Accredited laboratories must demonstrate that they are meeting current goals while striving to achieve new goals. To do this, specifically defined quality objectives must be chosen that can be measured to demonstrate whether the lab is meeting those objectives.

INTERNAL AND EXTERNAL AUDITS

To ensure the integrity of the lab's quality assurance system, a laboratory will routinely perform self-audits. Along with self-audits, external audits from accreditation bodies may be performed to ensure quality assurance standards compliance.

THE QUALITY MANUAL

For both ISO 17025 and NELAP accreditation a physical copy of a quality manual is necessary. The quality manual is a document that details the laboratories quality assurance system. The manual contains information about employees and their credentials, protocols, SOPs, etc.

HOW DOES A LAB KNOW ITS RESULTS ARE ACCURATE?

As now previously described, a laboratory must utilize strict quality control standards to prove their accuracy and precision. This chart sums up some, but by no means not all, of the ways in which laboratories assess and defend their own accuracy (and precision). Find more detail about each of these quality measures on the next several pages.

Basic Ongoing Quality Measures	
Proficiency Tests/Ring Tests	Laboratory "blindly" analyzes a sample provided by a third party who knows the actual concentrations of the target analytes in the sample
Demonstrations of Capability (DOC)	Used to document a laboratory technician's suitability for performing a sample preparation or analytical method
Sampling Quality Control Samples	
Sample Acceptance Policy	Defines the sample conditions necessary for acceptance by the laboratory
Random/Representative Sampling Procedures and Policies	Procedures that the lab will use to obtain a sample that is adequately representative of its source
Sample/Matrix Specific Quality Control Samples	
Matrix Spike	A sample is spiked with known concentrations of target analytes to measure matrix specific accuracy
Matrix Spike Duplicate	A second sample is spiked with known concentrations of target analytes to measure matrix specific precision
Matrix Duplicate	A duplicate sample used to measure general precision
Preparation Batch Specific Quality Control Samples	
Method Blank	Monitors contamination during sample preparation
Laboratory Control Sample (LCS)	A blank spike or other laboratory reference sample used to measure accuracy
Laboratory Control Sample Duplicate (LCSD)	A duplicate blank spike or other laboratory reference sample used to measure precision
Instrument Specific Quality Control Samples	
Solvent Blank	Monitors instrument contamination during analysis
Initial Calibration Verification (ICV)	A calibration check using reference standards obtained from a different source than those used for the initial calibration
Continuing Calibration Verification (CCV)	A sample containing a known concentration of a reference standard used to confirm the ongoing calibration of an instrument, often run before and after an analytical batch

FIGURE 61: HOW DOES A LAB KNOW THAT ITS RESULTS ARE ACCURATE AND PRECISE?

Understanding The Various Types of Quality Controls Used by Cannabis Testing Labs

There are distinct types of samples that laboratories use to monitor the accuracy and precision of their data. These QC samples are broken down into batch specific, sample specific, and instrument specific samples.

BATCH-SPECIFIC QUALITY CONTROL SAMPLES

Batch specific quality control samples may be prepared and analyzed alongside every batch of prepared samples to monitor contamination, accuracy, and precision. If a batch-specific QC measure is unsatisfactory, it disqualifies the entire batch and all of the affected samples must be re-prepared.

METHOD BLANK

A method blank is quality control sample which monitors whether any analyte contamination is occurring during the sample preparation process. A sample that is known to have zero analytes of interest is prepared in the typical fashion as a normal sample would be prepared. The sample is analyzed, and the results should reveal that no analytes of interest are present. If the method blank reveals significant levels of target analytes, like cannabinoids, the laboratory must review their sample preparation procedures, identify the source of contamination, and re-prepare and re-analyze all samples associated with the failed method blank.

LABORATORY CONTROL SAMPLE (LCS)/LCS DUPLICATE

A laboratory control sample consists of a sample that contains known concentrations of target analytes. Sometimes this is a sample that is spiked with chemicals at certain concentrations. Other times, an LCS may simply be a well characterized material that the laboratory uses as a reference. An LCS is run for every analytical batch. If the LCS is determined to be "out-of-control", meaning that it falls out of the lab's specifications, then the entire associated batch of samples must be re-prepared and re-analyzed. A second LCS may be prepared for an analytical batch to measure ongoing precision.

SAMPLE-SPECIFIC QUALITY CONTROL SAMPLES

Laboratories also utilize a series of other quality control sample types to gain insight about specific samples and sample types, monitoring things like matrix effects. **Matrix effects** are effects unique to the sample type that affect the quality of analytical results. For instance, if a laboratory is testing a new sample type that they have never seen before, like a Cannabis infused candy, they might include sample-specific quality control samples which monitor whether the applied method is properly extracting all the cannabinoids from the candy. If the quality control sample reveals that the lab's recovery of cannabinoids is too low, a different method would have to be used.

Some of the sample-specific quality control sample types are described below.

MATRIX SPIKE/MATRIX SPIKE DUPLICATE

A matrix spike is specific to a sample and identifies interfering matrix effects that limit the ability to effectively extract analytes of interest from the sample. Typically, a client sample is chosen at random and prepared in duplicate. One sample will be prepared like usual and the other will be spiked with known concentrations of a reference standard. The results of the spiked and un-spiked sample will be compared to determine how efficiently the target compounds were recovered. Sometimes a duplicate spiked sample will be prepared to also measure precision.

MATRIX DUPLICATE

A matrix duplicate is another sample specific QC sample. A matrix duplicate is simply a duplicate preparation of a sample of a particular type. Labs typically prepare at least one matrix duplicate for each matrix type featured in an analytical batch. For instance, if a lab is analyzing Cannabis flowers and extracts, they would prepare a duplicate of a flower sample and a duplicate of an extract sample. The results of the duplicate samples are compared to ensure they are precise.

INSTRUMENT-SPECIFIC QUALITY CONTROL SAMPLES

In addition to batch-specific and sample-specific quality control samples, laboratories also utilize instrument-specific quality control samples, which monitor instrument performance and look for signs of contamination or loss of calibration. These types of samples are generally run with every analytical batch of samples. Some of the primary instrument-specific quality control sample types are described below.

SOLVENT BLANK

The solvent blank is a way of measuring instrument contamination and actively cleaning instrumentation. Solvent blanks are simply preparations of clean solvent which are analyzed to determine if any analytes have been left behind in the instrument from a prior analysis. This is particularly important for contaminant screenings like residual solvent and pesticide screenings. If instruments are not carefully monitored with solvent blanks, contaminants may build up in the instrument and the instrument may start reporting false positives.

Initial Calibration Verification (ICV)

An ICV is a sample used to test the initial calibration of an instrument and is typically a reference standard obtained from a secondary source or secondary lot. This helps to ensure that the initial reference standard was trustworthy, and the established calibration curve is reliable.

Continuing Calibration Verification (CCV)

A CCV is another instrument specific QC sample. CCVs are typically pure reference standards, formulated to a known concentration, which are used to monitor instrument performance throughout an analytical run. Usually a CCV will be placed at the beginning (initial CCV) and end (final CCV) of an analytical run with the expectation that the results will match the expected target concentration. If a CCV is out of control, the lab must examine the instrument and determine whether maintenance or recalibration is required.

Why Do Test Results Vary Across Labs?

States that have legalized Cannabis and instituted mandatory product testing are beginning to see stark discrepancies across laboratories. Products seem to receive widely different potency results across laboratories. A report released in 2018 revealed that there was a huge variance in potency values produced by Cannabis testing labs in the state of Washington (Jikomes and Zoorob, 2018). The authors found that the chemotypes attributed to different strain names can vary substantially across laboratories – which is likely attributable to issues related to the "strain" concept discussed in earlier chapters of this book. Namely, strain names are largely unreliable, and plants can exhibit unique chemical profiles depending on environmental effects and genetic variability associated with seed propagation. It is easy to imagine that a variety of plants might receive the same strain identification, even if they are not genetically identical.

This report also discovered that among the laboratories investigated, some laboratories consistently reported high potency values, while others consistently reported low values, as compared to the overall spread of data analyzed. This sort of trend leads consumers to "number shop" – looking for laboratories that have a tendency to report higher THC values than others. Overall, this behavior leads to distorted data sets that make it difficult for researchers to work with and abstract meaningful insight. This trend also reveals that it's not just the heterogeneity of the products that is to blame for the disparities seen across testing labs.

The authors of the 2018 report comment that after controlling for various confounding variables, "these results suggest that the observed differences between laboratories cannot be explained by differences in the producers, product types, or strain names of the samples being processed by each lab." (Jikomes and Zoorob, 2018) This means, then, that the variability must come from details in a laboratory's protocols or quality system. Until greater quality standards are placed on testing laboratories, it will be impossible to ascertain whether an appreciable level of variability for Cannabis and cannabinoid product potency will remain.

Because of the discrepancies seen across laboratories, it is recommended that if you are a producer trying to collect data for product or process improvement, you should carefully vet laboratories and choose a lab that you trust. After picking a laboratory, stick with that laboratory throughout a project – otherwise you might end up with a bunch of data that is impossible to compare.

HOW CAN CANNABIS TESTING GO WRONG?

There are many ways in which Cannabis testing can go wrong. When trying to find a good Cannabis testing laboratory to work with, it is important to understand some of the common ways in which Cannabis testing can become compromised so that you can ask your lab probing questions to identify the quality of work that they are providing or claiming to provide. The following are some of the most common ways that Cannabis testing can go wrong in the laboratory followed by some questions that you should ask when deciding whether to use a laboratory's services or not.

IMPROPER TOTAL THC OR TOTAL CBD CALCULATION

When analyzing Cannabis for potency using a High-Pressure Liquid Chromatograph (HPLC), the results include the carboxylic acid forms of the cannabinoids, including THCA, CBDA, and CBCA, among others. To determine the total THC, the THCA and the THC are combined. It is tempting, but incorrect, to simply add them without applying the **decarboxylation correction factor**. Failure to use this conversion factor could be a sign of incompetence and unreliability, or an attempt to boost result numbers.

When the cannabinoid acids are heated and decarboxylated, they lose CO_2, and become lighter molecules. All in all, approximately 10-12% of the weight of a cannabinoid is lost after decarboxylation. So, 20% THCA (200 mg/g) becomes approximately 17% THC (170 mg/g) after decarboxylation. This conversion factor is approximately 0.88 and can be found throughout scientific literature, however you can calculate this correction factor yourself by simply dividing the molecular weight of THC (314.45 g/mol) by the molecular weight of THCA (358.47 g/mol) to reach the value 0.877 (314.45/358.47 = 0.877). In other words, THC is 87.7% of the mass of THCA.

Always pay close attention to cannabinoid test results produced via HPLC and ensure that the Total THC and Total CBD calculations are utilizing the proper decarboxylation correction factor and not simply adding up the carboxylic acid cannabinoids and neutral cannabinoids together.

Low Decarboxylation or Vaporization Efficiency (GC)

When a gas chromatograph is running, the first thing that occurs is a sample is injected into an inlet port where the sample is then quickly vaporized. This step is critical because if the sample is not vaporized at the proper temperature, the cannabinoid acids will not properly decarboxylate, resulting in dramatically low result numbers.

It is important for labs using gas chromatography to determine their decarboxylation efficiency to determine the accuracy of the equipment and the need for any corrections to be applied to the result. This can be done by taking a sample and manually decarboxylating half of it while preparing the other half as usual. Both samples are run through the machine and the difference is calculated. This is repeated multiple times to determine the decarboxylation efficiency.

At the time of this writing, most Cannabis testing labs are moving away from measuring cannabinoids with gas chromatographs, so the decarboxylation efficiency problem is becoming less significant. However, this issue is also related to the measurement of other Cannabis compounds, like terpenoids. This is especially true if the laboratory is using a headspace sampling method, instead of a liquid injection. If measuring terpenoids using a headspace sampler, it is important to ensure that the volatization of terpenes in the sample is adequate, otherwise the results obtained may be biased toward the terpenes with the lightest weight (and thus easiest to volatize) and heavier terpenes in the sample, like sesquiterpenoids, diterpenoids, etc, may be left behind.

Measuring "Ghost Peaks"

After repeated analyses on an instrument, residues may build up if certain components are not cleaned or replaced. If this happens, the instrument's detector will detect not only the sample passing through, but the leftover residues in the machine as well, leading to exaggerated results, or "ghost peaks." To avoid this, routine maintenance and servicing is necessary. Labs should also utilize "blank" injections of known clean solvent to detect ghost peaks before running any samples. If you are concerned about ghost peaks, simply ask your lab how they monitor and prevent instrument contamination or "analyte carryover".

Co-Eluting, or "Stacked" Peaks

When using relatively simple analytical techniques, like GC or HPLC, it is sometimes easy to be fooled into thinking that you are looking at one peak on your chromatogram, when in reality that peak represents two or more compounds that are similar enough in their chemistry that they passed through the instrument's detector at the same time, forming one giant peak. This is called "coelution." This is particularly a problem with measuring terpenoids, because there are a lot of them at similar weights and chemical configurations, but this is also an issue with cannabinoids. It is important when a lab is validating a testing method that they go to extra lengths to confirm that the peaks that they see on their chromatograms actually only represent a single compound each.

LACK OF REFERENCE STANDARDS OR ADEQUATE QUALITY CONTROLS

It is essential that laboratories use quality assurance practices, including quality control samples and reference standards, to monitor the accuracy of analysis results. A cannabinoid **reference standard** is a specially formulated sample that has a known concentration of cannabinoids present in it. When tests are run, the results can be compared and calibrated with the results of the reference standard to determine whether the instrument is performing correctly. Reference standards can be "spiked" onto a sample to measure how well an analytical method is "recovering" the target compounds.

For pesticide analysis quality control, for example, a sample is spiked with a known amount of pesticide. When the sample is analyzed, the result for that pesticide should correlate with the amount calculated to have been added to the sample. If it is off, the lab knows to examine their processes for sources of error.

It is tempting to try and produce results without using reference standards, especially for laboratories utilizing mass spectrometry which compares results against a database to tentatively identify compounds. However, it is entirely possible for mass spectra libraries to be inadequate for identifying compounds, or alternatively tentative chemical matches may be of such a low quality that they cannot be trusted with any high degree of confidence.

When evaluating laboratories, always ask them if they utilize reference standards for all the compounds that are measured and reported.

MANIPULATING CHROMATOGRAM PEAKS

One way that laboratories can fudge numbers is by manipulating the way that the instrument's computer software interprets the chromatogram peaks. It is possible to boost cannabinoid results, for instance, by redefining the amount of area on the graph that is representative of THC or CBD. This is why traceable records and auditing are important to ensure that laboratories are held accountable for the data they produce. Auditors are very sensitive to instances of "manual integration" of chromatogram peaks and require that laboratories maintain pre and post edit versions of any chromatograms that are manipulated along with the edit date, the initials of the editor, and a rationale for the edit. Manual integrations are a common activity in labs and do not necessarily indicate nefarious behavior, but repeated manual integration without a proper rationale is cause for concern.

USE OF EXCESSIVELY LENIENT QUALITY CONTROL PARAMETERS

It is entirely possible for a laboratory to have quality control parameters in place, but still deliver poor results, if those parameters are set too generously so that the laboratory allows itself a wide margin of error. For instance, a laboratory may allow technicians to use a standardized sample mass for result corrections, rather than the sample's actual mass, if that mass is within a certain range. A laboratory could say that if a weighed sample falls between 175 to 225mg, the result is corrected for a sample mass of 200mg. This would then allow technicians to consistently weigh samples under the standardized correction, ultimately causing results to be higher than they should be.

Other examples relate to other thresholds like accuracy and precision measurements. A laboratory could make their acceptable analyte recovery limits quite wide so that they never have an analytical batch that falls out of compliance with their own quality control parameters. This kind of behavior is particularly common in unregulated laboratory industries in states that have recently legalized medical or recreational cannabis, where laboratories testing Cannabis are not under scrutiny of third party or government agency auditors.

IMPROPER SAMPLING AND HANDLING OF SAMPLE MATERIAL

A common way that Cannabis testing goes awry is at the time of sampling and sample preparation. Client-provided samples tend to be the most cherry-picked samples from the available lot, perhaps not really representing an average of the lot. In addition, laboratories may feel pressure to manipulate samples by removing stems and trimming away excess plant material prior to sample preparation, further manipulating the final result. In some cases, laboratories have reported that samples have been received demonstrating unambiguous evidence of adulteration or manipulation, often in the form of inflorescences that have been sprinkled with sifted trichomes to boost cannabinoid content.

Great care must be taken while handling samples in the lab. Sterile gloves are used to avoid physical contact with the sample while also avoiding microbiological contamination. Our hands produce oils which mix with the oily trichomes of Cannabis, potentially manipulating the sample, if handled without gloves. If sample material comes into contact with an unsterile surface, the material must be discarded.

Samples must be well-mixed, or **homogenized**, before being prepared. If a sample is not properly mixed, or if a sample is "cherry picked", the analysis results might not be representative of the sample or the batch from which the sample was collected. For instance, when grinding up a Cannabis inflorescence, the trichomes are likely to dry sift to the bottom of the pile. If an analyst were to use the top portion of this sample in a potency preparation, they would get a lower result than if they tested the bottom of the pile. To avoid this problem, special homogenization equipment or methods for grinding samples within sterile test tubes is utilized so no material is lost or misrepresented.

Questions to Ask a Lab

In a September 2013 issue of *Natural Products Insider*, Dr. Steven Denalti, PhD published a list of ten questions to ask an analytical laboratory that are just as relevant to Cannabis testing laboratories as they are to any other natural products laboratory. Here is a summation of those questions:

Is your lab certified/accredited? If so, by what accrediting body?

Do you outsource any analyses? If so, to whom? What quality controls do you have in place to ensure my samples are not contaminated by any subcontracted facilities?

What are the credentials of the lab's staff? How much experience do they have performing these sorts of analyses?

What systems do you use for recording and managing data? How long would my raw data be stored and is the data available upon request?

Do you use validated methodologies for analyses and are method and procedural summaries available to review upon request? How do you validate your methods?

Do you have established laboratory instrument maintenance, servicing, and calibration schedules? Are these activities documented?

How are samples stored and protected from contamination?

What are typical turn-around times for each analysis? Will turn-around-times vary depending on the time of year?

How do you assure the validity of results if I am suspicious or unhappy with a result?

Keep in mind that these are just some of the questions you could ask to quickly evaluate a laboratory. After reading this chapter, what other questions might you ask your local laboratory?

Enduring Understandings

- Cannabis testing laboratories typically provide services to evaluate the potency and purity of Cannabis and Cannabis infused products.
- Some of the common tests performed by Cannabis testing laboratories are cannabinoids analyses, terpenoid analyses, microbiological testing, pesticide testing, metals testing, residual solvent testing, and sex testing.
- Chromatography is a process of separating a mixture into its unique chemical constituents.
- Mass spectrometry is a way of analyzing chemicals by evaluating the effects that their weight has on the trajectory of the chemical as it passes by a magnet.
- Polymerase chain reaction (PCR) is a technology used to amplify and measure DNA to detecting the presence of micro-organisms or particular genes.
- Analytical laboratories can utilize a variety of quality control methods to measure their own accuracy and precision.
- Due to product heterogeneity, natural batch-to-batch variation, lack of standardized methods across laboratories, and a lack of standardized sample methods, results across laboratories and across regions of the world can differ substantially.

Chapter 21:   INTERPRETING A CANNABIS ANALYSIS REPORT

Learning Questions
- What information is commonly found on a Cannabis COA?
- What does LOQ mean?
- What happens if someone disagrees with a lab's test results?
- How can Cannabis test results be converted to other units of measurement?

If you have ever had any Cannabis or Cannabis product tested by a laboratory for potency or contaminants, you have inevitably been faced with the task of deciphering a laboratory's "**certificate of analysis**", sometimes referred to as a "C of A", but more often referred to as a test report. These reports feature technical jargon, graphs, a myriad of numbers, interpretations, narrations, and a lot of other data.

Usually when someone is faced with a Cannabis test report, they ultimately want to know a few very basic things:

- What are the Total THC and Total CBD values?
- Were any contaminants detected?
- If so, what contaminants were detected and in what concentrations?

However, finding this seemingly simple information is not always so straightforward. Lab results can feature any assortment of technical jargon, columns of seemingly irrelevant data, and qualifier codes that appear to only have meaning to the laboratory, not the customer. Throughout this chapter, topics will be reviewed related to interpreting a Cannabis test report to identify some short-cuts to finding the information you need.

FIND THE PRIMARY INFORMATION

The first thing you should do when reviewing a test report is hunt down the primary pieces of data that answer your big question(s). If you ordered a potency analysis, immediately **search for the results for THC, THCA, Total THC, CBD, CBDA, and/or Total CBD**. If you ordered a contaminants screening, find the appropriate analysis section and **determine if any results other than "ND", "None Detected" or "<LOQ" are listed.** If "<LOQ" is listed for some analytes, while others are listed as "ND" or "<LOD", then the

lab may have detected trace amounts of the analyte in concentrations above the lab's limit of detection, but not above their limit of quantitation.

If there were any values listed for any contaminants, review those values and determine what units the values are being reported. For bacterial and fungal analyses, results are typically reported as **CFU/g**, or colony forming units per gram. Pesticide and residual solvent results are typically reported as **PPM**, or parts per million. Terpenoid and cannabinoid results are often reported as % w/w, or percent concentration by weight.

COMMON TERMS FOUND ON CANNABIS TEST REPORTS

Term	Description
LOD	Limit of Detection; The laboratory's lowest concentration that they can confidently detect
LOQ	Limit of Quantitation; The laboratory's lowest concentration that they can confidently detect and report – usually slightly higher than the LOD.
ND	"Not Detected" or "None Detected"; Indicates the lack of identified presence of something
Dry Weight	Dry weight results represent the concentration of the total dry, non-water, components of the sample. Dry weight results provide more value than wet weight results because dry weight results can always be corrected by moisture content to determine actual concentration of a sample.
Action Level	Concentration of an analyte required at which a sample "fails" for regulatory compliance or some other action is required
%	Percent; Parts per hundred; 1/100
ppm	Parts per million; 1/1,000,000
ppb	Parts per billion; 1/1,000,000,000
ppt	Parts per trillion; 1/1,000,000,000,000
g	Gram
mg	Milligram; 0.001g
mL	Milliliter; 0.001 L
mg/g	Milligram per gram; commonly used when reporting results for manufactured products
mg/mL	Milligrams per milliliter; commonly used when reporting results for liquid products; calculated by multiplying the mg/g result by the product's density in g/mL
mg/unit	Milligrams per unit; commonly used when reporting results for manufactured products; calculated by multiplying the mg/g result by the unit mass in grams
CFU	Colony Forming Units; Represent colonies identified on cultures which may be caused either by spores or living microbiological organisms present in the sample
CFU/g	Colony Forming Units per gram; Represents the number of colonies formed on a culture from one gram of sample.
TIC	Tentatively Identified Compound; a compound that was identified using mass spectrometry but not verified using reference standards.

FIGURE 62: GUIDE TO COMMON TERMS FOUND ON CANNABIS TEST REPORTS

EVALUATE THE RESULTS

Actual values should be reported for quantitative analyses, rather than a simple "pass/fail" designation. There are good reasons for this. For example, assume that there is a limit of 10,000 cfu/g of yeasts or molds allowed in Cannabis. **A pass/fail system for reporting microbiological results would not distinguish between Cannabis with non-detectable mold levels from a contaminated batch with 9900 cfu/g of black mold** – just below the allowable limit. Almost assuredly buyers at wholesalers and dispensaries would take such a discrepancy into consideration when deciding what product to purchase, however a pass/fail system of result reporting prevents such an informed decision-making process.

Test results should also be examined for **Tentatively Identified Compounds (TICs)**. These are usually seen in pesticide, residual solvent, or terpene analyses that use mass spectrometers and mass spectra libraries to identify compounds. **These values, usually of trace concentrations of compounds, are not truly quantitative or properly identified, however, until they have been verified against a chemical reference standard.**

HOW DID THE LAB CALCULATE "TOTAL" THC, CBD, CBG, ETC?

When reviewing cannabinoid potency results, it is important to determine how the "Total THC" and "Total CBD" values are calculated by the lab. First, look to see if the certificate of analysis notes what instrumentation was used for each analysis. If the instrument used for potency is an HPLC, immediately check to see if the **decarboxylation conversion factor** was applied to the THCA concentration to calculate total potential THC. When the decarboxylation factor is not applied correctly, the result becomes exaggerated, sometimes quite substantially.

As mentioned in previous chapters, decarboxylation refers to the process by which a carbon dioxide, or CO^2, group is removed from a carboxylic acid compound. When a bunch of THCA is decarboxylated to THC, a significant amount of weight is lost due to the loss of the CO^2. This is why it is inaccurate to simply add THCA and THC to calculate available or potential THC.

This is the proper equation for calculating total THC:

%THC + (%THCA x 0.877) = Max/Total THC

The decarboxylation factor is calculated by dividing the weight of the lighter compound by the weight of the heavier compound. For instance, the molecular weight of THC is 314.45 g/mol while the weight of THCA is 358.473 g/mol. Dividing these weights results in **0.877**, or an ~88% loss. For each compound, these decarboxylation factors might be slightly different, but for cannabinoids most of them are right around 0.88. So all in all, around 12% of the total weight of THCA is lost once it is heated and decarboxylated to THC.

Cannabinoid	Molecular Weight	Neutral Molecular Weight	Decarboxylation Correction Factor
THCA	358.478	314.469	0.877 (87.7%)
CBDA	358.5	314.464	0.877 (87.7%)
CBGA	360.5	316.48	0.878 (87.8%)
CBCA	358.5	314.46	0.877 (87.7%)
CBNA	354.4	310.4319	0.876 (87.6%)
THCVA	330.42	286.41	0.867 (86.7%)
CBDVA	330.42	286.41	0.867 (86.7%)

Max/Total THC Calculation

Using the following THC and THCa values, calculate the total or max THC.

THCa: 16.8%   THC: 3.4%   Max or Total THC: _____%

WHAT DO THEY MEAN BY "TOTAL CANNABINOIDS"?

It is common to see a value referred to as "total cannabinoids" on test reports from Cannabis testing laboratories. It is important to understand that there is not a Cannabis testing laboratory in operation that is reporting results for all 100+ cannabinoids that have been identified in Cannabis. For one thing, commercial labs cannot even obtain reference standards for most of them. At best, a Cannabis testing laboratory will report somewhere between 10 and 15 cannabinoids. For this reason, any value labeled as "total cannabinoids" is a bit misleading because it can only include the cannabinoids that the lab is actually quantifying. Don't be fooled by this specter of a test result.

ARE RESULTS IN DRY WEIGHT OR WET WEIGHT?

Sometimes a certificate of analysis might show two separate cannabinoid or terpenoid results, one for wet weight, and one for dry. In the natural products industry, results for the analysis of things like terpenes, vitamins, or cannabinoids are typically reported as dry matter. **Dry matter** refers to all the solids of a material, or everything that is not water. When a natural product is measured for vitamin content, for example, the concentration that is reported is the concentration of *solids* in the plant material that are vitamins.

To determine dry weight results, laboratories often either calculate each sample's moisture content or use a standardized procedure for drying samples completely before analysis, usually by using a programmable dehydrator or temperature-controlled oven. One way to measure the moisture content of a sample is to track the mass of a sample as it dries until the sample mass stabilizes. Then the starting weight and final weight can be compared to calculate the moisture content. This process of calculating moisture content through tracking the mass during drying is called "loss on drying." In addition, the length of time of drying and temperature may be tracked. A standardized drying temperature and time can be calculated and used to ensure all samples reach proper desiccation regardless of starting moisture content. There are other methods of measuring moisture content using various chemical reactions such as Karl Fisher titrations or sophisticated moisture content analytical equipment such as a moisture balance, which automates the loss on drying process.

The analyte concentration of a dry sample will always be slightly higher than in a wet sample. This is not because there are any less total molecules of cannabinoids present in the sample when it is wet compared to when it is dry, but rather because more of the total weight of the sample has become water, thus manipulating the overall concentration of cannabinoids by mass of the sample. The following pie charts demonstrate this change.

Example Compound Concentrations of 1g of Wet Cannabis

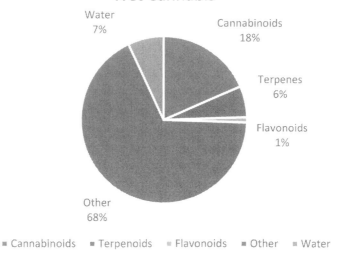

Example Concentrations in 1g of Dry Cannabis

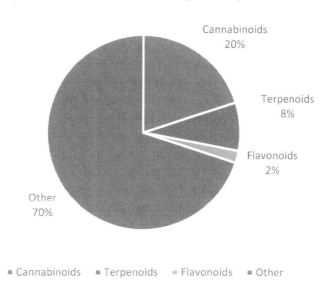

FIGURE 63: WET VS DRY WEIGHT CONCENTRATIONS OF CANNABIS COMPOUNDS

Wet weight corrections are most commonly seen in the pharmaceutical industry because slight changes in weight can have significant consequences when working with highly potent compounds consumed in very small quantities, like powdered drugs.

If both wet weight and dry weight results are listed on a certificate, try to find out how the dry weight correction was determined. Was the analysis performed on the wet sample and then adjusted to represent dry weight, or was the analysis performed on a dry sample and then adjusted to represent a wet sample? How were these adjustments performed? Was the samples true moisture content calculated, or was an assumed moisture content used?

The moisture level of a sample is often thought of as a predictor for microbial contaminants, but this not quite correct, because the water in a sample varies in its availability to microbial organisms like fungi and bacteria. The water in a sample is chemically "bound", or stuck in place, to varying degrees. A sample can potentially have significant water content, but the water could be very immobile and thus unavailable to microbes. This is why measuring **water activity,** or the mobility of water in a sample, is important. Water activity is measured by sealing a sample in a chamber and then measuring the humidity of the air in the chamber over time until it stabilizes.

WHO CERTIFIED THE RESULTS?

Other things to note include **the identity of the representative certifying the certificates of analysis**. This person should be able to attest to the validity of the results. A disconnected party does not satisfy this requirement. This signature should be by someone who is managing the lab or reviewing and verifying results as they are produced, as required by ISO and NELAC standards. **The date of the analysis** should also be noted. A certificate of analysis is only valid for a determined length of time set by the lab. Typically, this is approximately ninety days. After the validity date, the batch should be retested to produce a more accurate snapshot of the chemical profile of the material after long term storage.

DISPUTING TEST RESULTS WITH A LAB

It is common for anyone getting Cannabis testing performed regularly to run into situations where one might want to better understand the results or dispute the results of a testing lab. Most professional laboratories serving Cannabis clients will be happy to address concerns that may arise from laboratory results. Typically, the reasons that test result disputes arise is because of a less-than-expected potency value or an unexpected pesticide detection.

HANDLING UNEXPECTED POTENCY RESULTS

Potency result discrepancies may be caused by any number of reasons. Sometimes a CBD:THC ratio of a Cannabis flower may be different than what is typical for the associated cultivar, or "strain". Sometimes this may be due to unexpected genetic variability, especially in seed cultivation. Other times strains may be incorrectly labeled, leading the cultivator to expect a particular chemotype of resin yield which it simply cannot produce. The following are more factors that may affect the cannabinoid potency of a Cannabis flower sample:

- Excess leaf (untrimmed or lightly trimmed Cannabis)
- Excess moisture (if lab does not report results in dry weight)
- Excess stem
- Sampling conditions (random vs. client provided; homogeneity)
- Premature harvest

Keep in mind that when dealing with natural products like Cannabis flowers, it is completely normal to see some mild variation in potency results. If a Cannabis batch is tested by three different labs and the three labs report the total THC as 21%, 17%, and 19% respectively - these are considered to be essentially the same result and is *not* indicative of foul play or inadequate laboratory method standardization.

Sometimes the manufacturing of Cannabis extracts can produce unexpected results, particularly in regard to distillation. The result that many Cannabis distillate manufacturers have learned is that a distilled product may be anywhere from 30% to over 80% pure, which seems counterintuitive. When a distillate manufacturer receives a test result revealing that the product is only 30% THC or CBD, it leaves them scratching their head. The answers to this enigma can be found in the lab's chromatograms for the distillate sample.

A close inspection of a distillate sample's chromatogram typically reveals a variety of "mystery peaks", representing unique chemical compounds in the distillate which were not present in either the beginning flower, or intermediate extract. Throughout the course of the distillate production process, the Cannabis resin is exposed to a variety of temperatures, pressures, stirring, oxygen, and light – all of which provide conditions suitable for chemical reactions to take place in the extract. Scientists are still in the process of identifying exactly what these compounds are, with many speculating that they are various THC or CBD isomers.

If you suspect that a potency result that you have received from a lab is incorrect, ask to meet with the lab director or other available lab representative to review your results with you. The lab should be able to share what quality controls were in place to ensure the validity of your result. Alternatively, if there is sufficient cause to doubt the validity of the initial result, the laboratory may reanalyze the sample to confirm the initial result.

COMMON CAUSES OF UNEXPECTED POTENCY RESULTS		
Sample Type	Common Causes	Remedy
Flowers	Excess leaf and stem;	Trim flowers adequately;
	Excess moisture;	Dry flowers until stems snap when bent;
	Premature harvest	Monitor cannabinoid concentration in plant using thin layer chromatography or other technique during flowering to optimize harvest time
Distillates	Exposure to excess heat, light, oxygen;	Ensure extraction process is tightly controlled with all systems properly sealed off from exposure to light and air;
	Inadequate system parameters	Avoid excess heat
Edibles	Using volume vs mass for recipes;	Always use *mass,* rather than volume, for product recipes requiring precise dosages;
	No test results for feedstock;	Always have Cannabis flower or extract ingredients tested to properly calculate recipes;
	Ignoring density conversions	If the edible is a liquid, always have the lab convert your potency result from % or mg/g to mg/mL based on the product's density;
	Ingredients with co-eluting compounds (i.e. essential oils)	If using complex ingredients, send the lab samples of ingredients as well as "blanks" of the finished product without cannabinoids so the lab can make sure that none of the ingredients are causing any interference with cannabinoids

FIGURE 64: Common Causes of Unexpected Potency Results

UNEXPECTED PESTICIDE OR SOLVENT RESULTS

Unexpected pesticide results often arise from the use of systemic or translaminar pesticides. These pesticide types linger for prolonged periods of time in the plant, potentially appearing in detectable concentrations months after application. Sometimes pesticide contamination occurs from sources such as run-off from neighboring farms, airborne pollution, contact with clothing that has previously come in contact with pesticides, or even from the use of irrigation supplies which have come into contact with pesticides. It is important to rule out all sources of pesticide contamination prior to contesting a pesticide detection result. Sometimes agrochemical products might even feature unlabeled active pesticides.

A lab error that could be responsible for false positive pesticide detections in Cannabis is pesticide residue carryover in the analytical instrument used to test the samples. If a sample that is contaminated with pesticides is run prior to a "clean" sample, it is possible for traces of those pesticides from the first sample to linger in the instrument and pass through during the analysis of the "clean" sample. Typically, laboratories have various quality control measures in place to detect these kinds of phenomenon including running clean solvent blanks periodically throughout analyses to detect residual pesticides in the instrument.

A lab error that could be responsible for false positive solvent detections is solvent contamination associated with the cleaning of lab tools. It is a common habit for lab technicians to clean tools in between handling. However, if a sample is to be tested for the presence of solvents, it is critical that the laboratory *not* clean tools when handling samples. Instead samples are cleaned ahead of time and often baked or dried to ensure they are free of solvent residue. Then the technician will use as many clean tools as needed to complete the job without performing any cleaning. If a tool becomes dirty, a new one is used. A laboratory should have detailed procedures for ensuring against and detecting solvent contamination at the time of sampling and sample preparation.

Should you suspect a false positive pesticide or solvent detection, ask to meet with the lab director or other lab representative to go over your results with you. The lab should be able to share with you any quality control information associated with your sample to prove that care was taken to avoid cross contamination and ensure the validity of the lab's results.

COMMON CONVERSIONS AND CALCULATIONS

Once you have test results in hand, it might seem challenging to convert those results into something meaningful. For instance, let's say that I wanted to make my own batch of Cannabis infused brownies, using some of my recently harvested homegrown Fire OG variety of Cannabis. I send a sample to the lab and receive results revealing that my

Cannabis is 20% THC. How does this tell me how much Cannabis to use in my recipe? How can I predict the final dosage of each brownie? To answer these and related questions, we must perform some basic conversions and calculations.

What Kind of Potency Result Do You Need?	
Product Type	Recommended Potency Result Type
Flower	%
Flower (to be used as ingredient)	Mg/g
Extract	%
Extract (to be used as ingredient)	Mg/g
Edible (solid)	Mg/g
Edible (liquid)	Mg/mL

FIGURE 65: WHAT POTENCY RESULT FORMAT DO YOU NEED?

The rest of this chapter will explore many commonly utilized math conversions and dosage calculations which I highly recommend learning.

HOW MANY MILLIGRAMS PER GRAM?

To properly produce consistent dosages, it is important to understand how to calculate how many milligrams of something, like THC, are in a product. Some test results may feature these conversions. Other times, you may need to perform the calculations yourself. Luckily, the math is not too complicated.

When dealing with percentages, it helps to break the word "percent" down and remember that you are dealing with numbers that are "per 100" (think "per century" if it helps). In other words, to convert a percentage to a fraction, you just take the number and divide it by 100. So, 25 percent THC also means 25 divided by 100, or 25/100. We want to measure milligrams, so we just add those units to form 25mg/100mg. We know we want our final units to be mg/g, so we need to get the bottom number of the fraction, or denominator, converted to grams. A gram (g) is comprised of 1000 milligrams (mg), so if we multiply 25mg/100mg by 10, we get 250mg/1000mg, or 250mg/g.

1g (gram) of Cannabis = 1000mg (milligrams)

25% THC = 250mg/g because 25% of 1000mg is 250mg.

25 *percent* (per 100) = 25/100 = 25mg/100mg = 250mg/1000mg = 250mg/g

And so, 16% THC = 160 mg/g

SHORTCUT: to convert percent to mg/g, simply multiply the percent number by 10. For example, 20% THC or CBD is equal to 200mg/g THC or CBD.

HOW MANY MILLIGRAMS PER MILLILITER?

To find out how many milligrams are in a liquid Cannabis product like a tincture, you may need to convert the potency result from percent to milligrams (mg) per milliliter (mL). To do this, you must first know the approximate **density** of the product. A Cannabis infused tincture will primarily consist of ethanol. The known density of pure ethanol is 0.789g/mL. This means that every 1mL of ethanol weighs 0.789 grams.

A product's mass per volume is its density and is often reported in grams per milliliter (g/mL). This means that **an accurately measured milliliter of the product should be weighed to determine its weight per milliliter**. This measurement must be accurate; otherwise any potency calculations made with it will be exaggerated.

To convert a potency result from percent to mg/mL, all you have to do is to calculate the mg/g result and then multiply that number by the product density. For instance, if a tincture contained 3% THC, it could then be determined that it contained 30mg/g THC. Assuming the product's density is 0.789g/mL, because it is primarily ethanol, we can multiply 30mg/g THC by 0.789g/mL to get 23.67mg of THC per mL of tincture.

Solvent	Density (g/mL)
Ethanol	0.789
Everclear (95%)	0.8
Everclear (75%)	0.84
Coconut Oil	0.924
Glycerin	1.26
Most Vegetable Oils	~0.920
Medium Chain Triglyceride (MCT) Oil	~0.93-0.96
Measures of Mass (Solids)	
1 gram (g)	= 1000 milligrams (mg)
1 kilogram (kg)	= 1000 grams
Measures of Volume (Liquids)	
1 liter (L)	= 1000 milliliters (mL)
1 deciliter (dL)	= 1/10 liter

FIGURE 66: COMMON SOLVENT DENSITIES AND MEASUREMENT CONVERSIONS

Typical Potency Ranges for Cannabis Products

Disclaimer: The following information is meant only to serve as a general guide to some of the common trends found among the potencies of Cannabis products. There are always exceptions.

Product Type	Typical Potency Range (Total THC or CBD)
Inflorescence (flower)	5 – 25%
Cannabis Leaves (trim)	1 – 8%
Tinctures and MCT Solutions	0.1 – 10%
Edibles and Topicals	Highly variable; 5 – 1000mg per unit
Concentrates (sifted hash)	30 - 50%
Concentrates (rosin)	40 - 60%+
Concentrates (reduced ethanolic extract)	40 – 65%+
Concentrates (CO2 extract)	45 – 70%+
Concentrates (butane, propane, etc)	60 - 80%+
Distillates	70 – 90%+
Isolate	95%+

FIGURE 67: TYPICAL CANNABIS PRODUCT POTENCY RANGES

Inflorescence (Flowers)

The typical potency ranges for dried and cured Cannabis inflorescence is anywhere between 10% and 25%. It is common for flowers to fall somewhere between 13% and 25%. It is uncommon, though possible, to see flower potencies above 25%. It is very rare to find flowers that reach 30% or more. It is important to note that Cannabis potency values are influenced by the amount of leaf and stem present. Tightly trimmed "buds" will have higher potencies.

Extracts

Sifted forms of concentrated Cannabis extracts such as **Kief** and **Bubble hash** often feature total THC or total CBD potencies between 25% and 45%. The potency of desolvated ethanolic extracts, sometimes referred to by names like "**Rick Simpson Oil**" (**RSO**) or **FECO (Full Extract Cannabis Oil)**, typically range between 45% to 70% total THC or CBD. The potency values of these types of products is less than that of other concentrated extract types primarily because these extracts contain a wide variety of non-cannabinoid plant compounds like chlorophyll, flavonoids, glycoproteins, and more.

BHO/PHO concentrated extract products usually have a total THC or CBD potency somewhere between 55% and 85%. **CO₂ extracted resins** usually have total THC potencies between 40-55% on average prior to refinement. Winterized versions of these extracts will often reach potency values between 60% and 75%. **Distilled** and **isolated** extracts can sometimes reach purities of 85% or more. Cannabinoid **isolates** are usually found at purities of 95%+.

HOW DOES COLOR RELATE TO POTENCY?

A "SLAB" OF "SHATTER"

The color of a concentrate can *sometimes* be an indicator of cannabinoid content, but there are many exceptions. The higher the THC or CBD potency, usually the lighter in color and more transparent the product will be, in general. Cannabinoids themselves do not have much color, except for sometimes a very faint yellow or orange hue. Flavonoids, chlorophyll, quinones, and other compounds contribute colors like shades of green, red, yellow, and orange. Additionally, as an extract ages and the polyphenolic components of the extract oxidize, the color can change, usually becoming darker. Waxes and fats affect the clarity and viscosity of extract products, distorting light as it passes through the extract. Therefore, if a product does not feature excess compounds other than cannabinoids and terpenes, the product should be relatively free of color and less opaque.

Concentrates between 50% and 70% cannabinoid content often display amber to orange-yellow color, respectively. Concentrates usually exhibit a yellowish tint at around 80% concentration. At 90% or greater THC or CBD concentration, most color is gone, and only faint yellow and gold color remains.

However, this is not to say that all light colored or transparent concentrates must contain high concentrations of cannabinoids. Product color can be manipulated using different techniques like charcoal filtering, celite filtering or solvent washing. Some otherwise transparent concentrates may feature additional ingredients like terpenes which ultimately dilute the product's cannabinoid concentration while maintaining product clarity. Also, be aware that extracted oils can appear darker in color when contained in bulk but can actually be quite light in color and transparent when handled in small amounts.

To summarize, color can *sometimes* relate to potency, but it does not *always* directly correlate to potency.

EDIBLES AND INFUSED PRODUCTS

Potency results for edibles are usually reported in mg per g, mg per mL, mg per serving or mg per product (brownie, sucker, chocolate, etc). The average potency of a Cannabis infused edible usually ranges between 0.1-6% THC or CBD by weight, or 1 to 60 mg/g. Many edible products are between 10 and 100 mg THC or CBD total, although there are some products available in legal Cannabis markets that range upwards to 1000 mg per serving.

The average potency of an edible is highly sensitive to product weight. 10 unique Cannabis infused suckers of the same production batch, even with adequate quality control, will each weigh differently. So, if the tested infused sucker is reported to contain 5mg/g of THC, the suckers could have a wide range of potencies, with a 5-gram sucker containing 25mg THC, but a 6.5 gram sucker in the same batch containing 32.5mg. That's a 77% increase in potency between suckers! This is a distinction that customers need to understand to achieve proper dosing.

EXAMPLE OF POTENCY VARIABILITY IN A 5mg/g THC EDIBLE		
	Sucker Weight (g)	Total mg THC
Sucker 1	5	25
Sucker 2	6.5	32.5
Sucker 3	5.2	26
Sucker 4	4.8	24
Sucker 5	6.8	34
Total mg THC Range Throughout Batch	24 – 34mg THC	

FIGURE 68: EXAMPLE OF POTENCY VARIABILITY IN A 5MG/G THC EDIBLE

A more representative way of displaying potency values for edibles would probably be best as a *range* of values. For instance, the label for a brownie could indicate 60 ± 3 mg/brownie. This lets the consumer know that each of the brownies in the batch do not have the same potency due to their different weights and natural variations, but no brownie in the batch should contain more than 63 mg/g THC or less than 57 mg/g THC. This would allow consumers to prepare for potential worst-case scenarios if they happen to be particularly sensitive to the effects of THC.

CANNABINOID RATIOS CAN TELL A STORY

Cannabinoid ratios can sometimes be used to determine certain qualitative information about the material. For instance, **THC breaks down into CBN when exposed to oxygen and heat**. If CBN is present in high concentrations in a sample, it could be possible that the material was stored improperly, and the THC has been breaking down. Likewise, CBD can break down to a compound called cannabinodiol, or CBND – which may actually have psychoactive effects similar to THC – although CBND has not been well studied.

This is one reason why it may be a good idea to retest Cannabis batches for potency every few months. A product that tests high in THC or CBD early after curing,

359

might measure significantly lower after poor storage over time. The presence of CBG and CBGA can also tell the story of a Cannabis sample. CBGA is synthesized to THCA, CBDA, CBCA, and then later to THC, CBD, and CBC, thus **high CBG and/or CBGA content could be an indicator of premature harvesting or a genetic issue affecting the enzymes that convert CBGA to THCA and CBDA (unless the plant is a CBG dominant cultivar).**

Additionally, various cannabinoids and terpenes may modulate the pharmacological effects of THC or CBD. Some examples of compounds that might reduce the psychotropic effects of THC are CBD, CBG, CBC, and limonene. High CBN, myrcene, and linalool levels all demonstrate sedative activity in various studies indicating a potential utility for insomnia. Citrus compounds like limonene and nerolidol have been thought to demonstrate antidepressant effects like CBD and CBC. **The complex interactions between competing and complementing compounds are little understood, making it difficult to predict the efficacy of a Cannabis product in treating a health condition.** The more research reveals about these compounds and their synergies, the more qualitative information will be able to be drawn from lab test results.

Enduring Understandings

- A certificate of analysis (COA) should always be certified by a qualified analyst with a signature present directly on the COA.

- An LOQ is a laboratory's limit of quantitation which is the lowest value that can be measured and distinguished from the background noise of the analytical instrument.

- A result of "<LOQ" is not necessarily the same as 0 or "not present".

- Total THC or Total CBD is calculating according to the formula: THC + (THCA * 0.877) or CBD + (CBDA * 0.877)

- The decarboxylation factor used in Total THC or Total CBD calculations is derived by dividing the molecular mass of the neutral cannabinoid into the molecular mass of the acidic cannabinoid and multiplied by 100.

- Percent concentration results can easily be converted into milligram per gram values by multiplying the percent concentration value by 10.

Pop Quiz:

Practice Converting Potency Results!

A Cannabis flower is determined to contain 23% THC. Convert this value to milligrams per gram (mg/g).

An ethanolic tincture is labeled as 10% THC. Convert this value to milligrams per milliliter. Use the solvent density chart for assistance.

Approximately how many milligrams of THC are in 1 gallon of Cannabis infused glycerin tincture that contains 10 mg/g THC?

Answers: 230mg/g; 78.9mg/mL; ~454mg

PART VI

CANNABIS RESEARCH RESOURCES

Chapter 22:
HOW TO FIND CANNABIS RESEARCH PAPERS

"You can Google Berberine and see what Berberine does in dozens of cell lines. But I think until you can really digest that host of data and think about it scientifically, it's not a good idea to make scientific conclusions or assumptions about any one of them."

Anthony Smith, PhD, BTS #6 Curious About Cannabis Podcast

Learning Questions
- What are some online resources for finding peer-reviewed Cannabis research articles?
- What are the various types of research that may be featured in a research article?
- What is the difference between statistical significance and clinical significance?

If you want to start to do your own science research, you need to know how to find reliable information. Peer-reviewed research journals are the best place to look for credible information on a topic. **Peer-reviewed journals** include **articles** written by experts in the field which are reviewed by peers that are also experts in the field. The peer-review committee submits changes and critiques on a proposed article which must be addressed before the article is published. This helps to ensure the quality of the articles published in the journal.

In this section, we will review a few different methods of finding peer-reviewed research articles online. You can use these methods to find papers listed in the resources section of the appendix or to find information about a topic that interests you.

GOOGLE SCHOLAR – SCHOLAR.GOOGLE.COM

Google scholar can be a great tool for beginning your search for reputable science papers. To begin, just navigate to http://scholar.google.com. There you will see a screen that looks very similar to the typical Google search screen.

There is an option here to either include patents in the search or not. Typically for searching for academic papers, you will not want this option checked.

After performing your search, a list of results will appear:

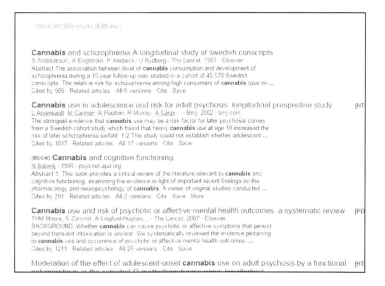

The PDF indicator lets you know that there is a PDF version of the document available online. Clicking the link will take you to the PDF where you can save and/or print the document.

Google Scholar also allows you to see "Related Articles." Clicking the Related Articles link will take you to a search results page with relevant articles listed.

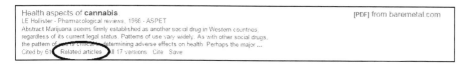

Google Scholar can be used to make collections of citations while you are performing research, so you can go back and review the various papers in your collection. It also allows you to see the various versions of the paper that have been found on the internet. It even tells you how many other papers have cited the paper you are reviewing.

PubMed

PubMed is an online library of biomedical research papers hosted by the US National Library of Medicine and the National Institutes of Health. Navigating to http://www.ncbi.nlm.nih.gov/pubmed will bring you to a page with a search bar at the top.

After performing a search, the following screen will appear. To narrow your search, use the options in the left sidebar. To limit the search results to only papers which are available in full text for free, choose "Free full text" under the "Text availability" sorting category. If you only want to view papers that are clinical trials, you can choose the Clinical Trial option under Article Types.

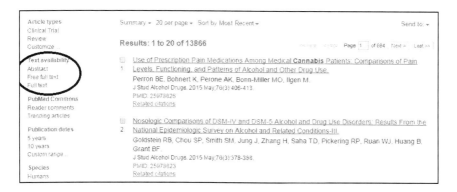

SCIENCEDIRECT

Another great source for finding scientific research papers is the ScienceDirect database. Navigating to http://www.sciencedirect.com will present a website with search options and a list of categories and subjects for browsing.

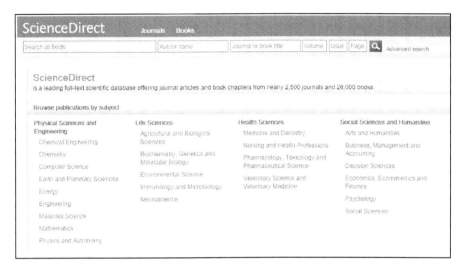

Performing a search leads to a screen very similar to the PubMed search screen. There are options to narrow your search on the left sidebar. You also have the ability to interact with multiple papers at once allowing you to buy, download, or save the citations of multiple papers simultaneously.

RESEARCHGATE.NET AND ACADEMIA.EDU

If you happen to be affiliated with a school and have a ".edu" email address, you can sign up for ResearchGate.net and Academia.edu and gain access to free full text versions of research papers that are shared by the authors to the broader research community. When using ResearchGate, if a paper is not available, you often have the option of requesting the paper directly from the author.

SCIHUB

SciHub is a digital repository of scientific publications, maintained by servers in various locations across the world, which provide users with access to almost any scientific paper, free of charge. All one needs to do is to search for a publication title, link, or DOI number and a PDF of the article will become available, if it is in SciHub's database. While this is a very powerful resource that is available on the web, please note that some of the content on SciHub may be provided illegally, and anyone that downloads a pirated copy of a scientific publication could be breaking piracy laws, depending on where they are located. Because of the issue of piracy and the challenging nature of knowing whether an article on SciHub is being provided legally or not, SciHub cannot be formally recommended as a resource. If you choose to use SciHub, please understand that you do so at your own risk.

HOW TO READ A RESEARCH PAPER

Reading a research paper can be very intimidating for anyone unaccustomed to the practice. A research paper comes in several primary components including: title, abstract, introduction, methods, results, and discussion. There are various methods used to read and interpret research papers. The following method can be used to quickly skim through papers to determine which papers are worth your time when you are trying to find out information about a specific topic:

1. Read the title and abstract to try and figure out what the point of the paper is and whether the paper is worth reading.

2. Read the introduction and determine the primary research question that the experiment is supposed to address as well as the researchers' prediction of the outcome of the research.

3. Look at the methods and results to determine if the experiment properly addressed the primary research question. What is the researcher or researchers finding(s)? What conclusions can you draw from the results? Were results statistically significant? Therapeutically/clinically significant?

4. Review the conclusion/discussion to find out what the researchers think their results mean. Do you agree with their conclusions? Does the data support their conclusions? What else needs to be known to draw further conclusions?

As you read through research papers, be prepared to look up definitions of unfamiliar terms. Research papers will also reference a variety of other research studies and articles, providing a wealth of resources to explore to gain a better understanding of the subject matter at hand.

TYPES OF RESEARCH

There are many different types of research study designs out there, with their own appropriate applications and limitations. Listed below are brief descriptions of some of the most common types of research studies you are likely to find when exploring Cannabis research papers:

- **Opinions**
    - o   Researchers and experts in various fields write opinion and editorial pieces occasionally for scholarly journals to weigh in on a topic of interest.
- **Case Reports**
    - o   Case reports or a case report series is simply a description of what one or more people experienced outside of a controlled setting.
- **Meta-Analysis**
    - o   A meta-analysis involves collecting data from across multiple studies and compiling them together to perform statistical analyses. Sometimes a meta-analysis may accompany a systematic review paper.
- **Review/Systematic Review**
    - o   A review paper is exactly what it sounds like – a review of the available literature on a certain topic. These kinds of papers are great for getting introduced to a topic before diving into details. There are a lot of helpful review papers available for Cannabis research, many of which are referenced throughout this book! I often recommend that new learners start with Ethan Russo's review paper, *Taming THC* which is available free online.
- **Case Control Study**
    - o   A case-control study is unique in that it starts at the end, so to speak, and works backwards to determine the potential cause of an effect. This is done typically by comparing attributes between two populations, performing some basic interviews to determine behavior patterns, lifestyle choices, etc and then the two populations are statistically evaluated.
- **Cross-Sectional Study**
    - o   A cross-sectional study is an observational study that looks at a population at a particular time or period of time.

- **Cohort Study/Prospective Observational Study**
  - A cohort study typically involves a group of individuals that exhibit a certain characteristic or feature some condition or treatment that are followed over time and compared to control groups that do not feature whatever characteristics, conditions, or treatments are being measured.
- **In vitro**
  - As mentioned previously, in vitro studies are petri-dish, or "test tube", experiments, typically involving cell cultures.
- **Randomized Control Trial**
  - RCTs are clinical trials that randomly assign participants to groups. If the RCT is blind, then the participants are unaware of what group they are assigned to. If the RCT is double-blind, then both the administrator of the study as well as the participants are unaware of who is in what group. The double-blind, placebo controlled, randomized trial is often considered a gold standard for research because it does the best to remove human bias or influence from the results.

TRY THIS! CANNABIS RESEARCH ACTIVITY

Using the resources presented in this chapter, find three peer-reviewed research papers on any Cannabis science topic of your choosing. Document the titles, authors, sources, and a summary of each article.

    1.   Title:

         Author(s):

         Link:

         Summary:

    2.   Title:

         Author(s):

         Link:

         Summary:

    3.   Title:

         Author(s):

         Link

         Summary:

STATISTICAL VS CLINICAL SIGNIFICANCE

The news media often throws around the word "significant" when referring to medical or other science research results without pointing out that scientists and mathematicians use the term "significant" quite differently than most of the public. It is important to understand significance from the point of view of a researcher to better comprehend results of research papers and understand what the results really mean in a practical sense. Researchers often talk about significance in one or two ways: **statistical significance** or **clinical significance**.

STATISTICAL SIGNIFICANCE

Statistical significance is a measure of the likelihood that an event is due to chance. This value is represented as a **P value**. Research papers often list P values in the Results or Discussion sections. If you do not see the P value there, check for any tables that might be present in the paper.

As a rule of thumb, the lower the P value, the less likely the event was due to chance.

For instance, a recent study examining the effects of high potency Cannabis on white matter in the brain reported that high potency users of Cannabis exhibited higher Axial Diffusivity ($p = 0.004$) and higher Radial Diffusivity ($p = 0.04$) in the *corpus collosum* than low potency users or non-users. These p values mean that there's only a 0.4% and 4% chance respectively of these results being due to chance. These results would be considered *statistically significant*. The research did not evaluate whether this effect was *clinically significant*. And yet numerous media outlets reported on this research result touting that high potency Cannabis has a significant effect on brain matter.

CLINICAL SIGNIFICANCE

Why is statistical significance not enough for clinicians to determine the usefulness of a research result?

The problem is that **it is entirely possible for a result to be statistically significant but still fail to be of clinical significance or importance**. For instance, a compound might be reported to provide statistically significant relief of pain or spasms, but if the compound only provides a small amount of relief, the result may not be considered clinically significant.

Clinical significance is sometimes measured as a value called the Minimal Clinically Important Difference score (MCID). The concept of MCID was first described in 1989 (Cook). It essentially refers to the smallest amount of improvement necessary for a treatment to be considered worthwhile. In his article *Clinimetrics Corner: The Minimal Clinically Important Change Score (MCID): A Necessary Pretense*, Chad Cook describes the development of this concept as such:

> *"...although statistically significant changes often occurred during use of instruments that measured change after intervention, in some cases the significant change had little clinical significance. Thus, their operational definition of a minimal clinically important difference was '...the smallest difference in score in the domain of interest which patients perceive as beneficial and which would mandate, in the absence of troublesome side effects and excessive cost, a change in the patient's management.'"*

Despite the introduction of the useful concept of MCID and other similar measures, these measures themselves have their own problems. Mostly, these measures rely heavily on reporting from patients, which can be laden with bias and error and often cannot be verified in an objective way. Another problem is that someone must define what a minimal clinically important value is. This usually ends up being the clinician.

REVIEWING AND INTERPRETING CANNABIS RESEARCH

When reviewing results from an experiment, there are some key things you can look for to determine the significance of the research results.

When reading the Results section of a Cannabis research paper, ask yourself these questions:

1) *What type of research was it? Cell culture? Rodent? Observational? Clinical? etc*

   There are a wide variety of types of research projects, each with unique applications and challenges. Identifying the type of research can help you decide how to proceed with evaluating the methods, results and conclusion.

2) *What was administered? THC? CBD? Whole plant extract? Vaporized Cannabis?*

   It is rare that Cannabis research utilizes herbal Cannabis. Instead, it is common to find research which utilizes synthetic cannabinoids, isolated phytocannabinoids (THC, CBD), or formulated plant extracts. It is critical to understand exactly what was administered when evaluating the therapeutic or clinical significance of the result. Synthetic cannabinoid and isolated cannabinoid studies will not represent typical Cannabis use like studies that utilize herbal Cannabis or whole plant extracts, especially given what is now known about the entourage effect.

3) *What is the sample size?*

An experiment's sample size will be listed as its n value. The main thing to understand about sample size is that smaller sample sizes produce less reliable results that do not adequately represent larger sample sizes.

4) *How likely is the result due to chance? What were the results compared to placebo? Has the study been replicated and if so, did the results agree or disagree with these results?*

Experimental results utilize p values to indicate how likely the result is due to chance. P values are typically found in the results or discussion section of the paper. The lower the p value, the less likely the result is due to chance. If the value is 0.05 or less, it is generally considered statistically significant.

If possible, search for similar experiments that have attempted to replicate the initial results, or, conversely, try to find out if the initial experiment is replicating any prior experiments and compare results. If the results agree, greater confidence can be established in the information.

5) *Is there sufficient data to suggest that the result is of clinical/therapeutic significance or importance?*

This is the hardest question to answer. Researchers can perform as many cell culture and rodent models of Cannabis and cannabinoid research all they want, but ultimately the data from these experiments never escapes a certain level of limitation in its scalability or practical applicability. It is not until research is conducted with humans, in clinical settings, with herbal cannabis and cannabis extracts, that experiments can produce results which can easily be said to be clinically significant or insignificant.

Enduring Understandings

- There are many ways to find peer-reviewed research articles online.
- Care should always be taken to review the methods and results of a research article to determine if the discussion and conclusions of the article authors are consistent with the actual results.
- "in vitro" research is research performed in test tubes or petri dishes on isolated tissues, cells, or chemicals (like chemical receptors).
- "in vivo" research is research performed in animals, typically rodents, monkeys, dogs, or humans.
- The results of in vitro research or non-human in vivo research are not always directly scalable to humans and should be evaluated with caution.
- Statistical significance is a measure of the likelihood that a result is due to chance.
- Clinical significance is a measure of the likelihood that a treatment will provide therapeutic value.

Chapter 23:
THE FUTURE OF CANNABIS RESEARCH:
OPPORTUNITIES AND CHALLENGES

Cannabis and cannabinoid science is an exciting and relatively new field of research with many exciting opportunities on the horizon, but due to several factors there are also many challenges facing Cannabis and cannabinoid research. Just a few of these opportunities and hurdles are outlined below.

RESEARCH OPPORTUNITIES

THE CANNABIS RHIZOSPHERE

There has been only a very small amount of research done to date looking at the ecology of the Cannabis root zone, or rhizosphere. Rhizospheres are fascinating subjects of ecological and agricultural research. By understanding how Cannabis roots affect soil and soil organisms, and how soil organisms and micro-organisms in turn affect Cannabis roots, it may be possible to develop more efficient Cannabis cultivation techniques allowing for more efficient nutrient cycling, better inherent pest control, and better water retention. Additionally, rhizosphere dynamics influence the chemistry of plant roots, primarily by changing the components of plant root exudates which are often composed of oils rich in triterpenoids and diterpenoids. As some companies begin pursuing true "whole plant" Cannabis products which incorporate all parts of the plant including flower, leaves and roots – understanding the dynamics that influence the chemistry of the roots will become critical. We may eventually come to a point where Cannabis roots are considered to have their own unique chemotypes as seen in the plant's resins.

CANNABIS ENDOPHYTES

As Cannabis cultivation and breeding gets more sophisticated, and an emphasis is placed on avoiding agrochemicals and maximizing the production of target compounds like cannabinoids and terpenoids, research is beginning to examine the microbiological communities present in and around the Cannabis plant and how they affect the growth and survival of the plant. As mentioned previously, while many of the endophytes present in Cannabis have been documented, their functions have not been well explored. By understanding Cannabis endophytes and their relationship to things like phytochemical production and pest resistance, future Cannabis breeding efforts can take these relationships into account and potentially breed plants that are more naturally vigorous, phytochemically rich, and resistant to pests and disease.

Mapping the Cannabis Genome

There is still a lot to understand about how Cannabis has evolved and how it utilizes different genes to express various phenotypical and chemotypical traits. It will be crucial that as many varieties of Cannabis as possible are genetically sequenced and cataloged for current and future research efforts. As the Cannabis plant genome is better understood, it is likely that Cannabis breeding efforts will become even more sophisticated. A better understanding of the Cannabis genome will allow taxonomists to better understand how different traits have moved through Cannabis populations over time. In addition, Cannabis breeders will be able to target their breeding efforts to upregulate various traits while downregulating others. Drug manufacturers are likely to use this information to better understand the biochemical pathways of Cannabis in the pursuit of developing novel cannabinoid medicines.

Protecting Genetic Diversity

Cannabis plants have been intensely hybridized to the point that the genetic diversity of the Cannabis plant has greatly suffered. This point is made at great length in McPartland and Small's 2020 paper about endangered high-THC cultivars called "A classification of endangered high-THC cannabis domesticates and their wild relatives". It is urgently important to seek out varieties of Cannabis that have not been contaminated by modern hybrids in order to preserve their germplasm for future research and cultivation.

Teasing Out Terpenoid Enantiomers

Throughout this book we mentioned that a persistent problem facing Cannabis terpenoid data is that most Cannabis testing laboratories are not identifying specific terpenoid enantiomers. We also mentioned that although terpenoid enantiomers may look nearly identical to one another, they can elicit vastly different effects from the body. An area of Cannabis research that desperately needs attention is this area of terpenoid enantiomer identification.

Is d-Limonene actually present in Cannabis? Or is it l-Limonene? Which enantiomers of linalool appear in Cannabis? These are important questions to answer, especially as producers are rushing to create terpenoid blends to mimic the terpene profiles of popular Cannabis cultivars. If these terpenoid blends feature terpenes from other botanical sources, they may not feature the same enantiomers as Cannabis, even if the scents are similar. This means that ultimately the effects of those non-Cannabis terpenes could be significantly different than would be produced from the Cannabis plant. We may find that certain Cannabis cultivars or chemovars feature unique terpenoid enantiomers compared to others, which would be useful for chemotaxonomy (classifying Cannabis varieties by their chemical profile). Understanding these enantiomers would also give both consumers and clinicians better data to work with to find products that are effective.

BETTER UNDERSTANDING THE ENTOURAGE EFFECT

Pharmacological science is currently moving away from the simplified model called "the receptor concept" which is the view that drugs elicit effects from the human body by simply binding to a receptor and causing an action. Researchers now understand that there is a whole symphony of activity happening when people consume food or drugs, especially polypharmaceuticals like Cannabis. Researchers also now understand that an otherwise benign compound might elicit unique, and sometimes profoundly powerful, effects when in the presence of other particular compounds. We refer to this action as "the entourage effect" – that certain compounds together elicit unique properties that are not attributed to any compound by itself. In essence, chemicals have the ability to act greater than the sum of their parts. However, researchers understand very little about what drives these effects or just how therapeutically significant the entourage effect is in the context of Cannabis.

Currently cannabinoid researchers are beginning to look for "allosteric effectors" of cannabinoid receptors – compounds which interact with chemical receptors in such a way as to boost the efficacy of cannabinoids when they happen to bind to the receptor. In a sense, these allosteric effectors can sometimes grab hold of a receptor and bend it or shake it in just the right way so that it is easier for ligands, like endocannabinoids or phytocannabinoids, to elicit effects. These kinds of effects on receptors are called allosteric effects, and the chemical agents that cause them are aptly named, allosteric effectors.

Future Cannabis research will undoubtedly continue to explore this concept of the "entourage effect" in order to lead to more effective product formulations. This type of research is likely to trickle out into other areas of pharmacological research as well.

CANNABIS AS A BIOREMEDIATION TOOL?

Ecologists are still trying to make sense of some of the claims of Cannabis being an effective bioremediation tool. Although it is true that Cannabis can uptake metals, and maybe other potentially toxic materials from the soil, it is still unclear how this compares to other bioremediators, like sunflowers, for instance.

There are relatively few research papers available that examine how Cannabis uptakes metals, so more research needs to be done there to collect a dataset that is sophisticated enough that restoration ecologists can use it to make decisions about whether or not to use Cannabis for bioremediation.

MICROBIOLOGICAL CANNABINOID FACTORIES

It is common in other industries to utilize bacteria and fungi to reproduce organic compounds once they are isolated and identified as valuable. Sure enough, this technique is already making its way into the Cannabis industry. Known as **cellular**

agriculture, this method of cultivating chemicals using bacteria will be used to provide greater amounts of minor cannabinoids like CBC, CBDV, and THCV for industrial purposes.

Understanding the Endocannabinoidome

The endocannabinoid system is quickly becoming too small of a concept to represent the complexities of lipid signaling in the body. As eluded to multiple times throughout this book, the endocannabinoid system is about far more than CB1 receptors, CB2 receptors, Anandamide, 2-AG, MAGL and FAAH. But even beyond the myriad receptors, ligands and enzymes involved with cannabinoid activity, there is a greater complexity. Depending on where these receptors, ligands and enzymes are located in the body – they may do different things. In essence, our bodies have various endocannabinoid systems distributed in a complex interconnected pattern throughout the body.

To further complicate things, when endocannabinoids are broken down, other active compounds are produced that interact with all sorts of other receptor targets in the body and facilitating actions – and those actions can vary depending on where in the body they are taking place. This concept of interconnected activities and systems is called the endocannabinoidome, and we are only beginning to piece together how these connected systems influence one another and how those activities may influence health and wellness (di Marzo and Wang, 2014). The future of endocannabinoid system research will certainly be focused on further elucidating this concept of the endocannabinoidome.

Finding Cannabinoids in Other Organisms

Cannabis is not the only plant to contain phytocannabinoids. *Herichrysum umbraculigerum*, a flower variety grown in South Africa, contains CBG-like compounds, presumably formed from a unique biochemical pathway than that which Cannabis utilizes to produce cannabinoids. It has been speculated that the plant *Leonotis leonurus*, also known as lion's tail or wild dagga (aka wild Cannabis), contains cannabinoids, including THCA, but this is yet to be confirmed in a peer-reviewed publication. Truffles have been found to contain endocannabinoid-like compounds. Additionally, a type of liverwort called *Radula perrottetii*, as well as related species *Radula marginata* and *Radula laxiramea*, contain a cannabinoid compound called perrottetinene, which is very similar in structure to THC and exhibits some affinity for CB1 receptors (Chicca et al, 2018).

Studying cannabinoids and terpenoids in Cannabis has begun to change the way that researchers look at other chemicals in plants. This is especially true after the discovery that a variety of non-cannabinoid compounds interact with cannabinoid receptors in the body, like the sesquiterpenoids beta-caryophyllene. *Echinacea purpurea*, or purple coneflower, contains alkylamide compounds that have been found to interact with cannabinoid receptors (Raduner et al, 2006). In addition, alkylamides from Echinacea can also inhibit the enzyme FAAH, affecting the breakdown of the endocannabinoid anandamide (Raduner et al, 2006).

Researchers will undoubtedly continue exposing other phytochemicals to cannabinoid receptors to identify what other sorts of compounds in our foods and medicines might be manipulating our endocannabinoid systems.

In addition, it turns out that some other phytochemicals actually resemble cannabinoids. For instance, in the *Rhodendron ferrugineum* plant, a chemical can be found called Ferruginene C which is uncannily similar in chemical structure to CBD (O's News Service, 2015). What other cannabinoid-like compounds are there in other plants that we have not uncovered yet and what therapeutic promise might they hold for treating issues related to the endocannabinoid system?

Examples of Non-Cannabinoid Compounds That Interact with the ECS

TERPENOIDS		
Beta-Caryophyllene	Sesquiterpenoid found in many plant essential oils	CB2 activity (Gertsch et al, 2008)
Isopimaric acid	Diterpene constituent of *Pinus roxburghii* bark	CB2 activity (Labib et al, 2018)
Ursolic acid	Triterpene constituent of *Pinus roxburghii* bark	CB1 activity (Labib et al, 2018)
FLAVONOIDS		
Cyanidin	Anthocyanidin flavonoid found in many red berries, fruit peels, etc.	CB1 and CB2 activity (Korte et al, 2009)
Delphinidin	Anthocyanidin flavonoid responsible for blue hues in flowers and berries	CB1 and CB2 activity (Korte et al, 2009)
POLYSACCHARIDES		
Polysaccharopeptide (PSP)	Polysaccharide extracted from turkey-tail mushrooms (*Trametes versicolor*)	CB2 activity (Wang et al, 2019)
ALKYLAMIDES		
Alkylamides from *Echinacea purpurea* and *E. angustifolia*	Alkylamides extracted from the roots of Echinacea plants	CB2 activity (Gertsch et al, 2004) PPAR-gamma activity (Spelman et al, 2009)

FIGURE 69: NON-CANNABINOID COMPOUNDS THAT MODULATE THE ECS

Semi-Synthetic Cannabinoids

The future of cannabinoid research is likely to consist of lots of tinkering with traditional cannabinoids to form what are sometimes referred to as "semi-synthetic" cannabinoids. This includes things like adding or removing functional groups from the molecule, adding carbons, taking away carbons, or hydrogenating the molecules. An example of a semi-synthetic cannabinoid is VCE-003 which is essentially a quinoid derivative of CBG. Another example of semi-synthetic cannabinoids gaining attention are the hydrogenated cannabinoids like hexahydrocannabinol (HHC) and hexahydrocannabinolic acid (HHCA) derived from THC and THCA. (see Chapter 16)

Understanding the ECS's Role in Immune System Functioning

Perhaps one of the biggest discoveries about the endocannabinoid system is that it is intimately connected to the control of immune system response. Particularly, the CB2 receptor has been widely speculated and demonstrated to exert a variety of effects on the immune system. Some of these effects seem to be immunosuppressive, while others seem to stimulate the immune system. Understanding these effects could help pave the way to far more efficacious treatments for auto-immune diseases and more!

Research Repeatability

One of the core principles of modern sciences is repeatability. If a study comes to a particular conclusion, the same conclusions should be reached if the study were to be duplicated by different researchers. So far there are very few Cannabis or cannabinoid research studies that have actually been replicated, which makes it very difficult to interpret the findings of the research that does exist. A major opportunity for future Cannabis and cannabinoid research lies in simply repeating past studies to determine if previous conclusions still hold up or not.

Challenges to Cannabis Research

Bad Data

There is a glaring problem facing many researchers in the face, and they might not even know it. It is their third-party analytical data. There are many doctors, nurses and other healthcare professionals that have attempted to amass databases of patient outcomes with Cannabis products, using the third-party laboratory data for information about the chemistry of products used, such as cannabinoid or terpenoid content. Generally they are hoping to identify patterns between the chemistry of Cannabis products and the outcomes patients experience so that they may be able to better predict how different Cannabis products may affect a person and what types of products may be best suited for different medical conditions. Unfortunately, some of that chemical data is wrong.

Cannabis testing has not been around for a long time. What we think of as modern Cannabis testing really began taking off around 2010 or so. Of course, there were research labs that had been performing analytical testing on Cannabis samples for many years prior to that – but usually it was only on Cannabis flower and usually focused on only a handful of chemical compounds. Today researchers, producers and consumers alike are interested in data about dozens of cannabinoids and terpenoids (as well as flavonoids and other compounds) and as laboratories have proceeded to validate testing methods to incorporate more of these compounds, an uncomfortable problem has been revealed.

It turns out that there are a lot of terpenoids that can look similar to one another on a chromatogram. Many terpenoids co-elute and appear as a single peak. Some cannabinoids elute at the same retention times as certain terpenoids. Some terpenoids elute at the same or similar retention times as certain cannabinoids. This problem gets compounded when a laboratory must test a more complex product like a Cannabis infused topical or food.

Laboratories are still trying to develop standardized methods for testing many of these complex Cannabis products, but the industry is certainly not going to wait for laboratories to perfect and standardize methods. So as regulators demand that laboratories provide data to facilitate Cannabis commerce, it is inevitable that a lot of unvalidated and outright bad data is circulating and will likely continue to be circulated for some time into the future. Different labs are using different testing methods, some are accredited, some are not, some perform rigorous formal method validation, some do not. Cannabis laboratory testing is still a maturing industry and it can be extremely difficult, if not impossible, to compare data between laboratories.

This variation in data quality can be controlled if researchers perform confirmation testing or rely on data from a single laboratory – however there would still be a burden to rigorously validate the methods used to produce the data to ensure that it is both accurate and precise. While generally the data for major cannabinoids like THC and CBD is often fairly accurate, exercise caution when reviewing data about minor cannabinoid concentrations, terpenoid concentrations or the concentrations of other minor or uncommon phytochemical constituents.

A PROBLEM WITH LAB RATS

As mentioned previously throughout this book, there is an ongoing debate about whether the results from *in vivo* rodent research can be extrapolated to properly represent humans. When discussing mental health research, we explored some of the common behavioral experiment models used for rodents and their inherent limitations. But there is another issue facing laboratory rodents that could have profound impacts for *in vivo* rodent research.

An issue with laboratory rodents bred in captivity is that they develop unique characteristics that can affect their genotypes, and thus their physiology, substantially. To put it simply – their cells age differently. This misstep of assuming that laboratory rodents must genetically and physiologically be similar to wild-type mice was not discovered in a sophisticated way until the early 2000s (Hemann and Greider, 2000; Weinstein and Ciszek, 2002).

This issue has many potential implications, such as that cancer drug research in rodents may be prone to underestimate toxic effects, distort or exaggerate the cancer risks of compounds, and even exaggerate potential benefits of those same compounds. Additionally, rodent derived tissues and cells are often used for preliminary *in vitro* research where the unique genetic difference of laboratory rodents, primarily in the form of lengthened chromosomal telomeres, can skew experimental findings by changing the way cells respond to stress. Ultimately this issue highlights another reason why we must be very cautious when interpreting the results of *in vivo* rodent studies and *in vitro* studies that utilize rodent derived cells or tissues, especially if those studies are examining things like tissue damage, cellular repair, lifespan, cancer dynamics, or oxidative stress.

This also highlights why it is important for researchers to focus Cannabis and cannabinoid research on human research, which will ultimately provide much greater value than *in vitro* cell or tissue culture medical research or *in vivo* rodent research that may provide results that are virtually meaningless in the context of a human.

PLACEBO AND NOCEBO EFFECTS

As clinical research of the efficacy of Cannabis as a treatment for various medical conditions is made more accessible, a big problem that any researcher must overcome is that of measuring the efficacy of the drug against the placebo effect. The placebo effect is a phenomenon in which a measurable effect is caused simply by the anticipation of an effect. **Just being in a clinical trial can cause participants to experience some measurable improvement of conditions**, complicating efficacy research.

Placebo effects can increase significantly the longer a study continues and the larger the sample size becomes (Tuttle et al, 2015). To limit the placebo effect, researchers must take great care to remain neutral and not use language or behavior that would suggest what effects a user might experience during a drug study. Another complication is that seasoned Cannabis users tend to be able to easily recognize real Cannabis from placebo and even alter their consumption behavior as a result – taking longer, deeper inhalations compared to novice users in one study (Cami et al, 1991).

To complicate this placebo puzzle even more, is the fact that research is now indicating that some placebo effects, like placebo analgesia (aka placebo pain relief), are actually mediated by the endocannabinoid system! Researchers studying the placebo effects seen in pain relief clinical trials discovered that the CB1 receptor is at least partially responsible for non-opioid placebo pain relief, as might be seen with non-steroidal anti-inflammatory drugs (NSAIDs) like ibuprofen or aspirin. (Benedetti et al, 2011)

Nocebo effects, on the other hand, are negative effects on health resulting from psychological effects. Examples of this in Cannabis use include things like paranoia and anxiety. Users that worry about experiencing anxiety may facilitate experiences of anxiety when exposed to either Cannabis or a placebo. This in turn affects heart rate and breathing, potentially compounding other negative health consequences. These detrimental effects may not necessarily be due to exposure to cannabinoids but may result from the psychological state of the user prior to exposure.

DRUG DELIVERY METHODS AND STANDARDIZED PRODUCT FORMULATION

Although pulmonary delivery of Cannabis and cannabinoid extracts is the most common drug delivery method used by Cannabis users, it is generally not an acceptable model for medical research. Smoking or vaporizing causes lung irritation and exposure to potentially harmful compounds. Pulmonary delivery also delivers psychoactive cannabinoids to the brain quickly, which increases abuse potential according to traditional pharmacological models.

Alternative drug delivery methods such as nasal mucosal, oral, and sublingual drug delivery systems are currently sought after by researchers. It is likely that future Cannabis research that involves humans will utilize inhalers and nose sprays to administer cannabinoids quickly to the blood stream without having participants potentially harm their lungs. The use of these administration methods also allows the use of standardized product formulations when conducting research, whereas using herbal Cannabis or even whole plant extracts may result in inconsistent formulations between batches, and thus inconsistent results in clinical research.

MEASURING ENDOCANNABINOID SYSTEM CHARACTERISTICS

Because endocannabinoids are only produced when they are needed, rather than being stored up or routinely circulated throughout the body, it can be very difficult to assess the state, or tone, of a person's endocannabinoid system. How will doctors in the future measure someone's endocannabinoid system? While it is possible to perform a spinal tap to look for the presence of endocannabinoids, there is the possibility that there may be nothing there to measure at the moment it is being measured. Likewise, a spinal tap only provides doctors with a chemical snapshot for a single moment in time, which may not actually indicate much concerning chronic states of being. Likewise, methods to measure endocannabinoids in saliva and other fluids have been developed, but still face challenges in broad research applications.

Perhaps researchers will identify compounds which correlate with endocannabinoids or cannabinoid receptor production, helping doctors infer the state of someone's endocannabinoid system without directly measuring it. A common example of this sort of measurement in action can be seen in measurements of prostate-specific antigen, or PSA, for determining the presence and virility of prostate cancer.

It may be that soon doctors will be able to take advantage of the endocannabinoid system to treat illness, but the problem of quantifying the endocannabinoid system must first be overcome.

LIMITATIONS OF PREVIOUS CANNABIS RESEARCH

While there have been a lot of research papers published about Cannabis, **much of this research consists of small sample sizes, unique conditions, a lack of standardized Cannabis material, short durations, and near-impossible reproducibility**. Researchers face the task of figuring out how to conduct research with materials that can be consistently reproduced for other research. This is another reason why smoked or vaporized Cannabis can be troublesome. Each harvest of will result in slightly different material. Preferred analytical methods for cannabinoid and terpene assaying need to be accepted and adopted to bring consistency to chemotype data produced by labs, which can then enable researchers to choose and enforce chemical criteria for clinical trials utilizing herbal Cannabis.

LEGAL HURDLES

Cannabis research in the United States still faces significant hurdles due to its illicit status federally. Cannabis is a classified as a Schedule I drug, meaning that it is indicated as having a high abuse potential with no medicinal use. Due to this restricted classification, any research requires several approvals from different government agencies like the Drug Enforcement Agency or the National Institute of Drug Abuse. If approved, typically Cannabis material for research must be provided by the federal government and can be of questionable quality, often not representing the quality of Cannabis most consumers encounter on a regular basis. The good news is that hemp is paving the way for Cannabis research to take place by universities, non-profit entities, and public companies that were not previously able to touch the Cannabis plant for fear of legal repercussions. Of course, the limitation to this is that this research will take place with CBD-rich Cannabis, rather than THC-rich Cannabis, and many of these institutions have a learning curve to work through regarding understanding the Cannabis plant and the various nuances affecting cultivation, harvesting, processing, extraction, and analytical testing.

Chapter 24: Concluding Remarks

Cannabis is truly a fascinating plant, regardless of the controversies and stigmas that human culture may associate with it. The human species has coevolved with Cannabis for a very long time, coaxing the plant to provide for many of our needs throughout history, and it is only relatively recently that this plant has been aggressively prohibited. Beyond its many industrial applications, Cannabis is responsible for producing hundreds of chemical compounds, many of which seem to pose significant therapeutic value, paving the way for a new wave of upcoming pharmaceuticals and natural products for years to come.

The Cannabis plant has helped researchers to uncover hidden aspects of human physiology, like the endocannabinoid system, leading health care workers and pharmacologists to rethink treatments for many common diseases like fibromyalgia, chronic inflammation, diabetes, and others. Studying the Cannabis plant has helped shed light on how our bodies process pain, regulate immune system responses, respond to trauma, and more. While there are risks associated with Cannabis use, which would be the case with any medicinal botanical, Cannabis appears to be relatively safe on a physiological level, when used responsibly.

This book, in all its noble attempts, only barely scratches the surface of many complex topics. **It is entirely likely that some of the information shared in this book may become obsolete and replaced with more refined interpretations and conclusions of the available information.** Throughout my academic career I encountered several mentors that would state some variation of the phrase, "Trust, but verify." For any of the information presented in this book, please trust, but verify. I have made every attempt that I could with the limited amount of time I had available to consolidate a vast assortment of information and present it as accurately and honestly as possible.

I have had to simplify some very complex topics, which always runs the risk of inaccurately representing the state of the science. I have also had to exclude a lot of information, otherwise this book would be over double its current length. I hope that through these various concessions, and despite them, that this book provides you with the resources you need to take your educational journey further to discover good information on your own. As research on all of the topics presented within this book continues over time, I intend to publish updated revisions of this book, as I have the bandwidth, to better reflect the insights and available data of the time.

It is my hope that this book has been helpful in your quest for learning and understanding the complicated and controversial topic of Cannabis. Throughout the rest of the book you will find research paper citations, recommended external learning resources and more so that you can continue to take your Cannabis education further, far beyond this book. Don't forget to also revisit the essential questions listed in the book's introduction and see how well you can now answer some of these questions!

This book features quotes from various interviews I have had with researchers, doctors, nurses, cultivators, etc. on the Curious About Cannabis Podcast. Another way you can take your Cannabis education further is by listening to episodes of the Curious About Cannabis Podcast and hearing these guests share their insights, experience, and knowledge. You can discover the Curious About Cannabis Podcast at www.CACPodcast.com.

Good luck on your continued quest for learning and **stay curious**!

Cannabis Crossword

Complete the crossword puzzle below!

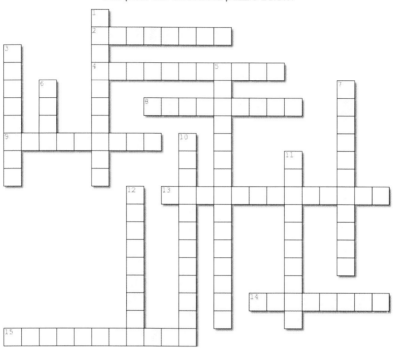

Across

2. terpene that smells like oranges
4. the primary binding site on a receptor
8. a type of trichome where cannabinoids are primarily found
9. wild-type landrace from Central Asia
13. breakdown product of CBD
14. alternative to 'strain'
15. chronic nausea and/or vomiting

Down

1. a secondary binding site on a receptor
3. naturalized Cannabis variety
5. cannabinoids produced by the body
6. Cannabis with less than 0.3% THC
7. CBD
10. wild-type landrance from South Asia
11. seedless female Cannabis plants
12. chemical phenotype

Cannabis Word Search

```
J L O I D I B A N N A C C R L
H I L O R E G I B A N N A C S
D E E X T R A C T I O N T W T
I R I E P I C U T A N E O U S
S P N K P X S P O N T A N E A
T E D H I M A L A Y E N S I S
I N I C A N N A B I S M D G Y
L E C S G L A N D U L A R G P
L G A L E T R I C H O M E M D
A C A N N A B I N O L T E F T
T U A L V E O L I A G H C Z I
E Q U A L A M R E D S N A R T
E N D O C A N N A B I N O I D
C H V F L A V O N O I D B I Y
C I X A M I R R E P S A F J R
```

ALVEOLI
ASPERRIMA
CANNABIDIOL
CANNABIGEROL
CANNABINOL
CANNABIS
DISTILLATE
ENDOCANNABINOID
EPICUTANEOUS
EXTRACTION
FLAVONOID
GLANDULAR
HEMP
HIMALAYENSIS
INDICA
SPONTANEA
TERPENE
TRANSDERMAL
TRICHOME

Cannabis Word Scramble

Unscramble the words below!

1. illsrepgsua _____

2. nenepi _____

3. lneienom _____

4. spuipcohpma _____

5. tcmuspre _____

6. lpidi _____

7. tauwrfeloo _____

8. rtparyhcmoghao _____

9. hdocnpriyo _____

10. ifncavnnla _____

11. lalsonmeal _____

12. eosaitxomr _____

13. lolianlo _____

14. siscpdiete _____

APPENDIX A: CITATION REFERENCES

Abrahamov, A., and R. Mechoulam. 1995. An efficient new cannabinoid antiemetic in pediatric oncology. *Life Sci* 56(23-24):2097-102.

Abrams DI, Hilton JF, Leiser RJ, et al. 2003. Short-term effects of cannabinoids in patients with HIV-1 infection: a randomized, placebo-controlled clinical trial. Annals of Internal Medicine. 139:258-266.

Adams IB, Martin BR. 1996. Cannabis: Pharmacology and toxicology in humans and animals. Addiction. 91(11):1585 - 1614.

Adams R, Hunt M, Clark JH. 1940. Structure of Cannabidiol, a Product Isolated from the Marihuana Extract of Minnesota Wild Hemp. I. J. Am. Chem. Soc. 62(1): 196-200.

Adams TC, Jones LA. 1975. Phytosterols of Cannabis smoke. J Agric Food Chem. 23(2):352-353.

Agrawal A, Nurnberger Jr, JI, Lynskey, MT, The Bipolar Genome Study. 2011. Cannabis involvement in individuals with bipolar disorder. Psychiatry Research. 185:459-461.

Ahmed SA, Ross SA, Slade D, Radwan MM, Zulfiqar F, ElSohly MA. 2008. Cannabinoid Ester Constituents from High-Potency Cannabis sativa. J Nat Prod. 71(4): 536-542.

Alavanja MCR, Hoppin J, Kamel F. 2004. Health Effects of Chronic Pesticide Exposure: Cancer and Neurotoxicity. Annu. Rev. Public Health. 25:155-97

Alavanja MCR, Samanic C, Dosemeci M, Lubin J, Tarone R, et al. 2003. Use of agricultural pesticides and prostate cancer risk in the Agricultural Health Study Cohort. Am. J. Epidemiol. 157:1-13

Alcorn J, Vuong S, Wu F, Seifert B, Lyon A. (2019). Pediatric Dosing Considerations for Medical Cannabis. Recent Advances in Cannabinoid Research. Chapter 10:181-200

Al-Ghezi ZZ, Alghetaa HF, Nagarkatti M, Nagarkatti P. 2017. Combination of cannabinoids, delta-9-tetrahydrocannabinol (THC) and cannabidiol (CBD), mitigate experimental autoimmune encephalomyelitis (EAE) by altering the gut microbiome. J Immunology. 198(1).

Alhouayek M, Lambert DM, Delzenne NM, Cani PD, Muccioli GG. 2011. Increasing endogenous 2-arachidonoylglycerol levels counteracts colitis and related systemic inflammation. FASEB J. 25(8):2711-2721.

Alhouayek M, Muccioli GG. 2012. The endocannabinoid system in inflammatory bowel diseases: from pathophysiology to therapeutic opportunity. Trends in Molecular Medicine. 18:615-625.

Allegrone G, Razzano F, Pollastro F, Grassi G. 2019. Determination of melatonin content of different varieties of hemp (Cannabis sativa L.) by liquid chromatography tandem mass spectrometry. SN Applied Sciences. 1:720.

Alter R. The Five Books of Moses: A Translation with Commentary. 2004. New York: W.W. Norton & Co.

Alvaro LC, Iriondo I, Villaverde FJ. 2002. Sexual headache and stroke in a heavy cannabis smoker. Headache: The Journal of Head and Face Pain. 42:224-226.

Alvheim AR. 2012. Dietary linoleic acid induces obesity through excessive endocannabinoid activity. University of Bergen.

Amada N, Yamasaki Y, Williams CM, Whalley BJ. 2013. Cannabidivarin (CBDV) suppresses pentylenetetrazole (PTZ)-induced increases in epilepsy-related gene expression. PeerJ. 1:e214. doi: 10.7717/peerj.214. eCollection 2013.

Ananth P, Ma C, Al-Sayegh H, Kroon L, Klein V, Wharton C, Hallez E, Braun I, Michelson K, Rosenberg AR, London W, Wolfe J. 2018. Provider Perspectives on Use of Medical Marijuana in Children with Cancer. Pediatrics. 141(1):e20170559

Andre CM, Hausman JF, Guerriero G. 2016. Front Plant Sci.

Antonisamy P, Duraipandiyan V, Ignacimuthu S. 2011. Anti-inflammatory, analgesic, and antipyretic effects of friedelin isolated from Azima tetracantha Lam. In mouse and rat models. Journal of Pharmacy and Pharmacology. Vol. 63, Issue 8.

Appendino, G. 2014. The International Cannabinoid Research Society (ICRS) Annual Meeting. (by way of Ryan Lee and O's News Service, O'Shaughnessy's Winter 2015/16 Issue)

Aqil M, Ahad A, Sultana Y, Ali A. Status of terpenes as skin penetration enhancers. Drug Disc Today. 12:1061-1067

Armbruster DA, T Pry. 2008. Limit of Blank, Limit of Detection and Limit of Quantitation. Clin Biochem Rev. 29:49-52

Ashman MR, G Puri. 2002. Essential Soil Science. Blackwell Publishing.

Ashton, HC. 2001. Pharmacology and effects of cannabis: a brief review. The British Journal of Psychiatry. 178(2):101-106.

Assmann G, Cullen P, Erbey J, Ramey DR, Kannenberg F, Schulte H. 2006. Plasma sitosterol elevations are associated with an increased incidence of coronary events in men: results of a nested case-control analysis of the Prospective Cardiovascular Munster (PROCAM) study. Nutrition, Metabolism, and Cardiovascular Diseases. 16(1):13-21.

Atwood, B.K. et al. (2010). JWH018, a common constituent of 'Spice' herbal blends, is a potent and efficacious cannabinoid CB1 receptor agonist. British Journal of Pharmacology 160 (3): 585–593.

Auwarter V, Dresen S, Weinmann W, Muller M, Putz M, Ferreiros N. 2009. 'Spice' and other herbal blends: harmless incense or cannabinoid designer drugs? Journal of Mass Spectrometry. 44(5):832-837.

Bang MH, Choi SY, Jang TO, Kim SK, Kwon OS, Kang TC et al. 2002. Phytol, SSADH inhibitory diterpenoid of Lactuca sativa. Arch Pharm Res 25: 643–646.

Barrett ML, Gordon D, Evans FJ. 1985. Isolation from Cannabis sativa L. of cannflavin – a novel inhibitor of prostaglandin production. Biochemical Pharmacology. 34: 2019–2024.

Basile AC, Sertie JA, Freitas PC, Zanini AC. 1988. Anti-inflammatory activity of oleoresin from Brazilian Copaifera. J Ethnopharmacol 22: 101–109.

Bechtold, J, Simpson, T, White, HR, Pardini, D. 2015. Chronic adolescent marijuana use as a risk factor for physical and mental health problems in young adult men. Psychology of Addictive Behaviors. Advance online publication. http://dx.doi.org/10.1037/adb0000103

Bedi G, Cooper ZD, Haney M. 2013. Subjective, cognitive and cardiovascular dose-effect profile of nabilone and dronabinol in marijuana somokers. Addiction Biology. 18:872-881.

Bektas A, Hardwick KM, Waterman K, Kristof J. 2019. The occurrence of hop latent viroid in Cannabis sativa with symptoms of Cannabis stunting disease in California. Plant Disease. https://doi.org/10.1094/PDIS-03-19-0459-PDN

Bellocchio, L., Cervino, C., Pasquali, R., Pagotto, U., 2008. The endocannabinoid system and energy metabolism. J. Neuroendocrinol. 20, 850–857.

Benedetti F, Amanzio M, Rosato R, Blanchard C. 2011. Nonopioid placebo analgesia is mediated by CB1 cannabinoid receptors. Nat Med. 17(10): 1228-1230.

Benowitz NL, Jones RT. Cardiovascular effects of prolonged delta-9-tetrahydrocannbinol ingestion. Clinical Pharmacology and Therapeutics. 18-287-297.

Bento AF, Marcon R, Dutra RC, Claudino RF, Cola M, Leite DF, Calixto JB. 2011. B-Caryophyllene inhibits dxtran sulfate sodium-induced colitis in mice through CB2 receptor activation and PPARγ pathway. AM J Pathol. 178(3):1153-1166.

Berge KE. 2003. Sitosterolemia: a gateway to new knowledge about cholesterol metabolism. Ann Med. 35(7):502-511.

Berman JS, Symonds C, Birch R. 2004. Efficacy of two cannabis based medicinal extracts for relief of central neuropathic pain from brachial plexus avulsion: results of a randomised controlled trial. Pain. 112: 299–306.

Bettarini F, Borgonovi GE, Fiorani T, Gagliardi I, Caprioli V, Massardo P *et al*. 1993. Antiparasitic compounds from East African plants: isolation and biological activtiry of anonaine, matricarianol, canthin-6-one, and caryophyllene oxide. Insect Sci Appl 14: 93–99.

Bidlack JE, SH Jansky. 2011. Stern's Introductory Plant Biology. McGraw-Hill. 12th Edition.

Biro T, Olah A, Toth BI, Czifra G, Zouboulis CC, Paus R. 2009. Cannabidiol as a novel anti-acne agent? Cannabidiol inhibits lipid synthesis and induces cell death in human sebaceous gland-derived sebocytes. Proceedings 19th Annual Conference on the Cannabinoids. International Cannabinoid Research Society: Pheasant Run, St. Charles, IL, p. 28.

Bisogno T, Melck D, Bobrov MY, Gretskaya NM, Bezuglov VV, De Petrocellis L, Di Marzo V. 2000. N-acyl-dopamines: novel synthetic CB(1) cannabinoid-receptor ligands and inhibitors of anandamide inactivation with cannabimimetic activity in vitro and in vivo. Biochem. J. 351:817-824.

Bisset NG, Wichtl M 2004. Herbal Drugs and Phytopharmaceuticals: A Handbook for Practice on A Scientific Basis, 3rd edn. Medpharm Scientific Publishers: Stuttgart; CRC

Blair A, Zahm SH. 1991. Cancer among farmers. Occup. Med. 3:335-54

Blair A, Zahm SH. 1995. Agircultural exposures and cancer. Environ. Health Perspect. 103:205-8

Bolognini D, Rock EM, Cluny NL, Cascio MG, Limebeer CL, Duncan M, Stott CG, Javid FA, Parker LA, Pertwee RG. 2013. Cannabidiolic acid prevents vomiting in *Suncus murinus* and nausea-induced behavior in rats by enhancing 5-HT1A receptor activation. Br J Phar. 168(6):1456-1470.

Bonn-Miller, MO, Babson, KA, Vandrey, R. 2014. Using cannabis to help you sleep: Heightened frequency of medical cannabis use among those with PTSD. Drug and Alcohol Dependence. 136:162-165.

Booth JK, Yuen MMS, Jancsik S, Madilao L, Page J, Bohlmann J. 2020. Terpene synthases and terpene variation in Cannabis sativa. Plant Physiology. doi: 10.1104/pp.20.00593

Bornheim LM, Everhart ET, Li J, Correia MA. 1993. Characterization of cannabidiol-mediated cytochrome P450 inactivation. Biochem Pharmacol.

Bradshaw J, Allard C. 2011. Endogenous cannabinoid production in the rat female reproductive tract is regulated by changes in the hormonal milieu. Pharmaceuticals. 4:933-949.

Bradshaw HB, Rimmerman N, Krey JF, Walker JM. 2006. Sex and hormonal cycle differences in rat brain levels of pain-related cannabimimetic lipid mediators. American Journal of Physiology – Regulatory, Integrative and Comparative Physiology. 291:R349-358

Braniste V, Al-Asmakh M, Kowal C, Anuar F, Abbaspour A, Toth M, Korecka A, Bakocevic N, Ng LG, Kundu P, Gulyas B, Halldin C, Hultenby K, Nilsson H, Hebert H, Volpe B, Diamond B, Pettersson S. 2015. The gut microbiota influences blood-brain barrier permeability in mice. Sci Transl Med. 6(263):263ra158.

Brenneisen R. 2007. Chemistry and analysis of phytocannabinoids and other Cannabis constituents. In: Elsohly M (ed.). Marijuana and the Cannabinoids. Humana Press: Totowa, NY, pp. 17–49.

Brown AJ, Wise A. 2001.Identification of modulators of GPR55 activity. Glaxosmithkline, WO0186305.

Buchbauer G, Jirovetz L, Jager W, Dietrich H, Plank C. 1991. Aromatherapy: evidence for sedative effects of the essential oil of lavender after inhalation. Z Naturforsch [C] 46: 1067–1072.

Buchbauer G, Jirovetz L, Jager W, Plank C, Dietrich H. 1993. Fragrance compounds and essential oils with sedative effects upon inhalation. J Pharm Sci 82: 660–664.

Burstein SH, Hull K, Hunter SA, Latham V. 1988. Cannabinoids and pain responses: a possible role for prostaglandins. FASEB J. 2(14):3022-3026.

Burstein SH, Hunter SA, Latham V, Renzulli L. 1986. Prostaglandins and cannabis. XVI. Antagonism of delta-1-tetrahydrocannabinol action by its metabolites. Biochem Pharmacol.35(15):2553-2558.

Burt BA. 2006. The use of sorbitol- and xylitol sweetened chewing gum in caries control. J Am Dent Assoc.137:190–196.

Cabral GA, Raborn ES, Ferreira GA. 2015. Phytocannabinoids and the Immune System. Handbook of Cannabis. Oxford University Press. 261-279.

Cami J, Guerra D, Ugena B, Segura J, de la Torre R. 1991. Effect of subject expectancy on the THC intoxication and disposition from smoked hashish cigarettes. Pharmacol Biochem Behav. 40(1):115-9

Cani PD, Plovier H, Van Hul M, Geurts L, Delzenne NM, Druart C, Everard A. 2015. Endocannabinoids – at the crossroads between the gut microbiota and host metabolism. Nature Reviews Endocrinology. 12(1): 133-143.

Caprioglio D, Mattoteia D, Pollastro F, Negri R, Lopatriello A, Chianese G, Minassi A, Collado JA, Munoz E, Taglialatela-Scafati O, Appendino G. 2020. The Oxidation of Phytocannabinoids to Cannabinoquinoids. J. Nat. Prod. Pre-Print. Published April 21, 2020.

Carabotti M, Scirocco A, Maselli MA, Severi C. 2015. The gut-brain axis: interactions between enteric microbiota, central and enteric nervous systems. Ann Gastroenterol. 28(2):203-209.

Carlini EA and Cunha JM. 1981. Hypnotic and antiepileptic effects of cannabidiol. Journal of Clinical Pharmacology. 21: 417S–427S.

Carvalho-Freitas MI, Costa M (2002). Anxiolytic and sedative effects of extracts and essential oil from Citrus aurantium L. Biol Pharm Bull 25: 1629–1633.

Cascio MG, Gauson LA, Stevenson LA, Ross RA, Pertwee RG (2010). Evidence that the plant cannabinoid cannabigerol is a highly potent alpha2-adrenoceptor agonist and moderately potent 5HT1A receptor antagonist. Br J Pharmacol 159: 129–141.

Cawthorne MA, Wargent E, Zaibi M, Stott C, Wright S (2007). The CB1 antagonist, delta-9-tetrahydrocannabivarin (THCV) has antioebesity activity in dietary-induced obese (DIO) mice. Proceedings 17th Annual Symposium on the Cannabinoids. International Cannabinoid Research Society: Saint-Sauveur, QC, p. 141.

Centers for Disease Control and Prevention. Smoking & Tobacco Use. Outbreak of Lung Injury Associated with E-cigarette Use, or Vaping. https://www.cdc.gov/tobacco/basic_information/e-cigarettes/severe-lung-disease.html (Accessed on Nov 11 2019)

Chandra, Suman; Lata, Hemant; Khan, Ikhlas A.; ElSohly, Mahmoud A. Photosynthetic response of Cannabis sativa L., an important medicinal plant, to elevated levels of CO2. Physiology and Molecular Biology of Plants. Vol. 17 (3). JUL 2011. 291-295

Choi HS, Song HS, Ukeda H, Sawamura M (2000). Radical-scavenging activities of citrus essential oils and their components: detection using 1,1-diphenyl-2-picrylhydrazyl. J Agric Food Chem 48: 4156–4161.

Chong Y, Shimoda S, Yakushiji H, Ito Y, Miyamoto T, Shimono N, Kamimura T, Akashi K. 2012. Fatal candidemia caused by azole-resistant Candida tropicalis in patients with hematological malignancies. J Infect Chemother. 18(5):741-746.

Christison A (1851). On the natural history, action, and uses of Indian hemp. Monthly J Med Sci Edinburgh, Scotland 13: 26–45. 117-121.

Chusid M. J., Gelfand, J. A., Nutter, C., Fauci, A. S. Pulmonary aspergillosis, inhalation of contaminated marijuana smoke, chronic granulomatous disease. Ann Intern Med 1975; 82: 682–3.

Citterio, S, Prato, N, Fumagalli, P, Aina, R, Massa, N, Santagostino, A, Sgorbati, S, Berta, G. 2004. The arbuscular mycorrhizal fungus Glomus mosseae induces growth and metal accumulation changes in Cannabis sativa L. Chemosphere. 59(1):21-29

Cornwell PA, Barry BW (1994). Sesquiterpene components of volatile oils as skin penetration enhancers for the hydrophilic permeant 5-fluorouracil. J Pharm Pharmacol 46: 261–269.

Craft RM, Leitl MD. 2008. Gonadal hormone modulation of the behavioral effects of Delta-9-tetrahydrocannbinol in male and female rats. European J of Pharm. 578:37-42

Crawford WJ, Merritt JC. 1979. Effects of tetrahydrocannabinol on arterial and intraocular hypertension. Int J of Clinical Pharm and Biopharmacy. 17:191-196.

Crippa, JA, Zuardi, AW, Martin-Santos, R, Bhattacharyya, S, Atakan, Z, McGuire, P, Fusar-Poli, P. 2009. Cannabis and anxiety: a critical review of the evidence. Hum. Psychopharmacol Clin Exp. 24(7):515-523.

Cudaback E, Marrs W, Moeller T, Stella N. 2010. The expression level of CB1 and CB2 receptors determines their efficacy at inducing apoptosis in astrocytomas. PLoS One 5 (1), e8702.

Cui N, Wang L, Wang W, Zhang J, Xu Y, Jiang L, Hao G. 2017. The correlation of anandamide with gonadotrophin and sex steroid hormones during the menstrual cycle. Iranian Journal of Basic Medical Sciences. 20: 1268-1274.

D'Argenio G, Valenti M, Scaglione G, Cosenza V, Sorrentini I, Di Marzo V. 2006. Up-regulation of anandamide levels as an endogenous mechanism and a pharmacological strategy to limit colon inflammation. FASEB Journal. 20:568-570.

Dalton WS, Martz R, Lemberger L, Rodda BE, Forney RB. 1976. Influence of cannabidiol on delta-9-tetrahydrocannabinol effects. Clin Pharmacol Ther. 19(3):300-309.

Darling MR, Arendorf TM, Coldrey NA. 1990. Effect of cannabis use on oral candidal carriage. J Oral Pathol Med. 19(7):319-321.

Darling MR, Arendorf TM. 1992. Review of the effects of Cannabis smoking on oral health. Int Dent J. 42:19-22.

Darlington CL (October 2003). "Dexanabinol: a novel cannabinoid with neuroprotective properties". IDrugs : The Investigational Drugs Journal 6 (10): 976–9.

Davalos SD, Fournier G, Boucher F, Paris M (1977). [Contribution to the study of Mexican marihuana. Preliminary studies: cannabinoids and essential oil (author's transl)]. J Pharm Belg 32:89–99.

Davis WM, Hatoum NS (1983). Neurobehavioral actions of cannabichromene and interactions with delta 9-tetrahydrocannabinol. Gen Pharmacol 14: 247–252.

de la Fuente A, Zamberlan F, Ferran AS, Carrillo F, Tagliazucchi E, Pallavicini C. 2020. Journal of Cannabis Research. (2):21. doi: 10.1186/s42238-020-00028-y

De Meijer E. 2015. The Chemical Phenotypes (Chemotypes) of Cannabis. Handbook of Cannabis. Oxford University Press. Chapter 5. pp. 89-110.

De Oliveira AC, Ribeiro-Pinto LF, Paumgartten JR (1997). *In vitro* inhibition of CYP2B1 monooxygenase by beta-myrcene and other monoterpenoid compounds. Toxicol Lett 92: 39–46.

De Petrocellis L, Ligresti A, Moriello AS. 2011. Effects of cannabinoids and cannabinoid enriched Cannabis extracts on TRP channels and endocannabinoid metabolic enzymes. B J of Pharmacol. 163:1479-1494.

De Petrocellis L, Orlando P, Moriello AS, Aviello G, Stott C, Izzo AA, Di Marzo V. 2012. Cannabinoid actions at TRPV channels: effects on TRPV3 and TRPV4 and their potential relevance to gastrointestinal inflammation. Acta Physiol (Oxf). 204(2):255-266.

De Petrocellis L, Ligresti A., Moriello A.S., Iappelli M., Verde R., Stott C.G., Cristino L., Orlando P., and Di Marzo V. 2013. Non-THC cannabinoids inhibit prostate carcinoma growth in vitro and in vivo: pro-apoptotic effects and underlying mechanisms. *British Journal of Pharmacology* 168 (1): 79–10

Degenhardt L, Hall W, Lynskey M. 2003. Exploring the association between cannabis use and depression. Addiction. 98 (11): 1493-1504

Denning D. W., Follansbee, S. E., Scolaro, M., Edelstein, H., Stevens, D. A. Pulmonary aspergillosis in the acquired immunodeficiency syndrome. N Engl J Med 1991; 324:654-62

Desserud PA, Naeth MA. 2012. An unexpected response of a bunch grass (rough fescue) to arbuscular mycorrhizae fungi. Ecological Restoration. 30(3):165-168.

Devane W, Hanus L, Breuer A, Pertwee R, Setevenson L, Griffin G, Gibson D, Mandelbaum A, Etinger A, Mechoulam R. 1992. Isolation and structure of a brain constituent that binds to the cannabinoid receptor. Science. 258(5090): 1946-1949.

Devane WA, Breuer A, Sheskin T, Jarbe TU, Eisen MS, Mechoulam R. 1992. A novel probe for the cannabinoid receptor. J Med Chem. 35(11):2065-2069.

Devane WA, Dysarz FA 3rd, Johnson MR, Melvin LS, Howlett AC. 1988. Determination and characterization of a cannabinoid receptor in rat brain. Molecular Pharmacology. 34: 605–613.

Devitt-Lee A. 2015. CBD-Drug Interactions: Role of Cytochrome P450. Project CBD. https://www.projectcbd.org/article/cbd-drug-interactions-role-cytochrome-p450

DeVuono MV, Parker LA. 2020. Cannabinoid Hyperemesis Syndrome: A Review of Potential Mechanisms. Cannabis and Cannabinoid Research. 5(2). https://doi.org/10.1089/can.2019.0059

Deyo R, Musty R (2003). A cannabichromene (CBC) extract alters behavioral despair on the mouse tail suspension test of depression. Proceedings 2003 Symposium on the Cannabinoids. International Cannabinoid Research Society: Cornwall, ON, p. 146.

Di Marzo V. 1998. 'Endocannabinoids' and other fatty acid derivatives with cannabimimetic properties: biochemistry and possible physiopathological relevance. Biochimica et Biophysica Acta. 1392: 153–175

Di Marzo V. 2018. New approaches and challenges to targeting the endocannabinoid system. Nat Rev Drug Discov. 17(9):623-639.

Di Marzo V, DePetrocellis L, Bisogno T. 2005. The biosynthesis, fate and pharmacological properties of endocannabinoids. Handb. Exp.Pharmacol. 168, 147–185.

Di Marzo V, Wang J. 2014. The Endocannabinoidome: The World of Endocannabinoids and Related Mediators. Academic Press. Elsevier.

Di Tomaso, E, Beltramo, M, and Piomelli, D. 1996. Brain cannabinoids in chocolate. Nature. 382:677-678.

Dioscorides P and Beck LY. 2011. De Materia Medica. Hildesheim: Olms-Weidmann.

Douds, DDJ, PE Pfeffer, and Y Shachar-Hill. 2000. Carbon partitioning, cost, and metabolism of arbuscular mycorrhizas. Pages 107-129 in Y. Kapulnik and DDJ Douds, editors. Arbuscular mycorrhizas: physiology and function. Kluwer Academic Publishers, Dordrecht, The Netherlands.

Dreher MC, Nugent K, Hudgins R. 1994. Prenatal Marijuana Exposure and Neonatal Outcomes in Jamaica: An Ethnographic Study. Pediatrics. 93(2): 254-260.

Drug Abuse Warning Network. 2012.

Dubertret C, Bidard I, Ades J, Gorwood P. 2006. Lifetime positive symptoms in patients with schizophrenia and cannabis abuse are partially explained by co-morbid addiction. Schizophrenia Research. 86:284-290.

Duffy B, Li L, Lu S, Durocher L, Dittmar M, Delaney-Baldwin E, Panawennage D, LeMaster D, Navarette K, Spink D. 2020. Analysis of cannabinoid-containing fluids in illicit vaping cartridges recovered from pulmonary injury patients: identification of vitamin E acetate as a major diluent. Toxics. 8(1):8.

Duncan M, Izzo AA. 2015. Phytocannabinoids and the Gastrointestinal System. Handbook of Cannabis. Oxford University Press. Chapter 12. pp. 227-244.

Duran M, Perez E, Abanades S, Vidal X, Saura C, Majem M, Arriola E, Rabanal M, Pastor A, Farre M, Rams N, Laporte JR, Capella D. 2010. Preliminary efficacy and safety of an oromucosal standardized cannabis extract in chemotherapy-induced nausea and vomiting. British Journal of Clinical Pharmacology. 2010. 70: 656–663.

Eichenbaum H, Cohen NJ. 1993. Memory, Amnesia, and the Hippocampal System. MIT Press.

El-Kattan AF, Asbill CS, Kim N, Michniak BB. 2001. The effects of terpene enhancers on the percutaneous permeation of drugs with different lipophilicities. Int J Pharm. 215(1-2):229-240

Elmes, M. W., Kaczocha, M., Berger, W. T., Leung, K., Ralph, B. P., Wang, L. et al. (2015). Fatty Acid-binding Proteins (FABPs) Are Intracellular Carriers for Δ9-Tetrahydrocannabinol (THC) and Cannabidiol (CBD). The Journal of Biological Chemistry, 290(14), 8711–8721. http://doi.org/10.1074/jbc.M114.618447

Elphick, M. R.; Egertova, M. (2001). "The neurobiology and evolution of cannabinoid signalling". Philosophical Transactions of the Royal Society B: Biological Sciences 356 (1407): 381–408.

ElSohly HN, Turner CE, Clark AM, ElSohly MA (1982). Synthesis and antimicrobial activities of certain cannabichromene and cannabigerol related compounds. J Pharm Sci 71: 1319–1323.

ElSohly MA, Slade D. 2005. Chemical constituents of marijuana: the complex mixture of natural cannabinoids. Life Sciences. 78:539-548.

Emboden, W.A., 1981. The genus Cannabis and the correct use of taxonomic categories. J. Psychoactive Drugs 13, 15–21.

Engel MA, Kellermann CA, Burnat G, Hahn EG, Rau T, Konturek PC. 2010. Mice lacking cannabinoid CB1-, CB2-receptors or both receptors show increased susceptibility to trinitrobenzene sulfonic acid (TNBS)-induced colitis. J Physiol Pharmacol. 61(1):89-97.

Engel MA, Kellermann CA, Rau T, Burnat G, Hahn EG, Konturek PC. 2008. Ulcerative colitis in AKR mice is attenuated by intraperitoneally administered anandamide. J of Physiology and Pharmacol. 59:673-689.

Engels FK, de Jong FA, Mathijssen RHJ, Erkens JA, Herings RM, Verweij J. 2007. Medicinal cannabis in oncology. European Journal of Cancer. 43:2638-2644

Eurachem – Quantifying Uncertainty in Analytical Measurement, Laboratory of the Government Chemist, London, 1995.

Evans FJ (1991). Cannabinoids: the separation of central from peripheral effects on a structural basis. Planta Med 57: S60–S67.

Falk AA, Hagberg MT, Lof AE, Wigaeus-Hjelm EM, Wang ZP (1990). Uptake, distribution and elimination of alpha-pinene in man after exposure by inhalation. Scand J Work Environ Health 16: 372–378.

Farag RS, Shalaby AS, El-Baroty GA, Ibrahim NA, Ali MA, Hassan EM (2004). Chemical and biological evaluation of the essential oils of different Melaleuca species. Phytother Res 18: 30–35.
402

Fattore L, Fratta W. 2011. Beyond THC: the new generation of cannabinoid designer drugs. Frontiers in Behavioral Neuroscience. 5(60): 1-12

Femenia-Fonta A, Balaguer-Fernandez C, Merino V, Rodilla V, Lopez-Castellano A. Effect of chemical enhancers on the in vitro percutaneous absorption of sumatriptan succinate. Eur J Pharm Biopharm. 61(1-2):50-55.

Fenselau C, Hermann G. 1972. Identificatoin of Phytosterols in Red Oil Extract of Cannabis. Journal of Forensic Sciences. 17(2):309-312

Fernandes ES, Passos GF, Medeiros R, da Cunha FM, Ferreira J, Campos MM, Pianowski LF, Calixto JB. (2007) Anti-inflammatory effects of compounds alpha-humulene and (-)-trans-caryophyllene isolated from the essential oil of Cordia verbenacea. Eur J Pharmacol. 569(3):228-236.

Fezza F, Bari M, Florio R, Talamonti E, Feole M, Maccarrone M. 2014. Endocannabinoids, Related Compounds and Their Metabolic Routes. Molecules. 19:17078-17106.

Food and Drug Administration. 2019. Harmful and Potentially Harmful Constituents in Tobacco Products; Established List; Proposed Additions; Request for Comments. 84 FR 38032. 08/05/2019. https://www.federalregister.gov/documents/2019/08/05/2019-16658/harmful-and-potentially-harmful-constituents-in-tobacco-products-established-list-proposed-additions

Fride E, Ginzburg Y, Breuer A, Bisogno T, Marzo VD, Mechoulam R. 2001. Critical role of the endogenous cannabinoid system in mouse pup suckling and growth. Eur J Pharm. 419:207-214.

Friedman PK, Isfeld D. 2011. Dimensions of Dental Hygiene.9:50–53.

Fuchs L. The great herbal of Leonhart Fuchs: De historia stirpium commentarii insignes, 1542 (notable commentaries on the history of plants). 1999. Stanford, CA: Stanford University Press.

Galilly R, Yekhtin Z, Hanus LO. 2015. Overcoming the bell-shaped dose-response of cannabidiol by using Cannabis extract enriched in cannabidiol. Pharmacology & Pharmacy. 6: 75-85.

Galli JA, Sawaya RA, Friedenberg FK. 2011. Cannabinoid Hyperemesis Syndrome. Curr Drug Abuse. 4(4): 241-249.

Gaoni Y and Mechoulam R. 1964. Isolation, Structure, and Partial Synthesis of an Active Constituent of Hashish. J. Am. Chem. Soc. 86(8): 1646-1647.

Gattefosse R-M (1993). Gatefosse's Aromatherapy. C.W. Daniel: Essex, MD.

Ghelardini C, Galeotti N, Salvatore G, Mazzanti G (1999). Local anaesthetic activity of the essential oil of Lavandula angustifolia. Planta Med 65: 700–703.

Geffrey AL, Pollack SF, Bruno PL, Thiele EA. 2015. Drug-drug interaction between clobazam and cannabidiol in children with refractory epilepsy. Epilepsia. 56(8):1246-1251. doi: 10.1111/epi.13060

George B. Wood and Franklin Bache, eds., 1851, The Dispensatory of the United States of America, 9th ed. Philadelphia: Lippincott, Grambo, 1851, pp. 310-311.

Gerard J and Johnson T. The Herbal: or, General History of Plants. 1975. New York: Dover Publications

Gertsch J, Leonti M, Raduner S, Racz I, Chen JZ, Xie XQ *et al.* (2008). Beta-caryophyllene is a dietary cannabinoid. Proc Natl Acad Sci USA 105: 9099–9104.

Gertsch J, RG Pertwee, V Di Marzo. 2010. Phytocannabinoid beyond the Cannabis plant – do they exist? Br J of Pharmacol. 160:523-529

Giessen E van de, Weinstein JJ, Cassidy CM, Haney M, Dong Z, Ghazzaoui R, Ojeil N, Kegeles LS, Xu X, Vadhan NP, Volkow ND, Slifstein M, Abi-Dargham A. 2016. Deficits in striatal dopamine release in cannabis dependence. Molecular Psychiatry. Advance online publication. doi:10.1038/mp.2016.21

Gil ML, Jimenez J, Ocete MA, Zarzuelo A, Cabo MM (1989). Comparative study of different essential oils of Bupleurum gibraltaricum Lamarck. Pharmazie 44: 284–287.

Giladi Y, Hadad L, Luria N, Cranshaw W, Lachman O. 2019. First Report of Beet Curly Top Virus Infecting Cannabis sativa L., in Western Colorado. Plant Disease. American Phytopathological Society. https://doi.org/10.1094/PDIS-08-19-1656-PDN

Gloss D, Vickrey B. 2012. Cannabinoids for epilepsy (Review). The Cochrane Library. Issue 6.

Godwin DA, Michniak BB. 1999. Influence of drug lipophilicity on terpenes as transdermal penetration enhancers. Drug Dev Ind Pharm. 25(8):905-915.

Goldschmidt L, Day NL, Richardson GA. 2000. Effects of prenatal marijuana exposure on child behavior problems at age 10. Neurotoxicology and Teratology. 22:325-336.

Gorzalka BB, Hill MN, Chang SC. 2010. Male-female differences in the effects of cannabinoids on sexual behavior and gonadal hormone function. Hormones and Behavior. 58:91-99.

Granja AG, Carrillo-Salinas F, Pagani A, Gomez-Canas M, Negri R, Navarrete C, Mecha M, Mestre L, Fiebich BL, Cantarero I, Calzado MA, Bellido ML, Fernandez-Ruiz J, Appendino G, Guaza C, Munoz E. 2012. A Cannabigerol Quinone Alleviates Neuroinflammation in a Chronic Model of Multiple Sclerosis. J Neuroimmune Pharmacol. 7: 1002-1016.

Grayson L, Vines B, Nichol K, Szaflarski JP. 2017. An interaction between warfarin and cannabidiol, a case report. Epilepsy Behav Case Rep. 9:10-11. doi: 10.1016/j.ebcr.2017.10.001

Greco R, Valeria G, Mauro M, Cristina T. (2010) The endocannabinoid system and migraine. Experimental neurology. 224:85-91

Grierson, GA. 1894. The hemp plant in Sanskrit and Hindi literature. Indian Antiquary. 260-262.

Gupta A, Epstein JB, Sroussi H. 2006. Hyposalivation in elderly patients. J Can Dent Assoc.72:841-846.

Guzman M. 2003. Cannabinoids: potential anticancer agents. Nat Rev Cancer 3(10):745-755.

Hall, W, Degenhardt, L. 2009. Adverse health effects of non-medical cannabis use. Lancet. 374:1383-91.

Habauzit V, Morand C. 2011. Evidence for a protective effect of polyphenols-containing foods on cardiovascular health: An update for clinicians. Therapeutic Advances in Chronic Disease. 3(2): 87–106

Hamadeh, R, Adehali, A, Locsley, RM, York MK. 1988. Fatal Aspergillosis associated with smoking contaminated marijuana, in a marrow transplant recipient. Chest. 94(2):432-433

Hampson AJ, Grimaldi M, Axelrod J, Wink D. 1998. Cannabidiol and THC are neuroprotective antioxidants. PNAS. 95(14):8268-8273.

Harris B (2010). Phytotherapeutic uses of essential oils. In: Baser KHC, Buchbauer G (eds). Handbook of Essential Oils: Science, Technology, and Applications. CRC Press: Boca Raton, FL, pp. 315–352.

Hart S, Fischer OM, Ullrich A. 2004. Cannabinoids induce cancer cell proliferation via tumor necrosis factor alpha-converting enzyme (TACE/ADAM17)-mediated transactivation of the epidermal growth factor receptor. Cancer Res. 64(6):1943-1950.

Hashibe M, Ford DE, Zhang ZF. 2002. Marijuana smoking and head and neck cancer. J Clin Pharmacol. 42:103S-107S

Hatoum NS, Davis WM, Elsohly MA, Turner CE (1981). Cannabichromene and delta 9-tetrahydrocannabinol: interactions relative to lethality, hypothermia and hexobarbital hypnosis. Gen Pharmacol 12: 357–362.

Hatoum NS, Davis WM, Elsohly MA, Turner CE. 1981. Cannabichromene and delta-9-tetrahydrocannabinol: Interactions relative to lethality, hypothermia and hexobarbital hypnosis. Gen Pharmacol. 12(5):357-362.

Hayes JS, Lampart R, Dreher MC, Morgan L. 1991. Five-year Follow-Up of Rural Jamaican Children Whose Mothers Used Marijuana During Pregnancy. West Indian Med J. 40(3): 120-123.

Hemann MT, Greider CW. 2000. Wild-derived inbred mouse strains have short telomeres. Nucleic Acids Res. 28(22): 4474-4478.

Hendriks H, Malingré TM, Batterman S, Bos R (1975). Mono- and sesqui-terpene hydrocarbons of the eseential oil of Cannabis *sativa*. Phytochem 14: 814–815.

Hendriks H, Malingré TM, Batterman S, Bos R (1977). Alkanes of the essential oil of Cannabis *sativa*. Phytochem 16: 719–721.

Hendrix PF, Parmelee RW, Crossley Jr. DA, Coleman DC, Odum EP, Groffman PM. 2014. Detritus Food Webs in Conventional and No-tillage Agroecosystems. BioScience. 36 (6):374-380.

Hermann H, Marsicano G, Lutz B. 2002. Coexpression of the cannabinoid receptor type 1 with dopamine and serotonin receptors in distinct neuronal subpopulations of the adult mouse forebrain. Neuroscience. 3(14):451-460.

Hill AJ, Weston SE, Jones NA, Smith I, Bevan SA, Williamson EM *et al.* (2010). Delta-Tetrahydrocannabivarin suppresses in vitro epileptiform and in vivo seizure activity in adult rats. Epilepsia 51: 1522–1532.

Hill M, Miller G, Ho W, Gorzalka B, Hillard C. 2008. Serum endocannabinoid content is altered in females with depressive disorders: a preliminary report. Pharmacopsychiatry. 41(2):48–53.

Hill TDM, Cascio M-G, Romano B, Duncan M, Pertwee RG, Williams CM, Whalley BJ, Hill AJ. 2013. Cannabidivarin-rich cannabis extracts are anticonvulsant in mouse and rat via a CB1 receptor-independent mechanism. Br J Phar. 170:679-692.

Hillig, K.W., 2004. Genetic evidence for speciation in Cannabis (Cannabaceae). Genet. Res. Crop. Evol. 51, xxx–xxx (in press).

Hillig, K.W., in press. A multivariate analysis of phenotypic variation in Cannabis. Syst. Bot.

Hillig, K.W., Mahlberg, P.G., 2004. A chemotaxonomic analysis of cannabinoid variation in Cannabis (Cannabaceae). Am. J. Bot. 91, 966–975.

Hoferl M, Krist S, Buchbauer G. 2006. Chirality influences the effects of linalool on physiological parameters of stress. Planta Med. 72(13): 1188-1192.

Hollister LE (1974). Structure-activity relationships in man of Cannabis constituents, and homologs and metabolites of delta9-tetrahydrocannabinol. Pharmacol 11: 3–11.

Huestis MA. 2007. Human Cannabinoid Pharmacokinetics. Chem biodivers. 4(8): 1770-1804.

Iffland K and Grotenhermen F. 2017. An Update on Safety and Side Effects of Cannabidiol: A Review of Clinical Data and Relevant Animal Studies. Cannabis and Cannabinoid Research. Vol. 2.1. http://doi.org/10.1089/can.2016.0034

Ismail M (2006). Central properties and chemcial composition of *Ocimum basilicum* essential oil. Pharm Biol 44: 619–626.

Iuvone T, Esposito G, Esposito R, Santamaria R, Di Rosa M, Izzo AA. 2004. Neuroprotective effect of cannabidiol, a non-psychoactive component from Cannabis sativa, on beta-amyloid-induced toxicity in PC12 cells. Journal of Neurochem. 89:134-141.

Izzo AA, Sharkey KA. 2010. Cannabinoids and the gut: new developments and emerging concepts. Pharmacol Ther. 126(1):21-38.

Jehanli A, Brannan S, Moore L, Spiehler VR. Blind trials of an onsite saliva drug test for marijuana and opiates. J Forensic Sci 2001;46(5):1214-1220.

Jiang, W. et al. (2005). "Cannabinoids promote embryonic and adult hippocampus neurogenesis and produce anxiolytic- and antidepressant-like effects". The Journal of Clinical Investigation. 115(11): 3104–3116.

Jirovetz L, Buchbauer G, Jager W, Woidich A, Nikiforov A (1992). Analysis of fragrance compounds in blood samples of mice by gas chromatography, mass spectrometry, GC/FTIR and GC/AES after inhalation of sandalwood oil. Biomed Chromatogr 6: 133–134.

Johnson JR, Jennison TA, Peat MA, Foltz RL (1984). "Stability of delta 9-tetrahydrocannabinol (THC), 11-hydroxy-THC, and 11-nor-9-carboxy-THC in blood and plasma". *Journal of analytical toxicology* **8** (5): 202–4

Johnson TN. (2008). The problems in scaling adult drug doses to children. Archives of Disease in Childhood. 93(3):207-211

Juergens UR, Dethlefsen U, Steinkamp G, Gillissen A, Repges R, Vetter H. 2003. Anti-Inflammatory activity of 1.8-cineol (Eucalyptol) in bronchial asthma: a double-blind placebo-controlled trial. Respir Med. 97(3):250-256.

Julien MS. Chirugie chinoise. Substance anesthétique employée en Chine, dans le commencement du III-ième siecle de notre ère, pour paralyser momentanement la sensibilité. Comptes Rendus Hebdomadaires de l'Académie des Sciences. 1849. 28:223–229.

Kagen S. L., Kurup, V. P., Sohnle, P. G., Fink, J. N. Marijuana smoking and fungal sensitization. J Allergy Cini Immunol 1983; 71: 389–93.

Kametani T, Furuyama H. 1987. Synthesis of Vitamin D3 and Related Compounds. Medicinal Research Reviews. 7(2):147-171

Kano, M., Ohno-Shosaku, T., Hashimotodani, Y., Uchigashima, M., Watanabe, M., 2009. Endocannabinoid-mediated control of synaptic transmission. Physiol. Rev. 89, 309–380.

Karas JA, Wong LJM, Paulin OKA, Mazeh AC, Hussein HM, Li J, Velkov T. 2020. The antimicrobial activity of cannabinoids. Antibiotics. 9:406. Doi:10.3390/antibiotics9070406

Karniol IG, Shirakawa I, Kasinski N, Pfeferman A, Carlini EA. 1974. Cannabidiol interferes with the effects of delta 9 – tetrahydrocannabinol in man. Eur J Pharmacol. 28(1):172-177.

Karschner EL, Darwin WD, McMahon RP, Liu F, Wright S, Goodwin RS, Huestis MA. 2011. Subjective and physiological effects after controlled Sativex and oral THC administration. Clinical Pharm and Therapeutics. 89:400-407.

Keifer M, Mahurin R. 1997. Chronic neurologic effects of pesticide overexposure. Occup. Med. 12:291-304

Kidambi S, Patel SB. 2008. Sitosterolaemia: pathophysiology, clinical presentation and laboratory diagnosis. J Clin Pathol. 61(5):588-594.

Kiers ET, MGA van der Heijden. 2006. Mutualistic stability in the arbuscular mycorrhizal symbiosis: exploring hypotheses of evolutionary cooperation. Ecology. 87(7):1627-1636.

Killestein J, ELJ H, M Reif, B Blauw, M Smits, BMJ Uitdehaag, L Nagelkerken, CH Polman. (2003). Immunomodulatory effects of orally administered cannabinoids in multiple sclerosis. Journal of Neuroimmunology. 137:140-143

Kimball ES, Schneider CR, Wallace NH, Hornby PJ. 2006. Agonists of cannabinoid receptor 1 and 2 inhibit experimental colitis induced by oil of mustard and by dextran sulfate sodium. American J of Physiology – Gastrointestinal and Liver Physiology. 291:G364-371.

Kinsey SG, Nomura DK, O'Neal ST, Long JZ, Mahadevan A, Cravatt BF, Grider JR, Lichtman AH. 2011. Inhibition of monoacylglycerol lipase attenuates nonsteroidal anti-inflammatory drug-induced gastric hemorrhages in mice. J Pharmacol Exp Ther. 338(3):795-802.

Korte G, Dreiseitel A, Schreier P, Oehme A, Locher S, Hajak G, Sand PG. (2009). An examination of anthocyanins' and anthocyanidins' affinity for cannabinoid receptors. J Med Food. 12(6):1407-1410.

Koskinen, J., Löhönen, J., Koponen, H., Isohanni, M., Miettunen, J., 2010. Rate of cannabis use disorders in clinical samples of patients with schizophrenia: a meta-analysis. Schizophrenia Bull. 36 (6) 1115-1130.

Koyama Y, Bando H, Yamashita F, Takakura Y, Sezaki H, Hashida M. 1994. Comparative Analysis of Percutaneous Absorption Enhancement by d-Limonene and Oleic Acid Based on a Skin Diffusion Model. Pharm Research. 11(3):377-383

Krishnaiah YSR, Satyanarayana V, Bhaskar P. 2002. Influence of limonene on thebioavailability of nicardipine hydrochloride from membrane-moderated transdermal therapeutic systems in human volunteers. Int J Pharm. 247(1-2):91-102.

Lamarck, J.B. de., 1785. Encyclope´die me´thodique. Botanique. 1 part 2, Panckoucke, Paris, pp. 694–695.

Langenheim JH (1994). Higher plant terpenoids: a phytocentric overview of their ecological roles. J Chem Ecol 20: 1223–1279.

Lata H, S Chandra, IA Khan, MA ElSohly. 2010b. High Frequency Plant Regeneration from Leaf Derived Callus of High delta-9-Tetrahydrocannabinol Yielding Cannabis sativa L. Planta Med 76:1629-1633

Lata H, S Chandra, N Techen, IA Khan, MA ElSohly. 2010a. Assessment of the Genetic Stability of Micropropagated Plants of Cannabis sativa by ISSR Markers. Planta Med. 76:97-100.

Legault J, A Pichette. (2010) Potentiating effect of B-caryophyllene on anticancer activity of a-humulene, isocaryophyllene and paclitaxel. J Parm and Pharmacol. 59:1643-1647

Leweke, F.M., Koethe, D., 2008. Cannabis and psychiatric disorders: it is not only addiction. Addiction Biology 13, 264–275.

Li J, Daughters RS, Bullis C, Bengiamin R, Stucky MW, Brennan J, et al. The cannabinoid receptor agonist WIN 55,212-2 mesylate blocks the development of hyperalgesia produced by capsaicin in rats. Pain 1999; 81:25–33.

Li Y, Owyang C. 2003. Musings on the Wanderer: What's New in Our Understanding of Vago-Vagal Reflexes? V. Remodeling of vagus and enteric neural circuitry after vagal injury. Am J Physiol Gastrointest Liver Physiol. 285:G461-G469.

Libzon S, Schleider LBL, Saban N, Levit L, Tamari Y, Linder I, Lerman-Sagie T, Blumkin L. 2018. Medical Cannabis for Pediatric Moderate to Severe Complex Motor Disorders. Journal of Child Neurology. 1-7. doi: 10.1177/0883073818773028

Linger P, J Mussig, H Fischer, J Kobert. (2002). Industrial hemp (Cannabis sativa L.) growing on heavy metal contaminated soil: fibre quality and phytoremediation potential. Ind Crop and Prod. 16:33-42

Linger, P, Mussig, J, Fischer, H, Kobert, J. 2002. Industrial hemp (Cannabis sativa L.) growing on heavy metal contaminated soil: fibre quality and phytoremediation potential. Industrial Crops and Products. 16:33-42

Linnaeus, C. 1753. Species Plantarum 2: 1027. Salvius, Stockholm. [Facsimile edition, 1957–1959. Ray Society, London, U.K.]

Llewellyn G. C., O'Rear C. E. A preliminary evaluation of illicit marihuana (Cannabis species) for mycotoxins. Dev Ind Microbiol Ser 1978; 19: 319–23.

Lopes NP, Kato MJ, Andrade EH, Maia JG, Yoshida M, Planchart AR *et al.* (1999). Antimalarial use of volatile oil from leaves of Virola surinamensis (Rol.) Warb. by Waiapi Amazon Indians. J Ethnopharmacol 67: 313–319.

Lorenzetti BB, Souza GE, Sarti SJ, Santos Filho D, Ferreira SH (1991). Myrcene mimics the peripheral analgesic activity of lemongrass tea. J Ethnopharmacol 34: 43–48.

Louw DR, Yang FW, Sutherland GR. 2000. The effect of THC on forebrain ischemia in rat. Brain Research. 857:183-187.

Lozano I. 2001. The therapeutic use of Cannabis sativa L. in Arabic medicine. Journal of Cannabis Therapeutics. 1: 63-70.

Ma EL, Li YC, Tsuneki H, Xiao JF, Xia MY, Wang MW, Kimura I. 2008. B-Eudesmol suppresses tumour growth through inhibition of tumour neovascularisation and tumour cell proliferation. Journal of Asian Natural Products Research. 10(2):159-167.

Maccarrone M, Gasperi V, Fezza F, Finazzi-Agro A, Rossi A. 2004. Differential regulation o ffatty acid amide hydrolase promoter in human immunce cells and neuronal cells by leptin and progesterone. European J of Biochem. 271:4666-4676.

Maccarrone M, Salvati S, Bari M, Finazzi A. 2000. Anandamide and 2-arachidonoylglycerol inhibit fatty acid amide hydrolase by activation the lipoxygenase pathway of the arachidonate cascade. Biochem and Biophysical Research Comm. 278:576-583.

Malingre T, Hendriks H, Batterman S, Bos R, Visser J (1975). The essential oil of Cannabis sativa. Planta Med 28: 56–61.

Malfitano AM, Ciaglia E, Gangemi G, Gazzerro P, LaezzaC, Bifulco M. 2011. Update on the endocannabinoid system as an anticancer target. Expert Opin Ther Targets. 15(3):297-308.

Marine KR, Cech JJ. Effects of High Water Temperature on Growth, Smoltification, and Predator Avoidance in Juvenile Sacramento River Chinook Salmon. North Am J Fish Manag. 2004; 24(1):198–210.

Marinelli S, Di Marzo V, Florenzano F, Fezza F, Viscomi MT, van der Stelt M, Bernardi G, Molinari M, Maccarrone M, Mercuri NB. 2007. N-Arachidonoyl-Dopamine Tunes Synaptic Transmission onto Dopaminergic Neurons by Activating both Cannabinoid and Vallinoid Receptors. Neuropsychopharmacology. 32:298-308.

Marks W., Florence, L., Lieberman, J., Chapman, P., Howard, D., Roberts, P. et al. Successfully treated invasive pulmonary aspergillosis associated with smoking marijuana in a renal transplant recipient. Transplantation 1996; 61: 1771–4.

Massa F, Marsicano G, Hermann H, Cannich A, Monory K, Cravatt BF, Ferri GL, Sibaev A, Storr M, Lutz B. 2004. The endogenous cannabinoid system protects against colonic inflammation. J Clin Invest. 113(8):1202-1209.

Mathew RJ, Wilson WH, Humphreys D, Lowe JV, Wiethe KE. 1992a. Middle cerebral artery velocity during upright posture after marijuana smoking. Acta Psychiatrica Scandinavica. 86:173-178.

Mathew RJ, Wilson WH, Humphreys D, Lowe JV, Wiethe KE. 1992b. Changes in middle cerebral artery velocity after marijuana. Biological Psychiatry. 32:164-169.

McDougle DR, Watson JE, et al. 2017. Anti-inflammatory omega-3 endocannabinoid epoxides. Proceedings of the National Academy of Sciences Jul 2017, 114 (30) E6034-E6043; DOI: 10.1073/pnas.1610325114

McGee, Harold (2004). *On food and cooking: the science and lore of the kitchen*. New York: Scribner. p. 714.

McGinty D, Letizia CS, Api AM (2010). Fragrance material review on phytol. Food Chem Toxicol 48 (Suppl. 3): S59–S63.

McKallip RJ, Nagarkatti M, Nagarkatti PS. 2005. Delta-9-tetrahydrocannabinol enhances breast cancer growth and metastasis by suppression o fthe antitumor immune response. J Immunol. 174(6):3281-3289.

McKernan KJ, Helbert Y, Kane LT, Ebling H, Zhang L, Liu B, Eaton Z, McLaughlin S, Kingan S, Baybayan P, Concepcion G, Jordan M, Riva A, Barbazuk W, Harkins T. 2020. Sequence and Annotation of 42 Cannabis Genomes Reveals Extensive Copy Number Variation in Cannabinoid Synthesis and Pathogen Resistance Genes. bioRxiv. Pre-print. Published January 05, 2020.

McPartland JM, Hegman W, Long T. 2019. Cannabis in Asia: its center of origin and early cultivation, based on a synthesis of subfossil pollen and archaeobotanical studies. Vegetation History and Archaeobotany. 28: 691-702.

McPartland JM, Mediavilla V. 2001a. Non-cannabinoids in Cannabis. In: Grotenhermen F, Russo EB (eds). Cannabis and Cannabinoids. NY: Haworth Press: Binghamton, NY, pp. 401–409.

McPartland JM, Russo EB. 2001b. Cannabis and Cannabis extracts: greater than the sum of their parts? J Cannabis Therap 1: 103–132.

McPartland JM, Small E. 2020. A classification of endangered high-THC cannabis (Cannabis sativa subsp. Indica) domesticates and their wild relatives. PhytoKeys. 144:81-112.

Mediavilla V, Steinemann S. 1997. Essential oil of Cannabis *sativa* L. strains. J Intl Hemp Assoc 4: 82–84.

Meehan-Atrash J, Luo W, Strongin RM. 2017. Toxicant formation in dabbing: the terpene story. ACS Omega 2017: 6112-6117

Meehan-Atrash J, Strongin RM. 2020. Pine rosin identified as a toxic cannabis extract adulterant. Forensic Science International. 312: 110301.

Mehrpouya-Bahrami P, Chitrala KN, Ganewatta MS, Tang C, Murphy EA, Enos RT, Velazquez KT, McCellan J, Nagarkatti M, Nagarkatti P. 2017. Blockade of CB1 cannabinoid receptor alters gut microbiota and attenuates inflammation and diet-induced obesity. Scientific Reports. 7:15645. doi:10.1038/s41598-017-15154-6

Mehmedic Z, Chandra S, Slade D, Denham H, Foster S, Patel AS *et al.* (2010). Potency trends of delta(9)-THC and other cannabinoids in confiscated Cannabis preparations from 1993 to 2008. J Forensic Sci 55: 1209–1217.

Mehmedic Z, Radwan MM, Wanas AS, Khan IA, Cutler SJ, ElSohly MA. 2014. In vitro binding affinity to human cb1 and cb2 receptors and antimicrobial activity of volatile oil from high potency Cannabis sativa. Planta medica. 80(10)

Merzouki A, Mesa JM. 2002. Concerning kif, a Cannabis sativa L. preparation smoked in the Rif mountains of northern Morocco. J Ethnopharmacol 81: 403–406.

Millar SA, Stone NL, Bellman ZD, Yates AS, England TJ, O'Sullivan SE. 2019. A systematic review of cannabidiol dosing in clinical populations. Br J Clin Pharmacol. 85(9): 1888-1900.

Milligan G. Orthologue selectivity and ligand bias: translating the pharmacology of GPR35. Trends Pharmacol Sci 2011;32:317–25.

Mokrysz C, Shaban N, Freeman TP, Curran HV. 2017. Acute effects of cannabis on the experience of speech illusion: a placebo-controlled study in adolescents and adults. European Neuropsychopharmacology. 27(1):S73

Moldzio R, Pacher T, Krewenka C, Kranner B, Novak J, Duvigneau JC, Rausch WD. (2012-05-07), "Effects of cannabinoids Δ(9)-tetrahydrocannabinol, Δ(9)-tetrahydrocannabinolic acid and cannabidiol in MPP(+) affected murine mesencephalic cultures", *Phytomedicine* **19**(8-9): 819–24

Mole Jr ML, Turner CE. 1973. Phytochemical screening of cannabis sativa L. I: Constituents of an Indian variant. Journal of Pharmaceutical Sciences. 63(1):154-156

Monti D, Saettone MF, Giannaccini B, Galli-Angeli D. 1995. Enhancement of transdermal penetration of dapiprazole through hairless mouse skin. Journal of Controlled Release. 33(1):71-77.

Moreau M, Ibeh U, Decosmo K, Bih N, Yasmin-karim S, Toyang N, Lowe H, Ngwa W. 2019. Flavonoid derivative of Cannabis demonstrates therapeutic potential in preclinical models of metastatic pancreatic cancer. Frontiers in Oncology. 9: 660.

Mothana RAA, Hasson SS, Schultze W, Mowitz A, Lindequist U. 2011. Phytochemical composition and in vitro antimicrobial and antioxidant activities of essential oils of three endemic Soqotraen *Boswellia* species. Food Chemistry. 126(3): 1149-1154.

Moyle PB. Inland fishes of California. Berkeley: University of California Press; 2002.

Musty R, Deyo R (2006). A cannabigerol extract alters behavioral despair in an animal model of depression. Proceedings June 26; Symposium on the Cannabinoids. International Cannabinoid Research Society: Tihany, p. 32.

Musty RE, Karniol IG, Shirikawa I, Takahashi RN, Knobel E (1976). Interactions of delta-9-tetrahydrocannabinol and cannabinol in man. In: Braude

MC, Szara S (eds). The Pharmacology of Marihuana, Vol. 2. Raven Press: New York, pp. 559–563.

Naftali T, Lev LB, Yablecovitch D, Half E, Konikoff FM. 2011. Treatment of Crohn's disease with cannabis: an observational study. Israel Medical Association Journal. 13. 455-458.

Nakazi M, Bauer U, Nickel T, Kathmann M, Schlicker E. 2000. Inhibition of serotonin release in the mouse brain via presynaptic cannabinoid CB1 receptors. Naunyn-Schmiedeberg's Arch Pharmacol. 361:19-24.

Nappe TM, Hoyte, CO. 2017. Pediatric Death Due to Myocarditis After Exposure to Cannabis. Clin Pract Cases Emerg Med. 1(3):166-170. doi: 10.5811/cpcem.2017.1.33240

Nanjwade, B. K., Patel, D. J., Udhani, R. A., & Manvi, F. V. (2011). Functions of Lipids for Enhancement of Oral Bioavailability of Poorly Water-Soluble Drugs. Scientia Pharmaceutica, 79(4), 705–727. http://doi.org/10.3797/scipharm.1105-09

Nanni O, Amadori D, Lugaresi C, Falcini F, Scarpi E, et al. 1996. Chronic lymphoctic leukemias and non-Hodgkin's lymphoma by histological type in farming animal breeding workers: a population case-control study based on a priori exposure matrices. Occup. Environ. Med. 53:652-57

Nissen L, Zatta A, Stefanini I, Grandi S, Sgorbati B, Biavati B *et al.* (2010). Characterization and antimicrobial activity of essential oils of industrial hemp varieties (Cannabis sativa L.). Fitoterapia 81: 413–419.

Noma Y, Asakawa Y (2010). Biotransformation of monoterpenoids by microorganisms, insects, and mammals. In: Baser KHC, Buchbauer G (eds). Handbook of Essential Oils: Science, Technology, and Applications. CRC Press: Boca Raton, FL, pp. 585–736.

Normen L, Dutta P, Lia A, Andersson H. 2000. Soy sterol esters and B-sitostanol ester as inhibitors of cholesterol absorption in human small bowel. Am J Clin Nutr. 71(4):908 – 913.

Notarnicola M, Tutino V, Tafaro A, Bianco G, Guglielmi E, Caruso MG. 2016. Dietary olive oil induces cannabinoid CB2 receptor expression in adipose tissue of ApcMin/+ transgenic mice. Nutrition and Healthy Aging. 4(1): 73–80.

Notcutt W, Price M, Miller R, Newport S, Phillips C, Simmons S, Sansom C. 2004. Initial experiences with medicinal extracts of cannabis for chronic pain: results from 34 "N of 1" studies. Anaesthesia. 2004. 59: 440–452.

Novak J, Zitterl-Eglseer K, Deans SG, Franz CM. 2001. Essential oils of different cultivars of Cannabis sativa L. and their microbioal activity. Flavour and Fragrance Journal. 16(4):259-262.

Novotna A, Mares J, Ratcliffe S, Novakova I, Vachova M, Zapletalova O, Gasperini C, Pozzilli C, Cefaro L, Comi G, Rossi P, Ambler Z, Stelmasiak Z, Erdmann A, Montalban X, Klimek A, Davies P, Satived Spasticity Study Group. 2011. A randomized, double-blind, placebo-controlled, parallel group, enriched-design study of nabiximols (Sativex®), as add-on therapy, in subjects with refractory spasticity caused by multiple sclerosis. European Journal of Neurology. 18: 1122–1131.

Noyes R Jr, Brunk SF, Avery DH, Canter A. 1975. The analgesic properties of delta-9-tetrahydrocannabinol and codeine. Clinical Pharmacology and Therapeutics. 18: 84–89.

O'Leary DS, Block RI, Koeppel JA, Flaum M, Schultz SK, Andreasen NC, Ponto LB, Watkins GL, Hurtig RR, Hichwa RD. 2002. Effects of smoking marijuana on brain perfusion and cognition. Neuropsychopharmacology. 26(6):806-816.

O'Shaughnessy WB. (1838–1840). On the preparations of the Indian hemp, or gunjah (Cannabis indica); their effects on the animal system in health, and their utility in the treatment of tetanus and other convulsive diseases. Transactions of the Medical and Physical Society of Bengal, 71–102, 421–461.

O'Shaughnessy's Online. 2014. McPartland's Correct(ed) Vernacular Nomenclature. http://www.beyondthc.com/mcpartlands-corrected-vernacular-nomenclature/

O'Sullivan SE, Kendall DA, Randall MD. 2004. Characterisation of the vasorelaxant properties of the novel endocannabinoid N-arachidonoyl-dopamine (NADA). Bri J of Pharm. 141:803-812.

Ogbe RJ, Ochalefu DO, Mafulul SG, Olaniru OB. 2015. A review of dietary phytosterols: their occurrence, metabolism and health benefits. Asian Journal of Plant Science and Research. 5(4):10-21.

Onaivi ES, Ishiguro H, Gu S, Liu QR. 2012. CNS effects of CB2 caannabinoid receptors: beyond neuro-immuno-cannabinoid activity. J Psychopharmacol. 26(1): 92-103.

Pacher P, Batkai S, Kunos G (2006). The endocannabinoid system as an emerging target of pharmacotherapy. Pharmacol Rev 58: 389–462.

Pacher P, Mechoulam R. 2011. Is lipid signaling through cannabinoid 2 receptors part of a protective system? Prog Lipid Res. 50(2):193-211.

Pagotto U, Vicennati V, Pasquali R (2205). The endocannabinoid system and the treatment of obesity. Ann Med 37(4):270-275.

Paris, R.R., E. Henri, and M. Paris. 1976. Sur les c-flavonoïdes du Cannabis *sativa* L. *Plantes Médicinales et Phytothérapie* 10:144-54.

Pedersen W. 2008. Does cannabis use lead to depression and suicidal behaviours? A population-based longitudinal study. Acta Psychiatrica Scandinavica. 118(5):395-403.

Penumarti A, Abdel AR. (2014) The novel endocannabinoid receptor gpr18 is expressed in the rostral ventrolateral medulla and exerts tonic restraining influence on blood pressure. J Pharmacol Exp Ther. 349:29-38

Perry NS, Houghton PJ, Theobald A, Jenner P, Perry EK (2000). In-vitro inhibition of human erythrocyte acetylcholinesterase by salvia lavandulaefolia essential oil and constituent terpenes. J Pharm Pharmacol 52: 895–902.

Pertwee RG, Ross RA. 2002. Cannabinoid receptors and their ligands. Protaglandins, Leukotrienes, and Essential Fatty Acids (PLEFA). 66(2-3):101-121. https://doi.org/10.1054/plef.2001.0341

Pertwee RG. 2008. The diverse CB1 and CB2 receptor pharmacology of three plant cannabinoids: delta-9-tetrahydrocannbinol, cannabidiol, and delta-9-tetrahydrocannabivarin. Br J Pharmacol. 153(2):199-215.

Pertwee RG. 2015. Handbook of Cannabis. Oxford University Press.

Peters M, Kogan NM. 2007. HU-331: a cannabuinoid quinine, with uncommon cytotoxic properties and low toxicity. Expert Opinion on Investigational Drugs. 16:1405-1413

Pindborg JJ, Barmes D, Roed-Petersen B. 1968. Epidemiology and histology of oral leukoplakia and leukoedema among Papuans and New Guineans. Cancer. 22:379-384.

Pinto L, Capasso R, Di Carlo G, Izzo AA. 2002. Endocannabinoids and the gut. Prostaglandins, Leukotrienes and Essential Fatty Acids. 66:333-341.

Pisanti S, Picardi P, D'Alessandro A. Laezza C, Bifulco M. 2013. The endocannabinoid signaling system in cancer. Trend Pharmacol Sci. 34(5):273-282.

Pollastro F, Minassi A, Fresu L. 2018. Cannabis phenolics and their bioactives. Current Medicinal Chemistry. 25(10):1160-1185

Ponto Ll, O'Leary DS, Koeppel J, Block RI, Watkins GL, Richmond JC, Ward CA, Clermont DA, Schmitt BA, Hichwa RD. 2004. Effect of acute marijuana on cardiovascular function and central nervous system pharmacokinetics of [(15)O]water: effect in occasional and chronic users. J Clin Pharmacol. 44(7):751-766.

Porter AC, Sauer JM, Knierman MD, Becker GW, Berna MJ, Bao J, Nomikos GG, Carter P, Bymaster FP, Leese AB, Felder CC. 2002. Characterization of a novel endocannabinoid, Virodhamine, with antagonist activity at the CB1 receptor. JPET. 301:1020-1024.

Pultrini Ade M, Galindo LA, Costa M (2006). Effects of the essential oil from Citrus aurantium L. in experimental anxiety models in mice. Life Sci 78: 1720–1725.

Ramírez Bg, E. A.; Blázquez, C.; Gómez Del Pulgar, T.; Guzmán, M.; De Ceballos, M. L. (2005). "Prevention of Alzheimer's disease pathology by cannabinoids: neuroprotection mediated by blockade of microglial activation". Journal of Neuroscience. 25(8): 1904–1913.

Ream GL, Benoit E, Johnson BD, Dunlap E. 2008. Smoking tobacco along with marijuana increases symptoms of cannabis dependence. Durg Alcohol Depend. 95 (3): 199-208. doi: https://dx.doi.org/10.1016%2Fj.drugalcdep.2008.01.011

Redecker, D., R. Kodner, and L.E. Graham. 2000. Glomalean fungi from the Ordovician. Science 289:1920-1921

Rice S, Koziel JA. 2015. Characterizing the smell of marijuana by odor impact of volatile compounds: an application of simultaneous chemical and sensory analysis. PLOS ONE 10(12): e0144160. https://doi.org/10.1371/journal.pone.0144160

Richardson JD, Aanonsen L, Hargreaves KM. SR 141716A, a cannabinoid receptor antagonist, produces hyperalgesia in untreated mice. Eur J Pharmacol 1997; 319:R3-4.

Riedel G, Fadda P, McKillop-Smith S, Pertwee RG, Platt B, Robinson L (2009). Synthetic and plant-derived cannabinoid receptor antagonists show hypophagic properties in fasted and non-fasted mice. Br J Pharmacol 156: 1154–1166.

Rock EM, Kopstick RL, Limebeer CL, Parker LA. 2013. Tetrahydrocannabinolic acid reduces nausea-induced conditioned gaping in rats and vomiting in Suncus murinus. Br J Pharmacol. 170(3):641-648

Rock EM, Sticht MA, Duncan M, Stott C, Parker LA. 2013. Evaluation of the potential of the phytocannabinoids, cannabidivarin (CBDV) and delta-9-tetrahydrocannabivarin (THCV), to produce CB1 receptor inverse agonism symptoms of nausea in rats. Br J Phar. 170:671-678

Rodrigues Goulart H, Kimura EA, Peres VJ, Couto AS, Aquino Duarte FA, Katzin AM (2004). Terpenes arrest parasite development and inhibit biosynthesis of isoprenoids in Plasmodium falciparum. Antimicrobial Agents Chemother 48: 2502–2509. Press: Boca Raton, FL.

Rog DJ, Nurmikko TJ, Friede T, Young CA. 2005. Randomized controlled trial of cannabis based medicine in central neuropathic pain due to multiple sclerosis. Neurology. 2005. 65: 812–819.

Romano B, Borrelli F, Pagano E, Cascio MG, Pertwee RG, Izzo AA. 2014. Inhibition of colon carcinogenesis by a standardized Cannabis sativa extract with high content of cannabidiol. Phytomedicine. 21:631-639.

Rosenblatt KA, Darling JR, Chen C, Sherman KJ, Schwartz SM. 2004. Marijuana use and risk of oral squamous cell carcinoma. Cancer Research. 64:4049-4054.

Rosenkrantz H, Fleischman RW, Grant RJ. 1981. Toxicity of short-term administration of cannabinoids to rhesus monkeys. Toxicol Appl Pharmacol. 58:118-131.

Ross SA, ElSohly MA. 1996. The volatile oil composition of fresh and air-dried buds of Cannabis sativa. J Nat Prod 59: 49–51.

Ross, S., ElSohly, H., ElKashoury, E., and ElSohly, M. (1996) Fatty acids of Cannabis seeds. *Phytochem. Anal.* **7**, 279–283.

Rothschild M, Bergstrom G, Wangberg S-A. 2005. Cannabis *sativa:* volatile compounds from pollen and entire male and female plants of two variants, Northern Lights and Hawaian Indica. Bot J Linn Soc 147: 387–397.

Ruhaak LR, Felth J, Karlsson PC, Rafter JJ, Verpoorte R, Bohlin L. 2011. Evaluation of the cyclooxygenase inhibiting effects of six major cannabinoids isolated from Cannabis sativa. Biological and Pharmaceutical Bulletin 34 (5): 774–778

Russo E. 2002. Cannabis treatments in obstetrics and gynecology: a historical review. Journal of Cannabis Therapeutics. 2:5-35.

Russo E. 2004. Clinical Endocannabinoid Deficiency (CECD): Can this concept explain therapeutic benefits of cannabis in migraine, fibromyalgia, irritable bowel syndrome and other treatment-resistant conditions?. Neuroendocrinology Letters. 25:31-39

Russo E. 2014. The Pharmacological History of Cannabis. Chapter 2. Handbook of Cannabis. Oxford University Press. p.23-29

Russo EB. 2007. History of Cannabis and its preparations in saga, science and sobriquet. Chemistry and Biodiversity. 4: 2624-2648.

Russo EB. 2011. Taming THC: potential Cannabis synergy and phytocannabinoid-terpenoid entourage effects. Br J of Pharmacol 163:1344-1364.

Russo EB, Burnett A, Hall B, Parker KK. 2005. Agonistic properties of cannabidiol at 5-HT-1a receptors. Neurochem Res 30: 1037–1043.

Russo EB, Marcu J. 2017. Cannabis Pharmacology: The Usual Suspects and a Few Promising Leads. Adv. Pharmacol. 80:67-134.

Ryberg E, Larsson N, Sjo¨gren S, Hjorth S, Hermansson N-O, Leonova J et al. 2007. The orphan receptor GPR55 is a novel cannabinoid receptor. Br J Pharmacol 152: 1092–1101.

Sagar, D.R., Gaw, A.G., Okine, B.N., Wong, A., Woodhams, S.G., Kendall, D.A., Chapman, V., 2009. Dynamic regulation of the endocannabinoid system: implications for analgesia. Mol. Pain 8, 5–59.

Salen G, Patel S, Batta AK. 2002. Sitosterolemia. Cardiovasc Drug Rev. 20(4):255-270.

Sallan SE, Zinberg NE, Frei E 3rd. 1975. Antiemetic effect of delta-9-tetrahydrocannabinol in patients receiving cancer chemotherapy. New England Journal of Medicine. 293: 795–797.

Sanchez-Duffhues G, Calzado MA, de Vinuesa AG, Caballero FJ, Ech-Chahad A, Appendino G, Krohn K, Fiebich BL, Munoz E. 2008. Denbinobin, a naturally occurring 1,4-phenanthrenequinone, inhibits HIV-1 replication through an NF-kB-dependent pathway. Biochem. Pharmacol. 76:1240-1250.

Sanchez-Duffhues G, Calzado MA, de Vinuesa AG, Appendino G, Fiebich BL, Loock U, Lefarth-Risse A, Krohn K, Munoz E. Denbinobin inhibits nuclear factor-kB and induces apoptosis via reactive oxygen species generation in human leukemic cells. Biochem. Pharmacol. 77:1401-1409.

Sarfaraz S, Adhami VM, Syed DN, Afaq F, Mukhtar H. 2008. Cannabinoids for cancer treatment: progress and promise. Cancer Res. 68(2):339-342.

Sarma ND, Waye A, ElSohly MA, Brown PN, Elzinga S, Johnson HE, Marles RJ, Melanson JE, Russo E, Deyton L, Hudalla C, Vrdoljak GA, Wurzer JH, Khan IA, Kim NC, Giancaspro GI. 2020. Cannabis Inflorescence for Medical Purposes: USP Considerations for Quality Attributes. J. nat. Prod. 83: 1334-1351.

Sauer, M.A., S.M. Rifka, R.L. Hawks, G.B. Cutler, and D.L. Loriaux. 1983. Marijuana: interaction with the estrogen receptor. J Pharm Exper Therap 224:404-7.

Sawzdargo M,Nguyen T, Lee DK, Lynch KR, Cheng R, Heng HH, George SR, O'Dowd BF. 1999. Identification and cloning of three novel human G protein-coupled receptor genes GPR52, wGPR53 and GPR55: GPR55 is extensively expressed in human brain. Brain Res. Mol. Brain Res. 64:193–198.

Scialdone M. United States Patent US9694040B2. Hydrogenation of Cannabis Oil.

Schwope DM, Bosker WM, Ramaekers JG, Gorelick DA, Huestis MA. 2012. Psychomotor performance, subjective and physiological effects and whole blood delta-9-tetrahydrocannabino concentrations in heavy, chronic cannabis smokers following acute smoked cannabis. Journal of Analytical Toxicology. 36:405-412.

Seidler A, Hellenbrand W, Robra BP, Vieregge P, Nischan P, et al. 1996. Possible environmental, occupational, and other etiologic factors for Parkinson's disease: a case-control study in Germany. Neurology 46: 1257-84

Shamloul R, Bella AJ. 2011. Impact of cannabis use on male sexual health. J of Sexual Med. 8:971-975.

Shou-Zhong, Y. 1997. The Divine Farmer's Materia Medica: A Translation of the Shen Nong Ben Cao Jing. Boulder, CO: Blue Poppy Press.

Siddiqui MZ. 2011. Boswellia Serrata, a Potential Antiinflammatory Agent: An Overview. Indian J Pharm Sci. 73(3): 255-261.

Silverstein SJ, Noel D, Heilbron D. 1978. Social drug use/abuse and dental disease. J calif Dent Assoc. 6:32-37.

Simopoulos, A. P. 2016. An Increase in the Omega-6/Omega-3 Fatty Acid Ratio Increases the Risk for Obesity. Nutrients, 8(3), 128. http://doi.org/10.3390/nu8030128

Singh UP, Singh NP, Singh B, Price RL, Nagarkatti M, Nagarkatti PS. 2012. Cannabinoid receptor-2 (CB2) agonist ameliorates colitis in IL-10-/- mice by attenuating the activation of T cells and promoting their apoptosis. Toxicology and Applied Pharmacology. 258:256-267.

Singh Y, Bali C. 2013. Cannabis extract treatment for terminal acute lymphoblastic leukemia with a Philadelphia chromosome mutation. Case Rep Oncol. 6:585-592.

Sinor AD, Irvin SM, Greenberg DA. 2000. Endocannabinoid protect cerebral cortical neurons from in vitro ischemia in rats. Neuroscience Letters. 278:157-160.

Small, E., 1979. The Species Problem in Cannabis 1. Science, Corpus Information Services, Toronto.

Small, E., Beckstead, H.D., 1973a. Common cannabinoid phenotypes in 350 stocks of Cannabis. Lloydia 36, 144–165.

Small, E., Beckstead, H.D., 1973b. Cannabinoid phenotypes in Cannabis sativa. Nature 245, 147–148.

Small, E., Cronquist, A., 1976. A practical and natural taxonomy for Cannabis. Taxon 25, 405–435.

Smith SC, Wagner MS. 2014. Clinical endocannabinoid deficiency (CECD) revisited: can this concept explain the therapeutic benefits of cannabis in migraine, fibromyalgia, irritable bowel syndrome, and other treatment-resistant conditions?. Neuro Endocrinol Lett. 35(3):198-201.

Squire, LR, Schacter DL. 2002. The Neuropsychology of Memory. Guilford Press.

Stahl E, Kunde R 1973. Die Leitsubstanzen der Haschisch-Suchhunde. Kriminalistik: Z Gesamte Kriminal Wiss Prax 27: 385–389.

Starks, Michael (1990). *Marijuana Chemistry: Genetics, Processing, Potency*. Ronin Publishing

Staudt R, Nitzsche J, Harting P. 2003. Supercritical Fluid Extraction Using Microwave Heating. Proceedings 6th International Symposium on Supercritical Fluids, Versailles, France, April 2003.

Storr MA, Keenan CM, Emmerdinger D. 2008. Targeting endocannabinoid degradation protects against experimental colitis in mice: involvement of CB1 and CB2 receptors. Journal of Molecular Medicine. 86:925-936.

Storr MA, Keenan CM, Zhang H, Patel KD, Makriyannis A, Sharkey KA. 2009. Activation of the cannabinoid 2 receptor (CB2) protects against experimental colitis. Inflammatory Bowel Disease. 15:1678-1685.

Storr, MA., Sharkey, KA. 2007. The endocannabinoid system and gut–brain signalling. Current Opinion in Pharmacology, 7(6), 575–582.

Stuart JM, Leishman E, Bradshaw HB. 2015. Reproduction and Cannabinoids: Ups and Downs, Ins and Outs. Handbook of Cannabis. Oxford University Press. 245-260.

Stumpf JL, Williams LD. 2020. Management of Cannabinoid Hyperemesis Syndrome: Focus on Capsaicin. Journal of Pharmacy Practice. Jul 2. 897190020934289.

Sullivan N, Sytze E, Raber JC. 2013. Determination of Pesticide Residues in Cannabis Smoke. Journal of Toxicology. Vol 2013. Article ID 378168

Sullivan SE. Phytocannabinoids and the Cardiovascular System. Handbook of Cannabis. Oxford University Press. Chapter 11. pp. 208-226.

Sun X, Dey SK. 2012. Endocannabinoid signaling in female reproduction. American Chem Soc Chem Neuro. 3:349-355.

Sundararaman P, Djerassi C. 1977. A convenient synthesis of progesterone from stigmasterol. J Org Chem. 42(22):3633-3634.

Szaflarski JP, Bebin EM. 2014. Cannabis, cannabidiol, and epilepsy – From receptors to clinical response. Epilepsy and Behavior. 41:277-282.

Taghinasab M, Jabaji S. 2020. Cannabis microbiome and the role of endophytes in modulating the production of secondary metabolites: an overview. Microorganisms. 8: 355

Tambe Y, Tsujiuchi H, Honda G, Ikeshiro Y, Tanaka S (1996). Gastric cytoprotection of the non-steroidal anti-inflammatory sesquiterpene, beta-caryophyllene. Planta Med 62: 469–470.

Thapa D, Lee JS, Heo SW, Lee YR, Kang KW, Kwak MK, Choi HG, Kim JA. 2011. Novel Hexahydrocannabinol Analogs as Potential Anti-Cancer Agents Inhibit Cell Proliferation and Tumor Angiogenesis. Eur J Pharmacol. 650(1): 64-71.

Thomas A, Baillie GL, Phillips AM, Razdan RK, Ross RA, Pertwee RG (2007). Cannabidiol displays unexpectedly high potency as an antagonist of CB1 and CB2 receptor agonists in vitro. Br J Pharmacol 150: 613–623.

Thomas A, Stevenson LA, Wease KN, Price MR, Baillie G, Ross RA et al. (2005). Evidence that the plant cannabinoid delta-9-tetrahydrocannabivarin is a cannabinoid CB1 and CB2 antagonist. Br J Pharmacol 146: 917–926.

Thompson GR, Rosenkrantz H, Schaeppi UH, Braude MC. 1973. Comparison of acute oral toxicity of cannabinoids in rats, dogs and monkeys. Toxicol Appl Pharmacol. 25(3):363-72.

Thors L, Belghiti M, Fowler CJ. (2007). The 'specific' tyrosine kinase inhibitor genistein inhibits the enzymic hydrolysis of anandamide: implications for anandamide uptake. Br J Pharmacol. 150:S951-S960.

Thors L, Belghiti M, Fowler CJ. (2008). Inhibition of fatty acid amide hydrolase by kaempferol and related naturally occurring flavonoids. Br J Pharmacol. 155:S244-S252

Tinto F, Villano R, Kostrzewa M, Ligresti A, Straker H, Manzo E. 2020. Synthesis of the major mammalian metabolites of THCV. J Nat. Prod. doi: 10.1021/acs.jnatprod.9b00831

Tomaso ED, Beltramo M, Piomelli D. 1996. Brain cannabinoids in chocolate. Nature. 382:677-678.

Treseder, K. K. 2004. A meta-analysis of mycorrhizal responses to nitrogen, phosphorus, and atmospheric CO2 in field studies. New Phytologist 164:347-355

Trezza V, Patrizia C. 2013. The endocannabinoid system as a possible target to treat both the cognitive and emotional features of post-traumatic stress disorder (PTSD). Frontiers in Behavioral Neuroscience. 100(7):1-6

Tsuneki H, Ma EL, Kobayashi S, Sekizaki N, Maekawa K, Sasaoka T, Wang MW, Kimura I. 2005. Antiangiogenic activity of B-eudesmol in vitro and in vivo. European Journal of Pharmacology. 512(2-3):105-115.

Turner, C.E., M.A. Elsohly, and E.G. Boeren. 1980. Constituents of Cannabis sativa L. XVII. A review of the natural constituents. J Nat Prod 43:169-304.

Tuttle AH, Tohyama S, Ramsay T, Kimmelman J, Schweinhardt P, Bennett GJ, Mogil JS. 2015. Increasing placebo responses over time in US clinical trials of neuropathic pain. Pain. 156(12):2616-2626.

Ujvary I, Grotenhermen F. 2014. 11-nor-9-carboxy-delta-9-tetrahydrocannbinol – a ubiquitous yet underresearched cannabinoid. A review of the literature. Cannabinoids. 9(1):1-8.

Vaddi HK, Ho PC, Chan SY. 2002. Terpenes in propylene glycol as skin-penetration enhancers: permeation and partition of haloperidol, Fourier transform infrared spectroscopy, and differential scanning calorimetry. J Pharm Sci. 91(7):1639-1651.

Van Wyk CW, Breytenbach HS, Dreyer WP. 1979. The epidemiology of preventable oral mucosal lesions in the Cape Peninsula. J Dent Assoc 34:672-676.

Vavilov, N.I., 1926. The origin of the cultivation of "primary" crops, in particular cultivated hemp. In: Studies on the Origin of Cultivated Crops. Institute of Applied Botany and Plant Breeding, Leningrad, pp. 221–233.

Vavilov, N.I., Bukinich, D.D., 1929. Zemledel'cheskii Afghanistan. Trudy po Prikl. Bot. Gen. Sel. Suppl. 33, 380–382, ([Reissued 1959, Izdatel'stuo Akademii Nauk SSSR, Moskva-Leningrad]).

Velasco G, Hernandez-Tiedra S, Davila D, Lorente M. 2015. The use of cannabinoids as anticancer agents. Progress in Neuro-Psychopharmacology and Biological Psychiatry. http://dx.doi.org/10.1016/j.pnpbp.2015.05.010

Velasco G, Sanchez C, Guzman M. 2012. Towards the use of cannabinoids as antitumour agents. Nat Rev Cancer. 12(6):436-444.

Versteeg PA, Slot DE, Velden U, Weijden GAvander. 2008. Effect of cannabis usage on the oral environment: a review. Int J Dent Hygiene. 6:315-320.

Voelker R, Holmes M. 2014. Pesticide Use on Cannabis. Cannabis Safety Institute white paper publication.

Volicer, L, Stelly M, Morris J, McLaughlin J, Volicer BJ. 1997. Effects of dronabinol on anorexia and disturbed behavior in patients with Alzheimer's disease. International Journal of Geriatric Psychiatry. 1997. 12: 913–919.

Volkow, ND, Baler, RD, Compton, WM, Weiss, SRB. 2014. Adverse Health Effects of Marijuana Use. The N Engl J Med 370:2219-2227.

Wade, DT, Robson P, House H, Makela P, Aram J. 2003. A preliminary controlled study to determine whether whole-plant cannabis extracts can improve intractable neurogenic symptoms. Clinical Rehabilitation. 2003. 17: 18–26.

Want H, Guo Y, Wang D. Kingsley PJ, Marnett LJ, Das SK, DuBois RN Dey SK. 2004. Aberrant cannabinoid signaling impairs oviductal transport of embryos. Nature Med. 10:1074-1080.

Wang D, Wang H, Ning W, Backlund MG, Dey SK, DuBois RN. 2008. Loss of cannabinoid receptor 1 accelerates intestinal tumor growth. Cancer Res. 68(15):6468-6476.

Ware MA. 2015. Synthetic Psychoactive Cannabinoids Licensed as Medicines. Handbook of Cannabis. Oxford University Press. Chapter 21. pp. 393-414.

Weinstein BS, Ciszek D. 2002. The Reserve-Capacity Hypothesis: Evolutionary Origins and Modern Implications of the Trade-Off Between Tumor-Suppression and Tissue-Repair. Exp Gerontol. 37(5): 615-627.

Whiting PF, Wolff RF, Deshpande S, Nisio MD, Duffy S, Hernandez AV, Keurentjes JC, Lang S, Misso K, Ryder S, Schmidlkofer S, Westwood M, Kleijnen J. 2015. Cannabinoids for Medical use: A Systematic Review and Meta-analysis. JAMA. 313(24):2456-2473.

Williams SJ, Hartley JP, Graham JD. 1976. Bronchodilator effect of delta1-tetrahydrocannabinol administered by aerosol of asthmatic patients. Thorax 31: 720–723.

Wirth PW, Watson ES, ElSohly M, Turner CE, Murphy JC (1980). Anti-inflammatory properties of cannabichromene. Life Sci 26: 1991–1995.

Y. Liu, F. Wu, Global burden of aflatoxin-induced hepatocellular carcinoma: a risk assessment, Environ. Health Perspect. 118 (2010) 818–824.

Yamamoto I, Gohda H, Narimatsu S, Watanabe K, Yoshimura H. 1991. Cannabielsoin as a new metabolite of cannabidiol in mammals. Pharmacol Biochem Behav. 40(3):541-546.

Yamaori S, Ebisawa J, Okushima Y, Yamamoto I, Watanabe K. 2011. Potent inhibition of human cytochrome P450 3A isoforms by cannabidiol: role of phenolic hydroxyl groups in the resorcinol moiety. Life Sci.

Yang Y, Wei MC. 2016. A combine procedure of ultrasound-assisted and supercritical carbon dioxide for extraction and quantitation of oleanolic and ursolic acids from Hedyotis corymbosa. Industrial Crops and Products. 79: 7-17.

Yao B, Mackie K. 2009. Endocannabinoid Receptor Pharmacology. Current Topics in Behavioral Neurosciences. 37-63

Zhu LX, Sharma S, Stolina M, Gardner B, Roth MD, Tashkin DP. 2000. Delta-9-tetrahydrocannabinol inhibits antitumor immunity by a CB2 receptor-mediated, cytokine-dependent pathway. J Immunol. 165(1):373-380.

Zuardi A, Crippa J, Dursun S, Morais S, Vilela J, Sanches R, Hallak J. 2010. Cannabidiol was ineffective for manic episode of bipolar affective disorder. J Psychopharmacol. 24(1):135-137.

Zuardi AW, Cosme RA, Graeff FG, Guimaraes FS. 1993. Effects of ipsapirone and cannabidiol on human experimental anxiety. Journal of Psychopharmacology. 7: 82–88.

Zuardi AW, Shirawaka I, Finkelfarb E, Karniol IG. 1982. Action of cannabidiol on the anxiety and other effects produced by delta 9-THC in normal subjects. Psychopharmacology. 76: 245–250.

Zweifel C, Stephan R. 2011. Spices and herbs as source of Salmonella-related foodborne diseases. Food Research International. 45:765-769.

APPENDIX B: GLOSSARY

Actinomycetes – also Actinobacteria; group of generally bacteria present in soils and water that give soil its characteristic smell. Actinomycetes produce a number of metabolites used in medicine.

Alkane – hydrocarbon compound with only single bonds

Alkene – hydrocarbon compound with one or more double bonds

Alkyne – hydrocarbon compound with one or more triple bonds

Allele – a form of a gene that is responsible for hereditary variation.

Allosteric Modulator – a compound that does not bind to the orthosteric site of a receptor, but instead binds to other sites and manipulates the shape and function of the receptor when a compound later binds to the orthosteric site.

Amnesia – deficit in memory

Analgesia – inability to feel pain

Analgesic – pain reliever

Angiosperm – flowering plant

Anther – the part of the stamen that holds pollen

Antiemetic – anti-nausea compound

AOI (Area of Interest) – when using the online Web Soil Survey program, this term refers to the area of which the user would like to find soil survey data

Apical Bud – also known as the terminal bud; the region of active growth at the top of the main stem of a plant

Apical Meristem – meristem region of active growth in the apical bud

Arbuscular Mycorrhizal Fungus – fungi of the phylum Glomeromycota; these fungi form symbiotic relationships with plant roots, exchanging phosphorous and other nutrients with the plant in exchange for carbon. Arbuscular mycorrhizae penetrate certain cells of the roots of the plant and then produce structures called arbuscules which are the sites where nutrients are exchanged with the plant.

Available Nitrogen - amount of Nitrogen present in molecular forms that are possible for the plant to process.

Available Phosphorous – amount of Phosphorous present in molecular forms that are possible for the plant to process.

Available Potassium - amount of Potassium present in molecular forms that are possible for the plant to process

Available Water – amount of water in soil that is available for a plant's roots to use

Bioremediation – remediation of contaminated landscapes using organisms such as plants and fungi to breakdown, absorb, or transform present contaminants.

Bipolar spectrum – spectrum of psychological dysfunction characterized by shifting mood states between depressed, manic, and hypomanic states

Bronchodilation - a bronchodilator is a substance that dilates the bronchi and bronchioles, decreasing resistance in the respiratory airway and increasing airflow to the lungs

Bryophyte – nonvascular plants (i.e. mosses)

Callus – a mass of undifferentiated cells produced by a plant in response to a wound or some other stimulus.

Calyx – collective term for the sepals of a flower

Cannabinoid – class of compounds that interact with cannabinoid receptors

Cannabis use disorder – spectrum disorder characterized by compulsive drug seeking and use behavior despite negative consequences in life responsibilities or relationships

Capitate – forming a head

Carbamates – a group of compounds derived from carbamic acid, commonly used as insecticides

Certificate of Analysis – an official laboratory document displaying the results of an ordered service signed by an appropriate laboratory representative

Chemical Weathering – the breakdown of rock through the changing of the chemical composition of the rock, usually through interaction with water and oxygen

Chemotaxonomy – method of categorizing something based on its chemical profile

Chemotype – the chemical profile of a living thing; the chemotype of Cannabis typically includes the cannabinoid and terpenoid content, and sometimes the flavonoid content

Chirality – a property of asymmetry; enantiomers are examples of chemical chirality

Colloidal Particles – in soil science, colloidal particles refer to the smallest particles in the soil that will suspend in solution, such as the clay and humus particles. These particles act as nutrient buffers and can cling tightly to positively charged ions.

Column – the part of a chromatograph that contains the stationary phase

Comorbidity – the co-occurrence of two or more illness, diseases, or conditions

Conjunctival hyperemia – red eyes

Cotyledons – the first leaves to sprout from a seed; the cotyledons are pre-formed in the seed before sprouting; also known as "seed leaves"

Cytokine – proteins important for cell signaling, especially for the immune system

Decarboxylation Conversion Factor – a correction factor applied to a carboxylic acid to calculate its potential decarboxylated content. For cannabinoids, this decarboxylation factor is approximately 0.88.

Deoxyxylulose Pathway – the chemical synethetic pathway responsible for the production of phytocannabinoids and terpenoids

Depression – a state of low mood and aversion to activity

Diabetes or Diabetes mellitus – a group of metabolic diseases characterized by high blood sugar levels over a prolonged period of time

Dimethylallyl pyrophosphate (DMAPP) – DMAPP joined with IPP forms GPP which is the precursor to CBGA, which goes on to form THCA, CBDA, and CBCA.

Dissolution – the separation of crystalline structures into their component ions in solution

Ectomycorrhizal fungus – mycorrhizal fungus that surrounds plant roots in a sheath and exchanges water and nutrients for carbon. Ectomycorrhizal often produce large fruiting bodies (mushrooms) and are associated with shrubs and trees.

Egg – the organic container of the zygote of a living thing

Embryo – the earliest stage of development of a plant in seed form. The embryo produces the premature cotyledons before sprouting.

Embryo Sac – ovule; produces an egg cell for fertilization with a sperm for reproduction

Enantiomer – in chemistry, two molecules with the same structure that cannot be superposed on one another ("left hand" vs. "right hand" analogy)

Endocannabinoid – compounds produced by the human body that act on cannabinoid receptors including anandamide and 2-Arachidonoylglycerol

Endocannabinoidome – complex interconnected series of physiological components associated with the functioning of the endocannabinoid system including non-cannabinoid receptors, pharmacologically active degradation products of cannabinoids, cannabinoid and non-cannabinoid receptor complexes, etc.

Endocannabinoid System – a lipid signaling system consisting of endogenous cannabinoid compounds, cannabinoid receptors and enzymes; the ECS is involved in various physiological processes such as appetite, pain modulation, mood, and memory.

Endosperm – nutrient storage unit in a seed that helps to provide nutrition for the developing embryo

External Reference Standard – reference standards obtained from outside of the laboratory to ensure the accuracy of internal standards and results

Fasting Insulin – insulin level prior to the first meal of the day

Fatty Acid – a class of compounds that have a long hydrocarbon chain that ends in a carbon-oxygen group bonded to a glycerol; for Cannabis, fatty acids are found primarily in the seed oil.

Fertilization – the moment when the egg and the sperm meet and the production of the seed contents begins

Flavonoid – a member of a group of polyphenolic plant pigment compounds that are water-soluble

Forced Swim Test - an experiment used to assay mood levels in rodents in scientific research

Free Radical – an atom or molecule that is very reactive due to an unpaired electron. Free radicals can cause rapid chain reactions that can destabilize other compounds, leading to more free radicals

Functional Group – a group of bonded atoms that give molecules particular characteristics (i.e. the carboxylic acid functional group is removed from THCA to produce THC)

Gas Chromatograph (GC) – instrument used in analytical chemistry to separate and measure the concentration of compounds in a solution. The solution is vaporized and steadily heated as it passes through a column, where the compounds pass across the stationary phase. A detector reports data about the separated compounds as they pass through.

Gene – a sequence of nucleotides on a segment of DNA that provides instructions for the production of proteins

Gene Pool – the genetic information among a population of individuals

Genotype – the genetic makeup of an organism

Geranyl-pyrophosphate – synthesized from the combination of DMAPP and IPP, GPP is the precursor to CBGa

Germination – the beginning of seedling growth when the embryo has received water and initiated growth

Germplasm – the living genetic material of an organism that is used for reproduction, like seeds or tissue

Glandular Trichome – a trichome possessing a spherical glandular secretion at the end. In Cannabis this is where the majority of common cannabinoids are produced

Glaucoma – group of eye diseases which can result in damage to the optic nerves and vision

Glomalin – a substance produced by fungi that are members of the glomeromycota that acts as a glue for various soil particles, essentially acting as a buffer for nutrients

GMP – good manufacturing practice

G-Protein Coupled Receptor – group of receptors that are a part of a large family of proteins that sense molecules outside of cells and control cell signaling and responses. Cannabinoid receptors are g-protein coupled receptors

Grafting – a method of propagation where a shoot is fused to another plant's rootstock so that a plant will grow that exhibits traits of both plants.

Gymnosperm – vascular plant that does not produce flowers (i.e. conifers)

High Pressure (Performance) Liquid Chromatography (HPLC) – an instrument used in analytical chemistry for the separation and identification of concentrations of compounds. HPLC is a cold method of analysis allowing for the identification of carboxylic acids and other compounds.

Hippocampus – area of the brain in the temporal lobe responsible for memory formation and storage among other things; the hippocampus is densely populated with CB1 receptors.

Hippocampus – part of the brain that belongs to the limbic system and is involved in memory and spatial navigation

Humus – the fraction of organic matter in soil which the organic matter is no longer recognizable

Hydrolysis – the breaking of a chemical bond through the addition of water

Hydrophilic – have an affinity for water

Hydrophobic – having no attraction for water

Hyperaccumulator – an organism that has the ability to accumulate and tolerate relatively high levels of metals in its tissues

Hyperalgesia – increased sensitivity to painful stimuli

Hyperemesis – excess nausea

Hypomania – mild state of mania

Immunomodulator – a compound that influences immune system response

In vitro – "in glass"; procedures performed in a petri dish or test tube are considered *in vitro*

In vivo – "in the living"; procedures performed on a living organism, typically a rodent

Inflammation - protective response that involves immune cells, blood vessels, and molecular mediators which causes pain, heat, redness, swelling, and loss of function.

Inflammation – response of the body to harmful stimuli characterized by pain, heat, redness and swelling

Inflorescence – a group of flowers on a main stem

Insulin – hormone used by the body to store sugar from the blood in various tissue types

Internal Standard – reference standard developed in-house and used to calibrate results and test instrument performance

Internode – space between nodes

Intraocular pressure – pressure within the eye

Isomer – molecule with the same formula as another molecule but with a different structure

Isopentenyl-pyrophosphate (IPP) – compound that when combined with DMAPP produces GPP, and consequently CBGa.

Isoprene –molecule with the formula $CH_2=CCH=CH_2$; base unit for terpenoids, aka isoprenoids

Killer T Cell – cells produced by the body that kill cancer cells as well as other damaged cells

Lateral Meristem – meristem region responsible for increasing the girth of the plant

Leaflet – Each individual leaflike structure that makes up an entire compound leaf

Leukoedema – blue, grey, or white appearance of mucosae; smoking can cause Leukoedema of the oral mucosa

Limit of Detection – the lowest analyte concentration that can be distinguished from a blank with at least 50% confidence

Limit of Quantification – the lowest concentration at which the analyte can be reliably detected at a confidence level that meets predefined quality assurance standards

Lipid – group of molecules including fats, waxes, sterols, fat soluble vitamins, monoglycerides, diglycerides, triglycerides, and phospholipids among other things. Lipids are used to store energy, contribute to the structure of cell membranes, and conduct signaling. The endocannabinoid system is a lipid signaling system.

Lipophilic – having an affinity for lipids

Lipophobic – not having an affinity for lipids

Macronutrient –nutrients required in great quantities for an organism to survive including Nitrogen, Phosphorous, and Potassium

Mania – state of great excitement, euphoria, delusions, and/or overactivity; one of the key components of bipolar spectrum disorder

Mass Spectrometer (Mass Spec or MS) – instrument used in analytical chemistry to detect the molecular weights of compounds that have passed through another instrument like a gas or liquid chromatograph

Mechanical Weathering – process of breaking down rock through physical processes like the expanding and condensing of water and ice in the cracks of rocks

Meristem – regions of active growth of a plant

Meroterpenoid – a compound containing a partial terpene structure

Micronutrient – nutrients required in small quantitites for an organism to survive including iron, cobalt, chromium, copper, iodine, manganese, selenium, zinc, and molybdenum.

Micropropagation – methods of propagation in which plants are cloned from meristem tissue in sterile environments. Plants are grown in a nutritive solution in test tubes. This allows for the propagation of high quantities of clones in a small amount of space

Mildew – a type of fungus that commonly grows on plants and produces a powdery appearance

Mobile Phase – in chromatography, the phase that moves and passes across the stationary phase

Mold – a type of fungus that commonly grows on plants and soil in humid environments and produces a fluffy stringy appearance in a variety of colors. Some molds are highly toxic and produce harmful mycotoxins.

Monoterpenoid – class of terpenes that have two isoprene units and a molecular formula of C10H16

Monotype – In taxonomy, having only one species, or type.

Morbidity – the presence of an illness or disease

NELAP – National Environmental Laboratory Accreditation Program

Non-Glandular Trichome – trichome lacking a spherical head and having a hair like appearance

Nonpolar – a compound with equal sharing of electrons

ORELAP – Oregon Environmental Laboratory Accreditation Program

Organochlorides – also known as Organochlorines, chlorocarbons, or chlorinated hydrocarbon; an organic compound with at least one covalently bonded chlorine. Organochlorides are a class of pesticides

Organophosphates – an organic compound with a phosphate group; a class of pesticides

Orthosteric Site – the primary site of action on a chemical receptor

Palmate – shaped like a hand or palm with appendages extending from a central location

Permanent Wilting Point – the point when water in the soil becomes unavailable for a plant's roots due to the tension the soil is exerting on the water.

Petiole – stalk of a leaf

pH – a measure of the positively charged hydrogen ions in a solution

Phenol – molecule consisting of an aromatic ring with a bonded –OH group; aromatic alcohol

Phenotype – the physical characteristics of an organism

Phloem – the part of the vascular system of a plant responsible for moving nutrients throughout the plant

Phytocannabinoid – cannabinoid produced by a plant

Polar – a compound with an unequal sharing of electrons

Polymerase Chain Reaction (PCR) – technique used in analytical chemistry to replicate a piece of DNA many times to measure

Polyphenol – a class of organic chemicals consisting of multiple phenol units. Phenol units are aromatic organic compounds with the molecular formula C_6H_5OH.

Polytype – in taxonomy, having more than one species, or type

Posttraumatic Stress Disorder (PTSD) – a psychological disorder typically following one or more traumatic events such as sexual assault, warfare, traffic accidents, terrorism, abuse, etc that is characterized by heightened states of fear, anxiety, antisocial behavior, flashbacks, and difficulty sleeping.

Protean Agonism – a state when a compound may agonize, or stimulate, a chemical receptor when the receptor is largely inactive, but may later change its activity to antagonize or inversely agonize the same receptor if the receptor is already active; derived from the Greek god Proteus who could change form depending on who was observing him.

Pyrethroids – a class of pesticides;

Reference Standard – a sample containing a known amount of a compound for the use of instrument calibration and result correction

Ring Test – the process of multiple analytical laboratories analyzing one sample with a known concentration of compounds and then sharing the results

Saprophytic Fungus – fungus that gains energy by breaking down dead organic matter. These fungi are responsible for the common mold seen on wet soils with heavy microbiological amendments

Schizophrenia – psychological disorder characterized by a variety of positive and negative symptoms including antisocial tendencies, hallucinations, delusions, false beliefs, confused thinking, catatonia, and mood swings

Secondary Mineral – a mineral that has been chemically weathered to become a different compound than the parent rock

Seed Coat – a protective layer of tissue around the seed

Serrate – having notched edges like the teeth of a saw

Sesquiterpenoid – class of terpenes with three isoprene units and a formula of $C15H24$. Sesquiterpenes are usually the primary terpenes left in dried and cured Cannabis as the more volatile monoterpenes volatize during drying.

Sessile – lacking a stalk; attached at a base

Soil Adsorption Coefficient – a number used to represent a compound's mobility in the soil

Solvent – a chemical used to dissolve other compounds to form a solution

Spinosyns – a class of pesticides generally approved for use in organic agriculture

Stamen – the pollen producing part of the reproductive system of a flower

Standard Deviation – a measure used to show the amount of variation in a data set

Standard Operating Procedure – detailed instructions for various procedures to achieve repeatability and assist quality assurance

Stationary Phase – the phase in chromatography which compounds pass across and separate

Stigma – part of the flower that receives pollen and passes it to the ovary

Style – the connection between the stigma and the ovary

Supercritical Fluid – a substance at a temperature and pressure at which the substance can pass through solids like a gass but dissolve compounds like a liquid. Supercritical fluid can be used to extract essential oils from plants.

Synthetic Seed – germplasm or callus from tissue surrounded in a nutritive gel

Supraphysiological – usually used in reference to a dose; a dose greater than would be typically found in a body

Tail Suspension Test – an experiment used to assay mood levels in rodents in scientific research

Taxonomy – branch of science dealing with the description and classification of organisms

Terminal Bud – also known as the apical bud; region of active growth at the tip of the main stem of a plant.

Ternary Diagram – a diagram for calculating soil texture type based on sand, silt, and clay percentages

Terpenoid – also known as isoprenoids; organic chemicals synthesized by plants that are responsible for the aromas and tastes of the plant

Terpenophenolic Compounds – compounds consisting of both isoprene and phenol units; cannabinoids are terpenophenolic compounds.

Thin Layer Chromatography – a method of compound separation and quantitation involving the exposure of a sample to a plate which is later exposed to a solvent which rises up the plate through capillary action. A dye is then applied to the plate to visualize the compound separations.

Tissue Culture – a method of growing tissue from an organism in a sterile environment like a petri dish or test tube.

Trichome – glandular or non-glandular growth from the skin of a plant.

Vasodilation – dilation of blood vessels

Venation – the shapes and patterns of the veins of a leaf

Winterization – process of precipitating heavy lipids from an oil by bathing the oil in alcohol and exposing the mixture to cold temperatures for an extended period of time

Xerostomia – dry mouth

Xylem – the part of the plant vascular system responsible for pumping water throughout the plant

Yeast – a type of fungus that is unicellular and reproduces through budding

Appendix C: Resources for Further Learning

Disclaimer: Resource listings are not an indication of endorsement of this book or the author by any listed associated authors, publishers, or affiliated organizations of entities listed in this appendix.

Suggested Books/Literature

The American Herbal Pharmacopoeia monograph for Cannabis inflorescence covers many aspects of the Cannabis plant from the botany and biochemistry of the plant to the analysis of the plant. Visit http://www.herbal-ahp.org to order a copy.

Handbook of Cannabis
edited by Roger Pertwee

The Pot Book: A Complete Guide to Cannabis – It's Role in Medicine, Politics, Science, and Culture
by Julie Holland

Cannabis: Evolution and Ethnobotany
by Robert Clarke and Mark Merlin

The Emperor Wears No Clothes
by Jack Herer

Marijuana Horticulture: The Indoor/Outdoor Medical Grower's Bible
by Jorge Cervantes

Hemp Diseases and Pests – Management and Biological Control
by JM McPartland, RC Clarke, and DP Watson

Marijuana Botany
by Robert Clarke

Cannabis: A Complete Guide
by Ernest Small

SUGGESTED WEB RESOURCES

American Association for Laboratory Accreditation: http://www.a2la.org
A2LA provides ISO accreditation programs and NELAP proficiency testing for analytical laboratories. They offer accreditation for medical Cannabis laboratories.

Americans for Safe Access: http://www.safeaccessnow.org/
Americans for Safe Access is a Cannabis education and advocacy group. Their website provides medical Cannabis related information on a variety of topics including health, law, and activism.

American Herbal Products Association (AHPA): http://www.ahpa.org/

Cannabinoid Hyperemesis Syndrome Resource: http://www.cannabinoid-hyperemesis.com/
Compiled information about CHS managed by CHS survivor and Cannabis advocate, Alice Moon, including information about symptoms, diagnosis, treatment, and ongoing research.

Cannabis Chemistry Subdivision of the American Chemical Society: https://dchas.org/cann/

Cannify: http://www.cannify.us/
Cannify is an online quiz that helps connect users, researchers, and health care professionals with relevant information about Cannabis in connection with a particular medical condition. Using results from hundreds of scientific studies, the Cannify Quiz uses a complex algorithm to generate personalized reports.

Connect by Confident Cannabis: http://connect.confidentcannabis.com/
Connect is a tool that allows users to evaluate the differences in chemotype between products that have passed through the Confident Cannabis software platform, used by Cannabis testing laboratories, producers, and retailers to share traceable information about Cannabis products.

Curious About Cannabis Podcast: http://www.CACPodcast.com/
The Curious About Cannabis Podcast is a spin-off resource from the Curious About Cannabis Book where author and science educator Jason Wilson interviews researchers, clinicians, chemists, cultivators, and others to critically explore essential questions about Cannabis. Find the Curious About Cannabis Podcast wherever you listen to podcasts.

Future 4200 Forum: http://www.future4200.com
The Future 4200 forum is an online forum primarily focused on sharing information about Cannabis processing technologies and techniques, however it does cover a wide variety of other Cannabis related topics as well. The forum has attracted the attention of a number of knowledgeable chemists, engineers, and other technical experts. While the forum is a repository of a lot of good information, as with any forum, it is important to be cautious when evaluating information. Trust, but verify.

The Good Scents Company Information System: http://www.thegoodscentscompany.com/
The Good Scents Company provides information about odor and flavor compounds found in fragrances, foods, essential oils, and more. This resource can be utilized to find information about smells and particular terpenes found in various products, like Cannabis. Their odor index can be found at: www.thegoodscentscompany.com/allodor.html You can find information about specific terpenes by visiting the "Found in Nature" section of the odor index.

Integrated Taxonomic Information System (ITIS): http://www.itis.gov/

International Cannabis Research Society (ICRS): http://www.icrs.co

International Institute for Cannabinoids (ICANNA): http://www.institut-icanna.com/en/

Kannapedia by Medicinal Genomics: http://www.kannapedia.net/
Kannapedia is a Cannabis strain genetics database which demonstrates the genetic relationships between different samples. The site features a massive phylogenetic tree representing their database that can make your head spin.

List of Cannabis Sativa diseases by McPartland (2003):
http://www.apsnet.org/publications/commonnames/Pages/Hemp.aspx

National Environmental Laboratory Accreditation Conference (NELAC) Institute:
http://www.nelac-institute.org/
The NELAC Institute handles environmental laboratory accreditations and more.

Natural Resource Conservation Service Web Soil Survey:
http://websoilsurvey.sc.egov.usda.gov/App/HomePage.htm

O'Shaughnessy's: http://www.beyondthc.com
O'Shaughnessy's is an excellent source for Cannabis science and research news and editorials.

Oregon Cannabis Education and Resource Center: http://www.oregoncannabiserc.org/

Oregon CBD: http://www.oregoncbdseeds.com/
Cannabis research and development company that produces federally legal CBD-rich, CBG-rich, and cannabinoid varin-rich hemp seeds in the United States.

Oregon State University Soil Testing Guide: http://smallfarms.oregonstate.edu/soil-testing
OSU provides great information about environmental laboratories that serve Oregon. Use their list of labs to find a lab that can test soil and water for pesticides and heavy metals. They also have a resource for interpreting soil test results and a guide to collecting soil samples.

Pesticide Database: http://www.pesticideinfo.org

Pesticide Properties Database: http://sitem.herts.ac.uk/aeru/ppdb/en/atoz.htm
This is a great website for obtaining detailed information about synthetic and naturally derived pesticides including data on mobility, persistence, toxicity, environmental impact, and more.

Phylos Galaxy by Phylos Bioscience: http://phylos.bio/galaxy/
Phylos Bioscience provides genetic services for Cannabis cultivators and hosts an online Cannabis strain "galaxy" which maps the genetic relationships between samples that they have tested.

Phytecs LLC: http://www.phytecs.com/
Phytecs develops and derives products from natural plant compounds that can support and restore optimal endocannabinoid system function. Check out their educational resources and recommended reading list.

Phytochemical Glossary: http://www.phytopia.com/cookbook/glossary.htm

Project CBD: http://www.projectcbd.org

PubChem: http://pubchem.ncbi.nlm.nih.gov/

Find chemical information from authoritative sources including information on over 103 million compounds and 264 million substances.

PubMed: http://pubmed.ncbi.nlm.nih.gov/

Find more than 30 million citations for biomedical literature from various medical and life science research journals and books.

ResTek ChromaBlogRaphy: http://blog.restek.com/

Restek provides laboratory instrumentation and supplies as well as training and education about analytical methods and technology. Their chromatography blog provides news and updates about chromatography instrumentation and methods.

Separation Science: http://www.sepscience.com/

Separation Science provides online learning and training opportunities surrounding all aspects of chromatography.

TLC Lab Supply: http://www.thctestkits.com/

TLC Lab Supply is a company providing thin layer chromatography kits and supplies to the public for testing products for cannabinoids.

Toxipedia: www.toxipedia.org

Find information about various toxins including pesticides and chemical contaminants.

World Health Organization Guidelines for Assessing Quality of Herbal Medicines with Reference to Contaminants and Residues: http://apps.who.int/medicinedocs/en/d/Js14878e/

This is an excellent overview of contaminants that can be found in herbal products, the common sources of those contaminations, and how to reduce the risk of contamination during growing, processing, and storage of herbal products.

INDEX

D

Index of Tables and Figures

NOTES

NOTES

NOTES

Want to **learn more?**

Featuring educational episodes on critical topics about Cannabis as well as exclusive interviews with Cannabis researchers, clinicians, producers, patients, and consumers – the Curious About Cannabis™ Podcast takes learners on an educational journey to critically explore essential questions about the world's most controversial plant.

Check out the Curious About Cannabis™ Podcast by visiting **www.CACPodcast.com** or search for the Curious About Cannabis™ Podcast wherever you listen to podcasts! You can also subscribe to the Curious About Cannabis™ channel on YouTube!

Support Curious About Cannabis™ on **Patreon** and Join Our Community of the Curious!

Made in the USA
Las Vegas, NV
25 June 2021